A HISTORY OF BRITISH NATIVE PONIES

Photo : Daphne Machin Goodall

Exmoor mares and two-day old foal, Codsend Moor, Withypool,
2nd May 1962

A HISTORY
OF
BRITISH NATIVE
PONIES

FROM THE BRONZE AGE

TO THE PRESENT DAY

A. A. Dent

and

Daphne Machin Goodall

WITH 32 PAGES OF PLATES

58 LINE DRAWINGS IN TEXT

AND 6 MAPS

J. A. ALLEN

LONDON

British Library Cataloguing in Publication Data

Dent, Anthony
   A history of British ponies.
   1. Ponies — Great Britain — History
   I. Title   II. Goodall, Daphne Machin
   636.1'6'0941   SF315

   ISBN 0–85131–436–8

First published in 1962 by Galley Press Limited under the title *The Foals of Epona*

Reproduced from the original and first published by J. A. Allen & Company in 1988

Published in Great Britain by
J. A. Allen & Company Limited,
1, Lower Grosvenor Place, Buckingham Palace Road,
London, SW1 0EL

Printed and bound in Great Britain

EPONAE SANCTAE REGINAE
ET GENIO BRITTONUM
AUCTORES LIBENTER VOTUM SOLVUNT

FOR that I sawe it lay not in me to perfourme this worke so as it might answer to every man's expectation, and specialie of such as are readier to find faultes than to amende them, I did almost repent me of mine enterprise and good desire; and the rather, for that I had no one Author to followe, that eyther wrote of these matters to the full, or in such order as did satisfye my mynde, but should be driven to deal with a great number of Authors whose sayings and experiences together with mine owne smal knowledge I must not onely orderly dispose but also apply the same to the use of this our countrey.

Thomas Blundeville of Newton Flotman in Norfolk, 1565.

I know not the original of this word, unless it be corrupted from *puny*.

Samuel Johnson's *Dictionary*,
1755, under the heading PONY.

Acknowledgments

PASSAGES now forming parts of certain chapters in the first part of this book have appeared, not always in the identical phrasing, in articles in the following: *The Dalesman, Riding, Arab Horse Society News, The Horseman's Year, Pony, History Today* and *The Chronicle* (Virginia).

Our thanks are due to the respective editors for permission to incorporate this material.

Preface

OF THE making of books there is no end, but in the making of books about horses there is an intolerable deal of repetition. The reader therefore is asked to forgive us if this book comes to a stop at the point where so many other books, including many good ones, begin. For practical purposes this means somewhere about the beginning of the nineteenth century, in the histories, whether official or unofficial, of our native breeds. An honourable exception is the preface to the original volume of the *Shetland Pony Stud Book*, which quotes laws of the Stuart period to show in vivid detail exactly how ponies were bred and fed in the northern islands. We shall quote these passages again without an apology simply because the old stud book is scarce and hard to obtain, and because they form a vital link in our story.

This is a long story, and parts of it are lost. Some because they were never written down, since the men who knew most about it were utter strangers to pen and ink:

I learned never read on book,

as one of Langland's characters has it. Some were indeed written down, but not in works of literary value, such as are copied and printed from age to age. The written record of some of these things still exists, but it is in notes of such mundane matters as estate rent rolls, wills, feudal musters, inventories of outgoing and ingoing tenancies, account books of now deserted abbeys and priories, ransacked occasionally by economic historians to whom a horse is a horse and nothing more precise than that, but otherwise buried in a thousand muniment rooms and municipal archives. If we had nine lives apiece there would be time to resurrect all this dead parchment.

As it is we intend to take you, by means of fragmentary written records but also by means of strikingly numerous visual pictures, on a journey far back in time, to an age where the men of Britain did not speak of ponies but only of horses, because the only horse they knew, the companion of their daily life in peace and war, *was* a pony, and in modern parlance a mountain or moorland pony at that. But it is not a long journey in space. We shall not go far beyond the bounds of Britain and Ireland. We may have a glimpse of Spain or Scythia through a telescope, and there will be brief excursions without passport to France and the Low Countries and Norway. We intend to trace backwards the hoofprints of a wayfaring that has lasted, and will last, as long as grass grows on these islands.

Contents

CHAPTER   PAGE

    Preface   vii
    List of Illustrations in Text   ix
    List of Plates and Maps   x
    Foreword to Second Edition   xi
1   THE INVADERS   1
2   THE LADY OF THE FOALS   7
3   ROMAN BRITAIN   35
4   THE ENGLISH AND THE VIKINGS   53
5   EARLY MIDDLE AGES   85
6   LATER MIDDLE AGES   113
7   TUDOR TIMES   128
8   STUART TIMES   150
9   HANOVERIAN TIMES   171
10 GEOGRAPHICAL INTERLUDE   195
11 THE FAR NORTH, THE HIGHLANDS AND
    ISLANDS   199
12 GALLOWAY, THE DALES AND THE FELLS   215
13 THE EASTERN COUNTIES AND THE ROADSTERS   230
14 EXMOOR, DARTMOOR AND THE NEW FOREST   246
15 WALES   262
16 IRELAND   275
17 CONCLUSION   287
    Appendix I: Roman Postal Service   289
          II: Monastic Horses   290
          III: Limitations of Bits as Evidence   291
          IV: Memory of the Roman Post-Horse   292
    Select Bibliography of Sources   293
    Index   297

List of Illustrations in Text

Figure   *Page*

1. Chargers disembarking from Norman landing craft.   1
2. Norman advance guard.   2
3. Sussex pack-pony.   3
4. South Saxon farmer harrowing.   3
5. South Saxon Thane hunting.   4
6. Pack-horses.   4
7. Donkey grazing.   4
8. Donkey in cart.   5
9. Count Guy de Ponthieu hawking on mule.   5
10. Mounted grooms escaping from Hastings.   6

All above from Bayeux Tapestry.

Headpiece to Chapter 2: Celtic coin of the Turones showing single-horse chariot.   7

11. The Lady of Lynwood: goddess and horseman on New Forest pottery.   8
12. Goddess and horseman on Scythian saddlecloth.   9
13. Epona feeding mules.   12
14. A common Gallic picture of the Equestrian God.   14
15. The Steppe Horse at the other side of the world.   18
16. The earliest unquestionable picture of domestic horses.   26
17. Ancient and recent sea-going skin-covered vessels.   29
18. Rock carving from Scandinavia. Sea-going ship and two-horse chariot.   33

Headpiece to Chapter 4: Jointed snaffle from early Saxon ship grave, at Nydam.   53

19. Viking horse gear.   75

Tailpiece to Chapter 4: English horses and Irish hounds about A.D. 1000 from *Canterbury Psalter.*   84

20. *Left:* Chaucer's miller mounted on capul.   120
    Right: Shipman on a rouncy. From *Ellesmere MS.*   120
21. Spanish jennet at the end of the fifteenth century. *Woodcut dated 1499.*   121

Headpiece to Chapter 7: Late fifteenth-century woodcut. Caxton's *Game and Play of the Chess*, showing a high official travelling on business.   128

22. Facsimile of a statute of Henry VIII concerning horse-breeding.   138
23. Irish chief with pony and horseboy, 1581.   156
24. English palfreys, 1558.   158
25. James I, hawking.   161
26. Subjects of James I, hunting.   162
27. Funeral of the Earl of Essex.   166
28. Slide-car at Inverness, about 1730, called in Gaelic *car-slaoid.*   180
29. Inverness, 2-wheel cart, about 1730, of a pattern called in Welsh *car-meidre.*   180
30. Country cart from Upper Clydesdale, eighteenth century; illustration from *The Gentle Shepherd*, by Allan Ramsay.   187
31. Burns ploughing.   188

Figure	*Page*
32. Illustration from *St Ronan's Well* showing heroine riding galloway.	189
33. 'Spangle, a favourite poney of H.R.H. the late Princess Charlotte.'	191
34. Mineral train, from industrial light railway prospectus, 1824.	193
35. The small West Highland pony with pack saddle.	209
36. The small West Highland type of shooting pony, ridden.	212
37. The Kyloe steer, by Thomas Bewick.	224
38. The Old English road horse, by Thomas Bewick.	225
39. Stud card of Young Active, 1832, from the collection of Mr Ernest Hutton.	233
40. Marshland Shales, 1824.	238
41. Early stud cards of harness horses, mainly of the nineteenth century, from the collection of Mr Ernest Hutton.	242
42. North Star, 1861.	244
43. Cornish pack-horses carrying sand, by J. Rowlandson, about 1790.	255
44. Cornish pack-horses, 1788, by J. Rowlandson.	256
45. Cornish ponies pulling sled in tandem, and mounted milkmaid, by Rowlandson, 1812.	256
46. View of Llanberis, with ponies in foreground, 1788.	264
47. Leading hay, near Carnarvon Castle, 1774.	265
48. Snowdon from Capel-Cerig, about 1780.	266
49. Inside car, 1843.	279
50. Outside car, 1843.	279
51. Wheel car, 1843.	280
52. Irish landlord and Irish tenant, 1852.	281
Tailpiece: Celtic coin of the Aulerci Cennomani (department of Mayenne)	288

References in the text, or in other captions, to these figures, are simply by number.

List of Plates

Mares and foal on Exmoor. *Photo by D. M. G.*	*frontispiece*
Plates 1–41	between 86 and 87
Plates 42–78	between 182 and 183

For details see Notes on pages 87 et seq. and 183 et seq.

References in the text, in Notes, or in other captions, to these pictures are in the form P1, P2, etc.

List of Maps

	Page
1. North-west Europe, 50 Fathoms Dryer	25
2. Three Waves from the North Sea	76
3. The Sea Way from Spain	123
4. British River Names	196
5. British Native Ponies: Breeding Areas	197
6. Galloway, the Dales and the Fells	216–17

Foreword to Second Edition

NOTHING STANDS still. The fortunes of British ponies have perhaps seen
more far-reaching turns, for better and for worse, in the quarter-century
since the first edition of this book appeared, than in the sixty-odd years
between the death of Queen Victoria and the day we first put finger to
keyboard. First a stimulus to breeding before the First World War when the
government, quite contrary to British precedent, actually intervened to
counter the free play of supply and demand by offering premiums to owners
of breeding stock likely to get the sort of hardy 'mount for all seasons' that
had proved so difficult to procure during the South African War. It is
typical of War Office thinking that this economic support for certain native
breeds went on for years and years after the battle of Cambrai had shown
that the days of hide-and-hair cavalry were not just numbered: they had
gone with the wind, and we no longer needed a military substitute for the
Boerepard. The Wehrmacht showed us that mounted infantry is best
mounted in lorries. While it was so showing us, things did stand still for a
while on the pony front because then the rural scene was dominated by two
things – the shortage of petrol and the stern effort to produce more food,
which meant, primarily, BREAD – which affected the pony not at all.
Unlike other equines it could exist comfortably without cereals, it played no
part in corn production, and it did not, then, require transport by the
internal combustion engine. The only adverse circumstance was the
ploughing up of marginal land, the kind of rough grazing on which ponies,
but not other farm stock, could do well.

Beginning in 1945 a spell of bad weather set in. Rationing became more
stringent than it had been while hostilities lasted – especially meat
rationing. Horse meat was not rationed, and while the horse butcher would
have preferred Shires and Suffolks he could not get enough of them, and
whole droves of ponies went the way of steak-and-kidney pies. Out of this
slough of despair many breeds were rescued by various organizations,
notably Glenda Spooner's Ponies of Britain Club, who persuaded those who
needed to be persuaded that the herds on mountain and moorland, bog,
forest and fen, were an unique and irreplaceable heritage that was worth
preserving. This re-awakened interest led, by the 1960s, to a boom in ponies
that threatened to be its own undoing by the 1970s: you can't have a boom
without a slump. The slump was disguised for quite a long time by the
overspill into an export market that had not previously existed. The
Germans looking round for something on which to spend the money they

had acquired by their Economic Miracle and which would 'lead them back to nature' by a less fatiguing way than slogging it out on foot from one Youth Hostel to another as the Wandervogel of the 1930s had done; the French, looking for something *chic* at which their child could achieve distinction; the Dutch, the Scandinavians, and others. But here again, nothing stands still: having imported a fair amount of breeding stock so that there are considerable studs of Highland ponies in Brittany and of New Forest in the Dordogne, mainlanders are breeding their own rather than incur the ever-increasing cost of transport. Most Shetland ponies throughout Europe have been bred in Holland; needless to say, they are far too big, now.

Having established their own standards of what our native breeds ought to look like, most importing countries, or rather the responsible government department, such as the *Service des Haras* in France, are being much more selective about approving imported stallions and mares for inclusion in the appropriate section of their official stud book: and it does not necessarily follow that a New Forest or Dartmoor pony that has had considerable success at English shows will be approved officially, across the Channel, for breeding purposes.

All attempts, not only ours, to reconstruct the past of the British pony, have been hampered hitherto by the scarcity of 'hard' physical evidence: there has been only one Newstead with its huge dump of skeletal Roman Army horses whose bones had been so jumbled together that it took months of careful toil to assemble the essential, identifying parts that could serve as a reconstruction of even *one* equine type. But of recent years archaeological technique has made it much more easy to assess the age, size, condition at death and conformation of animal remains. This has been recently demonstrated, in the City of London alone, by the discovery and 'interpretation' by modern techniques of the almost complete skeletons of a Roman and a tenth-century Saxon horse. Not to mention the skull of a Roman mule. There will be more such discoveries before we are done. Nor are the possibilities of art-finds exhausted yet. Between the appearance of the first and second editions of this book a plough in Dorset turned up a carved stone slab of Romano-British origin, second or perhaps third century of our era, showing the patron deity of some Thracian auxiliary squadron of the Roman Army mounted on a readily recognizable Exmoor pony.

But today, and tomorrow . . . Since fewer and fewer of our native breeds are now being bred in their native habitat and ever more in 'up-country' studs of one sort or another, there is a very real danger that the characteristics peculiar to the different pony breeds will be lost.

Two hundred years ago it was said that when the Arabian horse no longer breathes its native air, he ceases to be Arabian and this is equally true of the moorland pony – when he no longer needs to 'paddle' across marshland he will cease to be a moorland pony. Paddling is an essential gait for the moorland pony's survival; not the exaggerated 'daisy-cutting' trot now produced *ad nauseam* in the show-ring.

D.M.G.   A.A.D.

A HISTORY OF BRITISH NATIVE PONIES

CHAPTER ONE

The Invaders

If thou hast a care, tell not thine enemies:
Tell it to thy saddle-bow, and ride on, singing.

Proverb, attributed to King Alfred.

To BEGIN, not at the beginning, but at the most significant point half way along the corridor of years that separates us from the Britain of Cassivellaunus and Julius Caesar. For all practical purposes this picture will serve as the first entry of that principal actor, the Great Horse, into the theatre of Britain. The scene is Pevensey beach, and the time is October 1066. Norman sailors and grooms are disembarking with the chargers of Duke William's knights (1). The Great Horse that was to become the ancestor of the Shire and the Clydesdale was not unknown in England but it was a rarity at this time. Nor was it used for its true function which was about to be demonstrated so fatefully on the field of Hastings. There were no squadrons of mailed cavalry in the English army, but King Harold and his immediate following had a few Great

1. Chargers disembarking from Norman landing craft.

1

Horses which they used for staff purposes. As the doomed housecarles and the Kentish militia filed out of the woods and took up their positions astride the road from Hastings to London, Harold rode along the ridge that runs east and west between two tiny tributaries of the River Brede adjusting the ranks and receiving reports of what each commander could see on his front. He did the same during two lulls in the fighting, but once in contact with the enemy he sent his horse to the rear and fought on foot with the housecarles.

While the Normans kept the very full manes of their horses, it would seem that the English owners hogged theirs, but this may possibly be a

2. Norman advance guard without helmets galloping from Pevensey to Hastings.

device of the artist to distinguish the English commanders, since the casual 'reader' is otherwise almost bound to assume that any mounted figure in the Bayeux Tapestry is a Norman. This invasion is one of the only two accessions of equine stock, of the first importance to this country, that have taken place since Iron Age times. The Norman war-horse was typical of the large powerful strains of Diluvial stock whose homeland is the south shore of the Channel, the North Sea and the Baltic, between Brittany and Holstein. We tend to think of the other accession, the oriental horse whether Barb or Arab, as happening with a bang some time about the reign of William III. But the closer we look into history the further back in time this event seems to recede. Even in the Bayeux Tapestry (2) the Norman advance guard sent off from Pevensey to seize a second base at Hastings seem to be mounted on a slightly different type, not quite so hairy, lighter of bone, with less massive quarters and slightly dished faces: the sort that would be needed when *milites festinaverunt Hestingam*—the knights made haste to Hastings.

Meanwhile, what of the native horses? Here is one (3), property of

3. Sussex pack-pony commandeered by Norman foragers.

a gentleman in Sussex, as the sales catalogues say. Alas, poor gentleman, he will never see his little mare again. The Normans brought no transport animals with them, and their foragers have seized the little mare to carry sacks of looted meal and to round up a herd of beef on the hoof. Perhaps they even took her out of the plough, but not very likely because the only tillage work commonly done by horses was harrowing (4),

4. South Saxon farmer harrowing with horse.

which has to be taken, to be effective, at a pace slightly faster than bullocks can knock up. Even then only the worst horses were used for this job, and throughout the Middle Ages in wills, inventories, etc., we shall find the *hercarius*—the harrow-puller—assessed at such knackers' prices that they must have represented the dregs of the equine population. Probably the little Sussex mare who is so dwarfed by the Norman troop-horse carrying his rider purposefully towards the cookhouse

5. South Saxon Thane hunting with hounds and sling.

was used for hunting, like this (5). At any rate she is not so long in the back nor so cold-blooded about the head as the harrow-horse. We may perhaps regard her as a female ancestor of the New Forest. On the other hand she may have been a pack-horse like these (6): only pack-horses would be coupled by the halters like this.

6. Pack-horses.

The pack-horse enjoyed very low esteem among the Normans. It ranked well below a good mule.

> Vus no avrez palefrier ne dester
> Ne mul ne mule que puissez chevaucher,
> Getez serez sur un malvais sumer.

You should have neither palfrey nor destrier to ride, nor a mule either male of female, but shall be tossed on to a bad pack-horse.

Again, describing minimal losses to be expected on a campaign:

> N'i perdrat Charles li reis ki France tient
> . . . ne runcin ne sumer

King Charles who holds France shall not lose so much as a cob nor a pack-horse.

For tillage and draught there were a few donkeys and mules available before the Conquest. Here is one grazing (7) and one in harness (8).

7. Donkey grazing.

8. Donkey in cart.

Dashingly drawn, with great economy of line, the attitudes of donkey and driver recall the inimitable costermongers of Phil May. As this eleventh-century cockney spiv speeds on his way to the battlefield scenting a nice little deal in army surplus stores, he spares a passing insult for the Sussex ploughman.

The Normans also brought with them a few mules of great strength and impressive stature, such as is being ridden by Count Guy in (9),

9. Count Guy de Ponthieu hawking on mule.

though they were usually reserved for the use of ecclesiastics. These gigantic hybrids were the offspring of the Great Mares by a special kind of jackass known as a *baudet de Poitou* which grew up to 14 hands or even 14 hands 3 inches, and was able to get a massive mule up to 16 hands. As these animals died off in England, however, they do not seem to have been replaced very fast, since few laymen went to the trouble of importing any of the huge Poitevin jackasses for that purpose.[1]

Before the Normans began their first assault on the English position,

[1] But the 'Minster' Stud at Burton-on-Trent, famous for horse-breeding in Anglo-Saxon times, appears in a document of 1116 as owning about three dozen mares, no stallions, but three Spanish jackasses. Obviously it had gone over to the mule business. A century earlier it had owned sixteen stallions. (See Chapter 4.)

the Duke's minstrel Taillefer rode out of their lines across the brook and up the slope of no-man's-land, juggling with his sword and singing the *Song of Roland*, which celebrates the deeds of a Frankish, not a Norman, hero who lived more than two centuries before Hastings. The chronicler does not say how many of its 291 stanzas Taillefer had sung before the English killed him, but one of them which occurs quite early in the poem is very indicative of the way Normans thought about the function of the horse in war: it describes the Moslem host preparing for action before Roncesval.

> Laissent les muls et tous les palefreiz
> Es destriers muntent, si chavalchent estreiz

> [The Saracens] leave their mules and all their palfreys
> And mounting their war-horses form up in close order.

Of course no Saracen ever did any such thing; their tactics were to ride round and round the enemy on 'palfreys' peppering him with arrows. But it was now a long time since any Frenchman, let alone any Norman, had fought a Saracen, and the Norman mind could not conceive of an effective army that did not use exactly the same technique as themselves, which was to manœuvre, until almost in contact with the enemy, on light horses, then to put on their armour and mount their great horses, which, fit and rested, would be able to deliver a crushing blow.

The Normans do seem to have recognized degrees of speed as between war-horses, as we have repeatedly in the *Chanson de Roland* lines like this:

> Puis sunt montez sur lur curanz desters
> Then they mounted their running war-horses.

But whether these amounted to a separate breed, represented by (2) in the Bayeux Tapestry, is an open question.

The Anglo-Saxons conceived the military function of the horse as a useful conveyance for that tedious prelude to battle, the approach march, and if the worst came to the worst, for a quick getaway. For this

10. Mounted grooms escaping from Hastings.

purpose the native pony was quite good enough (though (10) shows a *sauve-qui-peut* by surviving generals' grooms and batmen on their imported steeds). But all that, together with a good many other old English traditions, was over, when the sun went down on the 14th October 1066 and the wolves came out of the forest.

CHAPTER TWO

The Lady of the Foals

Fine and fair was his swan-white robe,
The first that fastened a horse by the bridle.

The Sons of Llywarch the Old.

THE WOLVES came out of the forest. It would be someone's duty to chase them back again and keep them there, to follow them up and fight them on their own territory. Hitherto it had been the duty of thane-right-worthy men, but who would do it now? [1] This question must have ranked high among the doubts and perplexities of many English husbandmen whose late landlords lay dead on the field, or were fled over the wide sea to take service at Micklegarth, or were dispossessed and eating the bread of servitude on some other man's land. The question of rents and taxes would settle itself; after all, there had been

[1] The West Saxons were not alone in their view that for kings and noblemen hunting constituted a duty as well as a pleasure. 'Yet amid the wars and many hindrances of this present life and amid the assaults of the pagans and his daily illness, the king ceased not from the governance of the kingdom and from the pursuit of every kind of hunting.' Thus wrote Bishop Asser in his biography of King Alfred, which was intended for Welsh rather more than for English readers. There was no discrepancy between British and Saxon ideas about what constituted the proper conduct of a king. As for Alfred, he resembled all the other members of the house of Cerdic of whom we have any personal knowledge, in having rather delicate health; it is a wonder that the dynasty lasted so long, since the expectation of life (quite apart from accidents) of individual members was rather short. The last representative, Edward the Confessor, lived as long as most of them and reigned longer than all, yet he was not what one could call a robust or a pleasure-seeking type. His custom was to hunt every day during the season, when religious observances did not prevent this, until dinner time, and transact public business after that.

rents and taxes before, and there was no reason to suppose that the new king would want more taxes than the old one. As for the new landlord up at the Hall, he had a new set of housecarles, but they did not look like bigger eaters or harder drinkers than the last lot, even though his horses looked as if they would take a lot more keeping in oats than the old thane's.

But the forest—there was still a lot of it. Hastings itself lay near the eastern end of the Wood of Anderida, Andredesweald, that stretched away to the north far up into Surrey and swept round to the west, only

11. The Lady of Lynwood: goddess and horseman on New Forest pottery. Top of her head restored. Deliberately drawn hideous and terrifying.

skirting Southampton Water, to the Avon and the borders of the Dorset heaths. Farther north there were more and even greater forests, especially beyond Humber.

The thanes, who were now to be called the gentry, had taken care of the wolves. And before them the nobles of the British tribes, both before and after the Romans came. Ever since farming began it had been a part of the unspoken social contract that those whose skill at arms enabled them to live without labour of their hands should keep the wolf from the fold and the deer out of the crops. It was partly for this that they needed horses.

At the other end of Andredesweald, in the part that King William called his New Forest, is a valley called Lynwood—the Wood of Lime Trees. A thousand years and more before Hastings there had been in this valley a thriving pottery, producing a coarse but serviceable black ware. We have today a large vessel made by one of the potters for his own use. Its capacity is several gallons, and it was used to moisten the clay while it was being worked. Not with a view to sale, therefore, but for his own satisfaction, the potter had drawn this design on the lid (11).

The merest sketch of a goddess attended by horsemen. The name of the goddess is Epona. It bears a striking resemblance to a much more finished picture, worked in felt appliqué, on a Scythian saddle-cloth five hundred years older (12).

12. Goddess and horseman on Scythian saddlecloth.

The Scythian who worked the felt was not a full-time saddler nor was the potter of Lynwood a full-time potter. Both were part-time horse-breeders as many people in the New Forest and in Scythia still are.

Who was Epona? She was a Celtic, more specifically a Gallic and a British goddess, associated with a cult of horses that may have been itself derived from a horse-totem cult of the remote past. In the Old Stone Age there are rock paintings of mares in an advanced stage of pregnancy which seem to have religious significance: they are, if you like, a prayer for a good foaling season. The difference between the palaeolithic and the Iron Age horse cult, to which latter Epona belongs, is that to the hunters of the Old Stone Age the horse was just another kind of deer without horns, so much meat on the hoof; whereas to the Iron Age Celts it was the embodiment of majesty and nobility, that had been their companion for every step of their long journey from the original Aryan homeland beyond the Caspian Sea to the outer shores of Britain and the edge of the habitable world. Epona was almost the only goddess who was worshipped in the same guise by both the continental and the insular Celts. Her name means simply THE GREAT MARE, but there were many pseudonyms for it such as THE GREAT QUEEN (in Welsh, Rhiannon), THE HOLY QUEEN, Macha, which was her name in Ireland, and others.

The next oldest representation from Britain after the Lynwood water-pot is also from the south, from some site not exactly known on the downs of Wiltshire. It shows the goddess seated on a throne with her hands on the heads of two foals about the size of month-old New Foresters. This statuette (it is in bronze, only about five inches high) strikes the keynote of the whole cult.

Though eventually Epona's cult became that of horsemen in general, and attracted an even wider circle of devotees than that, in her essence she was a breeder's goddess before all things. Both before and after the Roman Conquest both Britons and Gauls revered her as their Lady of the Foals. Like the Black Demeter of Thessaly who was worshipped in the guise of a woman with the head of a mare, and like the more 'classical' Greek deity Artemis, she was believed to preside over the mating of mares and the birth of foals,[1] but she was also another aspect of the universal Earth Mother so dear to Indo-European legend, representing the earth in its beneficent aspect of fruitfulness, as was also the Black Demeter. No doubt the mare's head of the latter is a memory of the totem phase of the cult, the horse-mask worn by the priestess in a ritual dance; but all vestiges of totemism had disappeared by the time from which the surviving relics can be dated.

Due to a certain combination of circumstances, the image and the name of Epona became very widely diffused about the Roman Empire between the time of the final conquest of Britain by the Romans and the suppression of all pagan cults by Constantine, the emperor who was born in the barracks at York. In the first place, Roman cavalry was not really Roman at all. It consisted entirely of auxiliaries, the first regiments of whom had been Gauls under their own chieftains, such as we read about in the *Commentaries* of Julius Caesar. When we consider that chiefs such as Ambiorix and Vercingetorix were accustomed to command bodies of fifteen thousand and twenty thousand horse, it comes as no surprise to learn that, at the time of the invasion of Britain, Caesar's inspector-general of cavalry was a Gallic and not a Roman officer. Consequently Gaulish, and after them other Celtic, cavalry formations had a prestige in the Roman service that was never matched by any other sort of auxiliary; and every cavalry unit, no matter what its origin, took its tone from Celtic fashions. As every regiment in the Roman Army had its patron god or goddess whose chapel stood in the middle of the fortified barracks beside the regimental pay-office, most of them opted for the cult of the Gallo-British Epona.

For the Gauls and the Britons themselves she was the obvious choice. For reasons which any psychologist can explain, soldiers always go for a mother-figure in a big way, especially when serving overseas, and it was

[1] Again, like Artemis, she exercised a benevolent influence over human birth. Evidence of the transfer of her cult from Celtic to Germanic peoples is supplied by Grimm, who reported in the nineteenth century that German peasant midwives, in a case of protracted labour, would make a horse feed from the patient's apron.

the Roman policy always to post recruits to some station as far away from their birth-place as possible, but to keep units of the same tribal origin together. To the homesick British trooper in some godforsaken outpost beside the Danube or the Nile or the Euphrates, the image of Epona in the regimental shrine meant Home: and home was the orchard at the back of the farm-house, with a couple of old mares and their foals and Our Mam coming out to shut up the chickens at twilight.

So the commonest version of the image that we have seen, in plaque form, is of a woman sitting in a little paddock, surrounded by in-foal mares, who are eating apples out of her hand, or, occasionally, hay out of her lap. Or else she is seated on a throne, as in the Wiltshire statuette, or as in (P9) with her hand on the head of a foal in a gesture of bene-diction. In a Gallic carving, full of the vigour and the delight in con-voluted patterns that are such a feature of native Celtic art, we see her seated sideways on a mare of real quality, with a fine sweeping stride (P7), herself wearing a simple woollen dress such as British and Gaulish ladies wore in the Iron Age. Contrast her with (P8), from a Roman cavalry barracks in the Rhineland, where the whole picture has been squared up to make it fit the standard-type plaque, where the rider has been put into a smart Roman matinée gown and given the latest Roman hair-do, and at the same time provided with a tray holding two or three pounds of fruit instead of the single apple which was the Celtic symbol of plenty—a typically Roman vulgarity. The mare too has been squared up to fit into the frame, her hocks brought under her, her mane done up in plaits and her tail artificially 'set' either by nicking or some sort of show crupper; she is pacing along in the manner of the well-schooled but slightly overbent charger one sees carrying Roman generals on triumphal arches.

The original centre of the cult appears to have been Alesia, now called Alise-Ste-Reine, in the Côte d'Or. It is not difficult to guess who was the Sainte Reine in question. And it is from this region, amongst some of the noblest vineyards in the world, that the most significant of the images of Epona has been recovered. Among all the two hundred and fifty-three inscriptions and monuments to the Lady of the Foals which have been catalogued and reproduced by the devoted labours of M. Magnen, this is the most appealing. Not by reason of the somewhat doll-like image of the goddess herself, a typical piece of Roman provincial cheesecake which proves that commercial-religious art is not a modern phenomenon, nor by reason of the mare she is riding, who with her weak, long back and chuckle head is the sort of ancestress you might expect the Belgic Ardennais breed to have had. It is the foal, which is behaving so like a real foal. Something has distracted its wayward attention and it is going to investigate rather than follow its dam, goddess or no goddess; its nose is in the air and it is about to utter that high, piercing, maddening whinny that must strike an echoing chord in the heart of every horse-breeder in every age and every country (P4).

Although of animal origin, this name Epona was much too strongly imbued with religious flavour to be used of mortal women, but diminutives of it were sometimes given to Celtic girls of good family. Thus in the reign of Vespasian there occurred a serious mutiny among the auxiliary troops of the Roman Army stationed in Lower Germany. Nearly all the troops involved were serving in or near their own tribal territory, which shows how sound normal Roman policy in this respect was. One of the ringleaders was Julius Sabinus, a native officer, squadron leader in one of the Batavian cavalry regiments. He was joined by another German officer, Civilis, and Classicus, a Gaul. The mutinous units were soon joined by rebellious tribesmen both Celtic and German who had never been in the Roman service; for a time, in A.D. 70, they overran the whole of Belgic Gaul and Lower Germany: it would be an exaggeration to say they controlled it, but at least they ensured that no one else did, until the revolt was put down at the end of that year. For some reason Civilis received a free pardon but not his colleagues (did he turn Emperor's evidence?). Sabinus and his wife after years in hiding were apprehended and Sabinus executed. His wife was not a Batavian or any other kind of German. Her father was a chief of the Lingones, a Gallic tribe whose territory lay immediately north of the shrine of Epona at Alesia, a town notable for its resistance to Roman imperialism (or for seditious terrorism, according to which way you look at it). By order of the Emperor Vespasian the life of Sabinus's wife was spared, but being unwilling to live without him she deliberately offered such insults to the imperial person as could only result, as they did, in her death. Her name was Eponina.

Not all the worshippers of Epona were soldiers. We shall see later what part horse transport played in the daily life of the Roman Empire. Everyone connected with horses, but especially the lads in the racing stables, attached to every racecourse (that is, every major town) in the

13. Epona feeding mules or donkeys. Mural, now lost, from Circus of Maxentius in Rome.

empire, owed some allegiance to Epona, as did also the packmen and wagoners and the staff of the highly efficient ubiquitous imperial posting system. The racing establishments were very largely staffed by British slaves in any case. But as time wore on people whose business was not strictly with horses were attracted to the cult, principally muleteers and donkey-drivers, and a few images of Epona feeding mules and asses with hay from her lap exist in Mediterranean lands. It is almost certain that some design of Epona mounted on a donkey was the prototype, slightly adapted to new needs, of the Flight into Egypt pictures of the early Christian era.

Epona was just another aspect, originally, of the universal Earth Mother worshipped by all the Indo-Europeans, Scythians, Indians, Celts, Slavs and Germans alike. Long after Christianity had spread over this country from end to end the English had a ceremony to restore the fertility of barren fields, which began with extracts from the Church litany but reached its climax in a purely pagan invocation.

> *Hal waes thu, Folde, fira moder . . .*
> Blessed be thou, Earth, mother of men.
> Be thou fruitful in the embrace of the god,
> Filled with food for the nourishment of mankind.

There seems to be a direct continuity of ideas between this half-heathen Saxon hymn and the Celtic images of Epona with the foals eating hay out of her lap.

Both the Britons and the Gauls, in the cults of their various gods, erected statues and monuments which were not inscribed; thus the only 'labelled' representations of Celtic gods were produced under the Roman occupation, by which time many of the gods had been equated with Roman deities and had acquired some Roman attributes. We are faced with a repertoire of names of Celtic gods and a nameless gallery of their likenesses, which can only in part be matched together, as in the case of Sucellos the Good Striker, a kind of divine blacksmith easily identifiable by his hammer, like the classical Hephaestos and the Germanic Thor and Wayland. One of the most frequently occurring Gallic statues which defy identification is the figure of a horseman trampling underfoot the head and torso of a misshapen giant, the lower part of whose body is buried in the ground. Versions of this statue, of pre-Roman date, are very widely found all over Gaul. It symbolizes the triumph of light over darkness, the triumph of the air or the sun over the underworld: the earth is seen, not in the aspect of the benevolent Mother of All, but as the dark underworld or winter, the counterpart of the classical Pluto, the King of Hell. The equestrian god could reasonably be equated with the Gallic sun-god Lug, whose name is found in the old form of Lyons (Lugudunum) and also in the old form of Carlisle (Luguvallium) and in some Irish place names.

Luguvallium, about half a mile from the centre of modern Carlisle, was for many years the station of the crack Gallic cavalry regiment Ala Petriana, which had a thousand men and much more than a thousand horses on its strength, unlike all the other horsed units on the Hadrian Line, which had an establishment of only 512 all ranks. Whatever his name, this giant-killing god cannot have been conceived of, in the form

14. A common Gallic picture of the Equestrian God.

which his statues present, very early, since in the wars of the Gauls and the Romans about 200 B.C. all Gallic chieftains were mounted in chariots, and the Gallic chariot continued to appear on the battlefield until about 100 B.C. Two things are memorable about these statues; in every case the horse is of a more substantial type than the usual Gallic horse, and not a very handsome one; perhaps it represents the ancestor of the modern Ardennais, and (again perhaps) it was a Belgic speciality. The other thing is that it has quite obviously been trained to do this sort of thing; the horse is one of the rider's weapons.

We shall see in the next chapter further evidence of the prestige which Celtic, but especially Gallic, customs enjoyed throughout the Roman cavalry arm, strikingly demonstrated by the adaptation of this design to the standard regimental tombstones of Roman cavalry soldiers. The two other ranks whose tombstones we illustrate (P10, P11) belonged to Thracian units; the mounted figures are not representations of gods, but portraits of the deceased, and the prostrate figure under the hoofs is not a giant or an elemental earth-demon, but a real-life barbarian enemy; yet plainly the inspiration of the carving is derived from the Gallic divine horseman, whether he was Lug or another.

No shrines to the ancestors of the clan have been found in Britain, as they have in Gaul, but that is not to say that they did not exist. They were quite distinct from the tumuli where the body of the chieftain was buried, with suitable treasures, but they do appear to have contained the skulls, not only of the clan ancestors, but of enemies killed in battle or beheaded after capture, and sent after them to serve them in the next world. The lintels of some of these shrines in France are carved with rows of horses' heads, intended symbolically to provide for the journey of the soul to the land of the dead (P18).

In the burial proper the grave-goods always included saddlery and harness, sometimes a chariot, often a horse or horses. To a greater or less extent this was a universal custom among Indo-European tribes. Where it cannot be traced with certainty is among the tribes and in the places where cremation was practised. But we know from the practice of gipsies, even modern gipsies (who are of ancient Indo-European stock), that the burning of wagon and harness formed part of the cremation rite. Tacitus was impressed with the poverty and simplicity of the grave gear, compared with Celtic funerary pomp, at the German funerals he witnessed: but his experience was confined to the Rhineland and we have evidence from actual finds that the Germanic tribes of the sea coast had much more elaborate holocausts at the burial of a chief. The funeral of a pagan Anglo-Saxon will be described in a later chapter. The reason why the number of horses in Celtic and Germanic funeral offerings was never as great as among the Scythians whose graves have been excavated is that the Scythian princes had such vast numbers of horses, and also because they had little else *but* horses and the objects associated with them.

In a slightly disguised form the memory of this rite lasted into Christian times and throughout the Middle Ages. Right down to the Reformation the will of any English person of substance contains in the preamble 'and I leave my best horse as a mortuary to the Church of St Peter at Norton' (or Sutton or Eston or Weston, in Cumberland or Norfolk or Sussex or Devon), the parish where the deceased was buried. The horse was of course sold and the proceeds applied to the good of the church. But the bequest always included saddlery, showing the original intention to provide for the Ride of the Dead.

About the beginning of this century the name 'Celtic pony' was coined by an expert in zoology, whose competence we would not dispute, to denote a type or group of characteristic recurrent strains of horse whose existence and importance to our theme we recognize. But to us the choice of name seems an unfortunate one, for it tends inevitably to conjure up in the reader a false image—false in terms of human history. 'Nordic pony' would have suited us better if the word Nordic had not acquired a distinctly offensive smell since the middle 1930's; it is still redolent of the bogus anthropology and crackpot 'historical theory' of Rosenberg and Goebbels. We propose to say 'North Atlantic pony' hereinafter. We avoid the term Celtic in this context because Celtic can only be strictly applied to a group of languages. It can also be applied to a highly characteristic style of art some of whose practitioners certainly spoke Celtic languages—but did all of them?—in central and north-west Europe in the late Bronze and the earlier Iron Ages. The people whom the Greeks called Keltoi or Galatoi and who called themselves by a variety of names belonged to the Indo-European language group, who had their earliest known habitat in the grass lands around the Caspian Sea; they formed successive waves of emigration when bad grazing seasons and the pressure of Mongolian and Turkic neighbours drove them out of that region century after century until their descendants were spread all over Europe, Iran and northern India, and had imposed their language and religious and social ideas over wide tracts of the Old World. The Greek, the Italic, the Albanian and other groups preceded the Celts and settled on the north shore of the Mediterranean. After them were to come the Balts, the Germans, the Slavs, of the same language group, taking a more northerly course.

But of all these the Celts were the most widely spread. All the way along the Danube and over the Hellespont to Asia Minor (St Paul's Galatians), Bohemia, the Black Forest, northern Italy, Switzerland, Gaul, Belgium; and the two last widely separated waves spilling over the Pyrenees into Iberia and over the Channel into the British Isles—the ends of the earth as the ancients knew it. Thus the realm of the Celts stretches far beyond the habitat, at any time, of the North Atlantic pony; the latter includes Norway, but about the only place in north-west Europe where *no* characteristic Celtic remains have been found is the Scandinavian peninsula. (Denmark, especially Jutland, is another matter.) The Celtic culture was a horse culture, though not so exclusively so or so highly developed as that of the Scythians and related Indo-European tribes like Sarmatians and Antes, who seem to stand midway between the Persians, the Slavs and Celts. Scythian customs and art and technique deeply affected the Celts in all equestrian matters—which is as much as to say in all that affected the ruling class of the early Celts. The words of the British chief Caradog of Demetia, standing in chains before the Emperor Claudius after nine years of bloody resistance, are a conscious requiem for the free Celtic way of life: 'I had horses, men, arms, wealth. What wonder if I parted with them reluctantly? Yet if it pleases you Romans to be lords of all the world, do you expect that the world will gladly accept that servitude?' But unconsciously, by the order in which he lists the desirable things of life, this speech of Caradog reflects the scale of values by which the Celtic warrior-caste lived and died.

It is a sobering thought that horses, fully developed as they were then, were amongst the animals who witnessed man's first uncertain steps on this earth, when he emerged from—what? Even then many species of *Equus* had roamed the earth for over two million years—man by contrast is almost a newcomer, and perhaps one of the least developed, for he has not yet learnt to live in peace with his own kind. *Homo sapiens* has to learn what *Equus* has long since forgotten. But as we know that all animals are constantly changing, given time possibly *Homo sapiens* will change to the advantage of his fellow creatures.

Several learned men have devoted their lives to the study of *Equus* and it is due to them that today we know—almost beyond doubt—the early origin of the horse. Without going into a biological study of the crossing of black and white mice in order to prove how or why horses are certain colours, it will be sufficient if a brief outline is given of the horse's early development. We shall see how in the two thousand years since Caesar the horse changed and developed or disappeared under certain conditions, and we shall presently examine how he has further developed into those breeds which are today common to our island.

Darwin believed that horses had one common ancestor which was 'dun-coloured and more or less striped', which was domesticated in pre-historic times in central Asia. Others believe that horses had a multiple origin and included amongst their ancestors several quite distinct wild species.

J. Cassar Ewart said that if Darwin's theory was correct 'crossing members of the different breeds ought sooner or later to result in dun-coloured striped offspring'. This, however, never seems to happen unless one of the parents or one of the grandparents is dun-coloured and striped. A very common result of crossing horses is the production of chestnut offspring—the ground colour of hybrids between horses and zebras being very frequently chestnut, taken along with the fact that striped duns are obtained only when one of the parents is dun-coloured and striped, may support the view that the remote ancestor of the *Equidae* was of a chestnut or foxy-red colour; but it sheds no light on the origin of the domestic breeds.

It is not possible to understand the development and breeding of our present-day domestic horses unless we have some knowledge of the remote ancestors of *Equidae*. The evolution of the horse can be followed from the beginning of the Tertiary epoch up to the end of the Ice Age.

Most zoologists now assume that our domestic horses and ponies have sprung from three wild species, of which one species still exists apparently unaltered in *Equus przevalskii*, which is still to be found in the plateau district of the Altai Mountains. Dr Erna Mohr has recently published a booklet in which she states quite definitely that Przevalskii's horse does still exist—although not all the specimens in captivity which go under that name or that of the Mongolian wild horse are genuinely pure-bred. *Equus przevalskii* is known as the *Steppe* variety; it has long ears, an erect mane and a mule-like tail with a tuft round the root, a convex profile and a very long face bent downwards; the body is short, the limbs slender and the hoofs longer and narrower than in the *Forest* type; it is also less stupid than the *Forest*, which is 'best represented by more or less striped dun-coloured broad-headed elk-nosed horses, with the face nearly in line with the cranium, the ears broad and the eyes prominent'. These horses have a long body, strong limbs, thick joints and broad hoofs. In 1907 Professor Ewart wrote that though horses of this type are not found in a wild state, one occasionally comes across semi-domesticated members of the *Forest* variety in outlying parts of north-western Europe. Latter-day zoologists apparently also term this variety the Diluvial.

The third variety is described as the *Plateau*, which includes 'slender limbed horses with narrow heads, small ears, large eyes, a fine muzzle, a flat nose and long neck and small hoofs. A typical example of this variety now living is the *Celtic* pony of north-western Europe; less typical members are occasionally met with in Arabia, North Africa and

15. The Steppe Horse at the other side of the world—Japanese woodcut of American travellers riding and driving Manchurian ponies, about 1860.

Mexico'. No doubt the Tarpan, which still exists today, and the *Celtic* are one and the same.

In 1870 Professor Huxley came to the conclusion that modern horses had descended from *Hipparion*, a three-toed horse. Fossil remains occur in the Pliocene deposits, near Athens, and in the Siwalik Hills of India. More primitive forms still have been found in the Tertiary deposits of Europe. However, in 1876 Huxley thought that America was the original home of the species.

The earliest horse known was *Eohippus*, who came from a primeval mammal with five toes, some two or three million years ago, in the Eocene period. *Eohippus* was very small—only about twelve inches high. Remains have been found in the clay of Kent and Suffolk, and on the Continent and in North America. This little animal had four hoofs on each fore limb and three on each hind limb, but the middle toe of each foot was larger than the others.

So *Eohippus* had begun to develop and during many 'strivings in different directions—during a period of roughly two million years, eventually ended in the single-hoofed horses, asses and zebras, and almost at the beginning of the Tertiaries the horses parted company with their hoofed relatives which ultimately gave rise to the oxen, deer, camels and other ungulates in which the weight is supported entirely or mainly by the third-fourth toes, i.e. from the remote ancestors of the even-toed ungulates. Quite possibly these little *Equidae* were of a fawn colour, with either dark stripes or light spots'.

In the course of many thousands of years *Eohippus* was succeeded by other and rather more developed types. And so the Eocene period comes to a close and we enter upon the Miocene, which brought about a change of climate and for the horses a change of environment. The early Miocene horses were named *Mesohippus*. They ranged in size from 18 to 24 hands, but at the end of the Miocene there were horses standing nearly 14 hands. Gradually the middle toe became larger and the fifth meta-carpal became slender—rather like a 'splint' on a modern horse. During the later part of this period three distinct three-toed species lived in America, and these were *Hyperhippidium*, who was adapted for a forest life, *Mesohippus*, like a racehorse in build, extremely fleet and so able to live a free life on the open plains, and the last one *Protohippus*, whose conformation was intermediate and hence he spent his life partly in the forests and partly in the open. He was very small, only about 36 inches high—and although he seems to have been made rather on the lines of a Shetland pony, Professor Ewart says there is no proof of any present-day horses being descended from him—or that any of these three types were the ancestors of asses and zebras.

Remains of these early horses have also been found in other parts of the world, and 'in the Siwalik Hills of India the little three-hoofed *Hipparion*, before becoming extinct, gave rise to a one-hoofed descend-ant'. Remains of *Hippariones* have also been found in Greece. 'Of several species of the horses which inhabited the Old World during Pliocene times only two need be mentioned.'

For some reason, however, all the horses died out in North America during the Pleistocene period, although they seem to have continued for some time in South America.

About a thousand years ago the equine race missed recolonizing America by the narrowest of margins. Up to now archaeology has failed to reveal any definite remains of the Norse colony in what Leif the Lucky and Erik the Red called Wineland. But the written evidence of that settlement is too profuse and precise to be ignored. The later and more elaborate expeditions, mounted from Iceland, took live-stock with them. Horses are not specifically mentioned in the saga, but the word used—*fé*—could under certain circumstances imply horses as well as horned beasts. Cattle are only mentioned once, at a dramatic moment when the aboriginal *skraelings* (either Indians or Eskimos) were creeping up to surprise the settlement; the bull, who was turned out with the cows, saw them, and let out such a bellow that the *skraelings* turned and fled at the sight and sound of this strange animal. If the wheel of human destiny had spun but a little further—even if the human colonists had with-drawn—Cartier and Cabot might have been faced with countless herds of feral ponies, of mixed Shetland-Highland-Fjording-Gudbrandsdal descent, just as the western America pioneers met the vast herds of feral horses, descended from those turned loose by the Spanish *conquistadores*, roaming the plains along with the bison, the antelope and the caribou.

But archaeology has now shown us the sites of the Norse settlements of the same date in Greenland, in considerable numbers. The sites of these abandoned farmsteads contain the bones of all the domestic animals of Scandinavia, including the horse. This settlement lasted a little longer than did the Roman occupation of Britain—about five hundred years. It failed because within that time the climate of Greenland deteriorated sharply, and the Norsemen could not make the necessary adjustment to their way of life. Neither could their horses. Probably Greenland marks the limit of wet and cold and lack of calcium and sunlight which the horse can endure. The right type of pony flourishes in Shetland and Faeroe and Iceland, but the southern tip of Greenland is, and was, too much. There is a wild arctic bovine species—the musk-ox—but there has never been a wild arctic equoid species.

The end of Norse Greenland was not chronicled in writing; we know only that it occurred early in the fifteenth century, and that it must have been a horrible and gloomy one, not inevitable but brought about by a too-rigid clinging to the way of life the Greenlanders had practised in the old country. From the first it had been impossible to grow cereal crops to ripeness, yet they continued to depend on imported corn, supplemented mainly by milk products. For various reasons the corn ships ceased to make the Greenland voyage. As the climate worsened, the period of lactation in the sheep and cattle shortened to the point where there was not enough cheese or butter (even rancid butter) to last from one 'summer' to the next. In order to protect the live-stock from the weather and from the raiding Eskimo, it became the custom to house them all for nine months in the year, in spite of the fact that in the arctic summer haymaking is scarcely possible. In the last stage before the end, all the Greenlanders of Norse stock had scurvy and many were lepers, while all the live-stock were tubercular and rachitic. It would be interesting to know which went last—the sheep, the horses, the swine or the cattle. It might have been possible for the people to survive by reverting to nomadic pastoralism—to let the stock winter out, and to follow them, with tents and with snow-shelters, to the places where some grazing was still to be had under the snow. The animals might have adapted themselves. But for that better human clothes than their homespun woollens would have been essential. It would certainly have been possible to survive by reverting even further to a hunting economy, subsisting entirely on game and fish, which were both plentiful. But they preferred to die like men (some kind of men) than to live like beasts. So while, in the little stone churches whose foundations still lie in the

Greenland valleys, the priest celebrated a eucharist without bread and without wine, before a diseased and starving congregation, by the light of tallow candles (for without bees there was no wax) which the said congregation would have been only too glad to eat, the terrible little yellow men laughed and grew fat. They were terrible, these little slit-eyed Men from Midnight, because they came down *from the north*, from the land of cold and darkness and death. But they remembered what the Norsemen had forgotten, and lived without horses, by hunting alone.

However in the last phase of the Tertiary period horses were to be found in Asia, Europe and North Africa, but it is still not known how many species inhabited the Old World in preglacial times and how many survived the Ice Age in Asia and Europe. But it is certain that during the Pleistocene period several kinds of horses were found in Europe, horses of the *Forest* type in south England, in Prussia and in the Harz Mountains, and slender-limbed horses in the Rhône valley.

A wealth of information has been obtained from the bone deposits of Solutré, and of course the cave drawings by artists of the Reindeer period at Solutré, Lascaux, Altamira and more recently in the Sahara also show what the horses of prehistoric times looked like. There seems no reason at all to doubt the existence of the three varieties, *Steppe*, *Forest* and *Plateau*. These were not confined to one particular part of the world— and herds of all three were doubtless to be found in various parts of Europe—and if the *Forest* type was to be found in England, why not also the *Plateau*—the latter-day *Celtic* type? One imagines that even in prehistoric times there were crossings of the three species, therefore why not separate herds of the *Steppe-Plateau* cross, which in turn may have crossed with the *Forest* and so on *ad infinitum*, until we have the many and various mixed types which bring us within the limits of this story.

Professor Ewart further writes: 'An examination of the bones found at Solutré and elsewhere, and of the numerous carvings, engravings and drawings points to the conclusion that several species of horses inhabited Europe during the later portion of the Palaeolithic period, and further that during the Reindeer period some progress was made in domesti-cating the horse. It is difficult to say how many species of horses were crowded into the south of Europe during the cold phase which brought the Reindeer hunters from the north, but apparently in addition to varieties with a large head and large teeth there were varieties with strong limbs and broad hoofs and also varieties with slender limbs, a small head and a fine muzzle.' As already indicated, the *Steppe* horse (*E. przevalskii*) of the Gobi Desert has a very large head, but narrow hoofs and slender limbs, while the recent *Forest* horse has a short, proud head, broad hoofs and strong limbs. Further, it has been mentioned that the North Atlantic pony (a member of the *Plateau* variety) has a narrow head and slender limbs, and is otherwise very different from the *Steppe* and *Forest* forms.

'If it can be shown that there are grounds for believing the *Steppe*, *Forest* and *Plateau* varieties agree in their main points with three wild species hunted by Palaeolithic Man, an important step will have been taken towards proving the multiple origin of the horses now living under domestication, i.e. towards accounting for the marked differences which exist amongst modern horses.'

Now the *Steppe* horse does still exist in the Gobi Desert. Professor Ewart says that 'it is represented by three races living to the east, south and west of Kobado'. However, present-day information seems to show that there is probably only one herd of *E. przevalskii* left. What were thought sixty years ago to be genuine *przevalskii* horses appear to have been cross-bred with the domestic Mongolian ponies and eventually herds of these were semi-wild. However, it does exist; it is yellow-dun or bay-dun with black points and an eel stripe; occasionally it shows a faint shoulder stripe and perhaps very slight bars on the legs. All the callosities are present, which is not the case in the *Plateau* type. The foot is long and narrow and the heels more contracted—in the *Forest* horse the hoof is broad and otherwise well adapted for soft ground. In Przevalskii's horse the hard, narrow hoof is adapted for the hard, dry ground of the desert and steppe. 'The mane is erect and short with fairly long ears; the distance between the eyes and nostrils is great, partly because the eyes are nearer the ears, but chiefly because the face is relatively longer than in other types of horses.' The outline from eyes to muzzle is more or less convex. They are clean-legged, but with flat bone. It has five lumbar vertebrae (the *Forest* has six). There are, says Professor Ewart, few obstacles of a reasonable height which it will not clear, batter down or scramble over, and it willingly crosses water (which the *Forest* type dreads).

Taking all the information together, it does seem that the Reindeer cave artists of Solutré drew the *Steppe* horse—that he existed then, in herds in Europe, and that he has not changed but is identical with those horses still to be found in Mongolia. A skull from Remagen proves that about the same period narrow-browed, long-faced horses lived in the Rhine valley.

But also at Solutré there were found remains of stout-limbed, large-jointed and broad-hoofed horses. *Forest* animals most frequently have striped or spotted coats, to make their owners less conspicuous, and breeds long domesticated often begin life with a striped or spotted coat and these sometimes remain throughout life. From information gathered by M. Piette and M. Boule, it is assumed that in 'the broad-hoofed horse after Pleistocene the striping was more perfect than in any of the other varieties'.

It may hence be taken for granted that horses of the *Forest* type, i.e. horses having a general resemblance to the fjord horses of Norway, were common in the south of Europe towards the end of the Palaeolithic period, i.e. from twenty to thirty thousand years ago. A typical *Forest* horse, like a *Steppe* horse, is a dark yellow-dun with black points, which tends to become light brown or bay rather than red—hence, while intensification of the colour of the *Steppe* horse would probably result in a chestnut, a like change in the *Forest* horse would more likely produce a bay. The *Forest* horse has been known to be striped—even to the face, neck, shoulders and flank. The mane and tail are long and wavy. The hoofs are broad and rounded to enable him to walk on soft marshy ground. He has well-developed ergots and chestnuts. The head is broad and short, the ears are also broad and set wide apart: 'The outline of the face for some distance beyond the level of the eyes is concave, but about midway between the eyes and nostrils it becomes convex.' So that the face of the *Forest* horse rather resembles an elk, and like the elk he can feed on shrubs and leaves and grasses. The *Forest* horse has a strong, stout but rather long body, and short, strong legs, the tail set on low, and between the loins and the root of the tail the dorsal band lies in a shallow groove.

The *Forest* horse, like the *Steppe* horse, has eighteen pairs of ribs and six instead of five lumbar vertebrae. The action is free and high but owing to his conformation one would not expect him to gallop or jump or even trot for great distances. Here, very obviously, is the ancestor of our 'cold-blooded' horses.

Drawings in the Dordogne and Combarelles Caves show the *Forest* type quite distinctly—and one imagines that it is this type which latter-day scientists on the Continent call Diluvial—as they equally appear to refer to the *Plateau* or North Atlantic type as Tarpan.

During the Pleistocene period the *Forest* type seems to have had a wide distribution, for a skull was also found in Pomerania, and in the British Museum there are bones which indicate that horses of the *Forest* type were common in Kent and Essex and in the south of France.

There is also evidence left by the artists of prehistoric times that a third type of flat-nosed horse existed, and was to be found alongside the Roman-nosed and elk-nosed horses. These were horses with well-furnished tails, drooping hind quarters and long, slender limbs; and from these very probably have sprung our light ponies and, by artificial selection of centuries-long duration, very probably also the Barbs and Arabs. The present-day representative of this type is most likely the North Atlantic pony or Tarpan.

The head is small and narrow with a fine muzzle, small ears, large eyes, straight or concave face, heavy mane and tail. He has only two chestnuts—front chestnuts. Hoofs are intermediate between the *Steppe* and *Forest* variety. The vertebrae are larger, making the neck longer and chest deeper. He is yellow-dun in colour, with very faint, almost unnoticeable stripes.

Fifty years ago Professor Ewart compared the present day North Atlantic pony to the *Plateau* type. Probably the Tarpan, more recently discovered still to exist in Poland, is also a near relation to the North

Atlantic, but it is said that the coat of the Tarpan changes to white in winter.

All these varieties, or if you like sub-species, of horse had evolved before the British Isles were separated from continental Europe, an event which happened some time between 20,000 and 10,000 B.C. All of them were reasonably plentiful in northern and western Europe, and all of them could have walked into Britain dry-shod without any interference or help from man (such men as there were in those times). To get an idea of what this part of the world looked like in the period between the final retreat of the ice-sheet and the sinking of the land that made the North Sea and the Channel, one need only regard a physical map of the area with special attention, say, to the fifty-fathom contour of the sea bed. This line represents the coastline at a given point in the post-glacial period. It shows us Europe already with a deeply indented coastline to the north-west, with islands lying off it, as now. (See facing page.)

Only the islands are not Britain. They are, reading from north to south: Iceland (a slightly larger and closer Iceland than we have now); Faeroe (one big island about the size of Cornwall and Devon together); Shetland (also one big island); three islands to the west of it now drowned and known to fishermen as Faeroe Bank, Bill Bailey's Bank and Lousy Bank: an island about the size of Man in the centre of the present Rockall Bank, running up to a central peak the top twenty feet of which still stand out of the water, and a slightly larger island about 180 miles west of Clew Bay (the present Porcupine Bank). Ireland is a peninsula about one-third again the size of the present island, joined to the mainland by an isthmus from Donegal to Islay. A long fjord about thirty miles wide runs down the middle of what is now St George's Channel and the Irish Sea. All the Inner Hebrides are joined to the mainland, but the Outer Hebrides are what the inhabitants still call them—the Long Island, one continuous land from Barra Head to the Butt of Lewis. The Orkneys are just an extension of Caithness, with a quite narrow sound separating them from Shetland. The south shore of the Moray Firth instead of turning sharply to the south at Peterhead stretches away east to the Skagerrak. Many islands lie off it between Shetland and Norway, where there are now none. Half way along it there is a pair of huge inlets, the mouths of the Rhine, but a monstrous Rhine into which all the rivers of eastern Britain south of Aberdeenshire have emptied themselves. It flows northward through a vast flat plain that contains several lakes, and a low range of hills where the Dogger Bank now is. Its biggest tributary you may call the Channel River which gathers all the waters of northern France and southern England and rises in a hollow plain somewhere north-west of the Channel Isles. Between that point and Scilly ran the last land bridge with the Continent, and when this broke down it must have done so in the presence of a large and fairly advanced human population, because oral traditions of the disaster were handed down and are to be found in a shadowy form

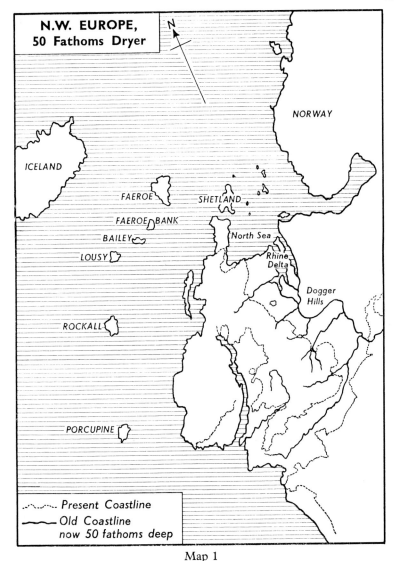

N.W. EUROPE,
50 Fathoms Dryer

NORWAY

ICELAND

FAEROE

SHETLAND

FAEROE BANK

BAILEY

North Sea

LOUSY

Rhine
Delta

Dogger
Hills

ROCKALL

PORCUPINE

..⌐\.⌐⌐.. Present Coastline
————— Old Coastline
      now 50 fathoms deep

Map 1

in the Arthurian accounts of the Land of Lyonesse. Let us say that Lyonesse was drowned in 15,000 B.C., in the great period of the Old Stone Age hunters, marooning our three types of horses. There now ensues a period of some 14,000 years during which no more horses can come to Britain, even if new types of horse evolve on the Continent, unless men bring them by sea. And no man made a ship good enough to carry live horses until some time in the late Bronze Age—say 1000 B.C.

It has also been suggested that Palaeolithic man not only hunted horses for food, but maintained herds of semi-wild horses as Laplanders today maintain herds of reindeer. He may also have domesticated horses, for there are in existence drawings and carvings showing horses with lines suggestive of headstalls or halters; and M. Piette says that for ten or perhaps twenty thousand years the halter was exclusively used, and even now in some parts of the world the halter has not yet given place to a bridle, i.e. to a head-piece adapted for carrying a bit. Nevertheless the oldest recognizable picture of people leading horses (foals) in halters is not Palaeolithic, only Mesolithic (16).

Though horses inhabited England in Palaeolithic times, their remains have not been found in Neolithic burial mounds. Therefore it is supposed that the horse was rarely used in Britain until the Bronze Age. In fact there are some reasons for believing that the horse became extinct in Britain towards the end of the Palaeolithic period, and did not reappear until Neolithic times—some say not until the Bronze Age. If the skulls in the British Museum from Walthamstow, Essex, belong to

16. The earliest unquestionable picture of domestic horses, from Canforos de Peñarubia, Spain.

the Neolithic Age, horses either did not become extinct in Britain during, say, the Reindeer period, or they were re-introduced sooner than is generally assumed by antiquaries.[1] Judged by their measurements *the Walthamstow horses were cross-bred animals*, and were hence probably domesticated—and closely approached the *Forest* and the *Plateau* variety.

'In forms adapted for arid sandy wastes, and for plateaux with the few fertile areas separated by wide and almost barren deserts, the coat is, with rare exceptions, of a dun, grey or rufous colour, with at the most white patches to serve as recognition marks. In varieties which from the outset are adapted for a forest life the coat is usually of a fawn colour and richly decorated with stripes or spots.

'The fjord horses of Norway, the horses of Iceland and of the western highlands and islands of Scotland and in fact horses all over the world— in Mongolia, Tibet, India and Arabia—characterized by a short, broad head, a short neck, a long body and short limbs ending in broad hoofs, have often a well-marked dorsal band, and in some cases vestiges of stripes on the face, neck and trunk. The view that these stripes have been inherited from members of the *Forest* variety is supported by crossing experiments.'

The foregoing is a summary of all we know about the horses living wild in Britain before the men of the New Stone Age arrived.

[1] But once the land-bridge between England and the Continent had sunk under the sea, they could only be introduced in ships, and no Neolithic boat could transport horses alive.

The oldest recognizable piece of harness found in Britain comes from a cave above the Heathery Burn near Stanhope on the Wear in County Durham. The cave was inhabited (apparently for many generations) by a family of copper-smiths who also smelted metal from the local pits. The date is rather early Bronze Age and none of the bronze bits they made has been preserved. But the cheek-pieces have. They are made of deer's antler, not bronze, and are like the corresponding part of what is now called a Liverpool driving bit. Probably made for the artisan's own use, and showing that these metal workers, like the tinkers who are their last living successors in the same tradition, travelled about in wagons, doing repairs on the spot, or making the models most in demand in the district where they happened to be working. Their base is close to the centre of modern Dales pony breeding.

It is possible that the early domestic horses were even smaller than the wild prototype. For long zoologists were reluctant to consider the longhorn cattle of the Windmill Hill people as descended from the urus, the gigantic wild ox which survived wild in eastern Europe until well into historic times, simply because the Windmill Hill cattle were so much smaller than the wild oxen. But consider the circumstances of their capture and the conditions under which the first generations of domestic grazing animals were kept. In the first place, the best adult specimens would never be caught alive. Only the sickly wild cows, only the unsound wild mares. Of wild calves and foals, the late-born would be most likely to be captured, handicapped as they were by being born after the spring flush of grass, unable to keep up with the herd on migration and saved from the wolves only by the intervention of man. Saved. Better perhaps for these foals if the wolves had got them than for those unskilled, soil-scratching proto-peasants to bring them up by hand. What could the Neolithic 'farmer' produce to wean a foal or a calf? At best gruel, if he could spare the precious grain. But to make gruel implies the ability to boil water. Boiling water can be done without metal kettles, but it takes a lot of learning and involves dropping red-hot stones one by one into an earthen pot of cold water; it is a slow process, and the farmer's dinner has to be cooked in the same pot. Once weaning was over, there was no hay because, though corn can be reaped with the jawbone of an ass or pony set with small flints in the tooth-sockets, this is no tool for mowing. Having survived the winter by luck and a lot of browsing on gorse and brier shoots, munching of weathered acorns and the like, the young stock face the spring on such range of grazing as is consistent with security on the Neolithic farm. The capacity of Stone Age men to build fences was limited, and largely devoted to fencing the deer out of their grain-plots. So was their capacity to clear the forest with axes of polished slate. Unlimited range, not richness of pasture, kept the wild herds in good heart, as generous range still keeps our mountain breeds. Neolithic grazing was limited beyond our imagining. So just as the primitive longhorn, itself part-ancestor of some of our biggest beef-and-draught breeds, was a mere stunted caricature of *bos primigenius*, its wild ancestor, so the earliest domestic ponies may soon have degenerated into big-headed dwarfs like the pitiful cattle of India today.

Faults of conformation may also have been artificially developed simply because the few horses of the tribe were so precious. Just as some stallions in modern studs are half crazy with claustrophobia because they are 'too valuable' to get more than half an hour in the exercise paddock a day, or to enjoy even a semblance of normal herd life, so these immature 'sacred cows', and sacred colts too, were cabin'd, cribb'd and confined. If not penned up, then restrained by a variety of halters, tethers, clogs and hobbles all of the crudest design and workmanship calculated to distort young bones and stretch young sinews in the wrong directions. Later in life came working gear equally crippling. Little of this has survived, but early agricultural tools are poor things compared with the perfected hunting gear of the preceding age. The skin kayak, the harpoons, the nets, the wonderful laminated composite horn bows, even the boomerangs, of a fully developed hunting culture are things of beauty in themselves and of maximum efficiency within their range. But to judge by the progress in agricultural tool-making, the skilled bowyer and net-weaver must have turned into a miserable botcher of harness.

Only by the capture of more wild specimens could the existing domestic stock be improved, and all the time man in western Europe was losing his hunting skill. First, because many of the large grazing animals had vanished with the change of climate. The herds of reindeer and elk were no more to be found outside Scandinavia, and now many tribes in Britain hunted no game larger than the hare or the pig, perhaps many filled the pot with rats and squirrels. Second, because the demands of agriculture itself left no time to practise the art of venery, except for the very few. Only the specialist could now track the wild herds, intercept them at their drinking places or in defiles on migration routes, and catch them in nets or with lassos. And the specialist would demand a price of much corn for a live foal. The farmer, too, after many generations of ground-grubbing, had grown out of touch with large animals. When he ceased to live and die on the same terms as the wild herds, he gained something and also lost something—the paradoxical but none the less real sympathy of the hunter for the hunted, that mystery which the anti-blood-sport crusaders will never comprehend. This is apparent in their art. The naked carnivorous men of the Old Stone Age could draw stallions and stags to the life, to do honour to the divine spirit of the wild herds, even though the immediate purposes of the drawing were to compass the death, by hunt-magic, of the individual horse or deer. The house-dwelling, fully clad peasant could do no such thing.

In view of the fact that light passenger vehicles virtually ceased to exist in medieval Europe, because of the badness of the roads, how was

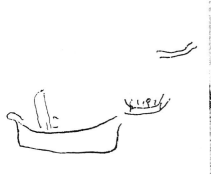

17. *Left :* Rock carving of early Bronze Age 'ship' made of wicker covered with hides, either of horse or seal, like (*right*) a Greenland umiak or 'women's boat'. Like the Galway curragh it will carry children, pigs, goats or sheep with legs tied, but not cattle or horses. (Cf. Pl.)

it possible for the Iron Age Celts to use chariots when they had no roads at all? There is no certain answer to this question because Celtic artists were impressionistic rather than realistic, and their pictures give us little idea of how their chariots were built. Nor do the remains recovered by archaeology contain any of the vital chassis parts in any but the most decayed state. Perhaps part of the answer lies in the statement of a Norwegian sailor, Captain Magnus Andersen. He was the man who commanded the facsimile of the Gokstad viking ship, a copy exact in every detail of the ninth-century original, on the historic voyage in 1893 from Bergen to New York. He said: 'The bottom of the ship was fastened to the ribs with withy below the cross-beams. The bottom as well as the keel could therefore yield to the movements of the ship, and in a heavy sea it would rise and fall as much as three-quarters of an inch. But strangely enough the ship was watertight all the same. Its elasticity was also apparent in other ways. In a heavy sea the gunnel would twist up to six inches out of line. All this elasticity combined with the fine lines, naturally made for speed. . . .' The only nails in the Gokstad ship were used to fasten the planks of the skin to each other. The skin as a whole was *sewn* to the frame timbers with willow withy.

Elasticity is probably the answer in the case of the Celtic chariots also. This involved, in the case of the viking ships, the use of a certain amount of green timber, so that these ships were not built to last, at least, not without periodical rebuilding. So perhaps the individual chariot had a very short life, but certain rigid parts were used over and over again. The only comparable vehicles are not chariots at all, but the travelling wagons used by the Iron Age Scythians of south Russia and Siberia. Some of these, contained in the deep-frozen graves of Scythian kings, have been preserved entire. They also were for use across country, and some of them were prefabricated and could be assembled or dismantled with no tools more complicated than a mallet. It is assumed that this was to facilitate the crossing of rivers by migrating hordes, but it may equally have been to enable rapid running repairs. This would involve the manufacture of interchangeable spare parts of standard size and shape. Not impossible in Iron Age Scythia or Britain. Every single part of the war-chariot was regarded as expendable, but between battles it was important to salvage wrecks for rebuilding, and what the R.E.M.E. now call cannibalization.

Gallic chariotry became a thing of the past before the Roman conquest of Gaul was over, so that no pictures of Gaulish chariots figure in Roman triumphal monuments. The chariots we see most often in Roman pictures are those of the hippodrome. These were probably modelled originally on the British war-chariot, but they bore the same relation to it as a racing sulky of our day does to a Victorian gig. The hippodrome chariot was stripped to the bare essentials, a mere sketch of a vehicle, like the ones in the Bronze-Age rock-carvings, which of course may not be realistic but a deliberate simplification by the artist, who has reduced his men to pin-figures and the horses to wire models.

But we should dismiss from our minds the thought that a ride in a British war-chariot contained any slightest element of comfort. Exhilaration, yes.[1]

The British war-chariot carried a crew of two, almost naked as the military ritual of an earlier age demanded. We learn from Tacitus (*Agricola*, 12) that it is the armed man who is the retainer and the driver who is the chieftain. His huge shield, with which he protected the driver, symbolized their relationship. In terms of a later military system, the driver is the knight, and the armed man is the shield-bearer—scutifer—escuyer—squire. The duty of the charioteer was to drive up the lanes between the squadrons of cavalry which the Britons employed together with chariots, protected from the barrage of sling-shot, javelins, arrows, etc., by the shield, and deposit his champion in front of the enemy lines. In all well-conducted armies (i.e. other Celtic armies) one of the enemy champions would then come out of the opposing lines and engage in single combat with him. When he won—if he won—the charioteer would pick him up again. Unfortunately for the Britons, the Roman army did not fight like that. Nevertheless one and all—Iceni, Catuvellauni, Trinovantes, Silures, Brigantes—continued to use this technique even when they knew the champions would be engaged in a mellay, not a duel. The reason can only be that these champions were armed with some weapon that could not be wielded effectively either from the

---

[1] While this book was in the press the results of recent excavations at Bagendon, a Belgic *oppidum* (stronghold), Cirencester, near Gloucester, were published. Among animal bones recovered, half belonged to the 'Celtic shorthorn' ox, showing that the local Dobuni were primarily cattlemen and their commonest meat was beef. Also the bones of several chariot ponies of size equal to the modern Dartmoor, and of the type called by Ewart *Plateau*. Also a mint producing exclusively coins with designs of horses. And a forger's den, *ditto ditto*.

chariot or on horseback. In practice this means only a big battle-axe or a two-handed sword. But nothing of the nature of the Lochaber axe has been found in British remains, so the weapon of their champions must have been the claymore, the 'great sword' later renowned as the characteristic arm of Highland infantry, and which is found abundantly in British iron-age sites. Tacitus said it had no point for thrusting. This method of fighting, practised later in Britain than in Gaul, was practised later still in Ireland, and from Irish sagas we learn the curious fact that the eating of horseflesh or any food derived from it, even unwittingly, produced a state of ritual uncleanness which prohibited the eater from driving for a period of weeks. This taboo was called 'geasa'.

These taboos persisted for many centuries after the heroic way of life in Celtic society had passed away. We have recently had a long and pain-ful demonstration of the fact that the sale of horseflesh for human consumption is still not feasible in Ireland, and an Englishman observed of the Highlanders near Inverness about 1730:

'The poorest Creature that loses a horse by death would sell him for 3*d*. to a soldier who made it part of his business to buy them, and he made not only 6*d*. of the carcass to feed the Hounds' (beagles kept by English garrison officers) 'but got two Shillings or half a Crown for the Hide. But the owner would not flay the Horse, though he knew very well how to do it, as almost everyone here is something of a Tanner; and the reason is that it is an employment only fit for the hangman.' He adds that the local children shouted this epithet after the soldier in the streets.

The question of Arab imports into these islands, and how early they can be dated, is fraught with difficulties. In the first place British archaeologists in excavating and dating a site are in the habit of examin-ing animal bones, if any, classifying simply as dog, pig, ox, horse, etc. without further particularization, and not preserving them. Yet it should be possible, here and there, to identify the genuine Arab from the density as well as the slenderness of the cannon bone, even after a few thousand years. A well-known technical guide to this subject, I. W. Cornwall's *Bones for the Archaeologist*, teaches how to distinguish equine from other animal skeletons, but not how to distinguish one breed from another, or, apart from dentition, how to tell the bones of young from those of adult horses. So that where an archaeologist reports laconically 'small horse' he may be dealing either with a pony or with a foal or yearling of some larger breed. The characteristic skull formation of the Arab as distinct from that of other breeds is nowhere discussed in this work.

Obvious candidates for the title of First Importer of Arabs are the Romans and the Phoenicians. With their ample technical resources and formidable thoroughness, the former may be expected to have brought Arab horses to Britain, just as they brought Chian wine and Colchester oysters to any part of the empire where they were wanted, *if* they had a use for Arab horses in Britain. (In fact archaeology does confirm the presence of Arab troop-horses in the military zone of Britain in Roman times.) Their importation would have depended in the days of the Antonines solely on the importance attached by the military commander to the need for fast light cavalry horses, expense being a secondary consideration. Roman shipping was intended primarily to convey corn and slaves from overseas provinces to the metropolis. Both are somewhat bulky cargoes, demanding the kind of hold-space that might conveniently be used to ship horses on the outward voyage.

About the Phoenicians we cannot be so positive. In the first place the Phoenicians who came to Britain (but really perhaps only to the Scilly Isles) did not come from the Palestinian ports of Tyre and Sidon but from the western Phoenician trading posts like Carthage in Africa and Tartessos in Spain. Therefore, if they brought horses, these were unlikely to have been Arabs but Barbs (that is, if the Barb *is* truly indigenous to North Africa and not a product of the Moslem invasions of the seventh century A.D.). Moreover the merchandise which the Phoenicians sought in Britain was heavy and compact. All they wanted, it seems, was copper, tin and zinc, smelted in ingots. This they bought with the more precious metals, silver and gold, minted or unminted, or traded for wine, which again is a heavy rather than a bulky cargo. We know very little about the carrying capacity of Phoenician ships, but we do know that fresh water is a limiting factor in the carriage of horses by sea. Even a pony will drink eight gallons a day on land, and the dry shipboard diet and presence of salt in the air would generate an even greater thirst. Before the invention of casks, water-skins were not easy to handle and stow on board, and clay water-jars were very heavy, and liable to fracture in a rough sea. Within the Mediterranean it was possible to make long and relatively quick voyages without being out of touch with land for more than forty-eight hours at a time. But to get from Carthage to St Michael's Mount meant first coasting along past the shores of Portugal and Galicia in a fairly straight line, with the opportunity to put in for fresh water as often as required. After Cape Finisterre, however, one could either set a straight course for Ushant and the Scillies, or coast around the Bay of Biscay, taking about three times as long to fetch Ushant, but keeping in touch with watering points. The former was possible and customary in medieval times, but it may not have been possible for more primitive seafarers, even if there was room for horses in their hold. The latter may have been so slow as to be uneconomic. Certainly the Phoenicians for these reasons cannot have carried many horses, and then only at such expense that in order to make a profit— and no Phoenician risked his capital for anything but a thumping profit —the price delivered at St Michael's Mount would be more than all but the very richest Britons would have been willing or able to pay.

Another drawback from which the Phoenicians suffered as shippers of Arab horses to the north was that the selection of good oriental horses demands a certain aesthetic sense as well as an eye to utility. The ancestral stock of the Phoenicians was Philistine, and the name of the Philistines has not become a byword for nothing. Of all the ancient civilizations theirs was the most materialistic. Technically brilliant, it was artistically worthless, wherever it went. What little we know about the architecture of Carthage is not inspiring. Its temples and palaces resembled nothing so much as a collection of super-cinemas in the worst style of the late 1920's, and Carthaginian coins often bear the image of a horse; it is a stiff and characterless picture, in a debased and clumsy imitation of Hellenistic art. The Carthaginian army contained no native cavalry; even the great Hannibal employed Gaulish and Iberian mercenaries in this role. The Carthaginians have been called a crabbed,

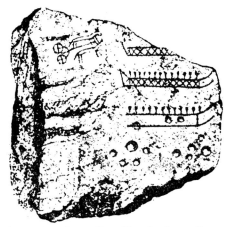

18. Rock carving from Scandinavia, later Bronze Age. The sea-going ship first appears simultaneously with the two-horse chariot in these monuments, where the chariot is always represented in the same form, whether in Sweden or in the Sahara.

morose and sadistic people. They were not the men to pick the horses that, in order to find a ready sale among Celtic chieftains, must, first of all, fill the eye.

On balance we think that, whatever Arab horses reached Britain before the Roman invasion, the most part walked overland from Massilia to Boulogne or perhaps to Brittany (Armorica), where the seaboard tribe of Veneti had the most serviceable ships suitable for ferrying live-stock.

Artistic evidence, though it tells us nothing of the means whereby they came to Britain, does assure us of the presence, among others, of a type of horse which we would not hesitate to call Arab. There is in all Celtic art a tendency to stylize since its true function was not to portray but to embellish. But sometimes the stylization almost takes the form of caricature, and some feature of the equine head, or the whole figure, is seized on and exaggerated because it makes a pattern which the artist finds appropriate to the space which he is decorating. Such traits as the bulging forehead, goggle eyes, flared nostrils, triangular skull and characteristic tail carriage of the Arab horse all lend themselves to this treatment and all are to be seen in various horse designs of insular Celtic art during the Iron Age. A later example, at second hand. Norwegian art, even medieval art, is strongly influenced by Celtic tendencies, and on P27 we see a twelfth-century Norwegian impression, stylized in just this way, of a horse with pronounced Arab features that have been treated almost in the manner of a cartoonist. We shall have cause to consider later on by what means a horse of this very oriental, warm-blooded type can have arrived in Norway to serve as a model for the artist. And if in Norway, why not in Britain?

CHAPTER THREE

Roman Britain

————————⟨⟨⟨⟨⟨⟨⟩⟩⟩⟩⟩⟩————————

To the goddess Epona and the clan spirit of the Leuci
in fulfilment of a vow by Tiberius Justinus Titianus,
orderly to the brigadier commanding XXII
(Antoniniana) Legion.

Inscription at Mainz.

THIS inscription is interesting, not because it has any direct reference to
Britain (XXII was stationed in the province known as Upper Germany,
and the Leuci were a Celtic tribe living about the headwaters of the
Moselle), but because of the background of this votary of Epona. He was
a legionary, Italian born, a Roman citizen either by birth or by virtue of
enlistment: not a member of the provincial or foreign auxiliaries.

From the beginning to the very end, the Roman legions, which were
essentially heavy infantry brigades trained also in field engineering, contained a small mounted element. This was not cavalry in the true sense.
It corresponded much more closely to the sub-unit which was on the
establishment of every German infantry regiment down to 1945, known
as a *Reiterzug* or mounted platoon. It was useful as an advance guard,
or as a rearguard, on the march, and could be employed effectively as a
fighting patrol. But very often it was used as a pool of mounted orderlies
to maintain communications, or as an escort for the brigadier. When
serving in this last capacity it is easy to see how easily our friend
Justinus might have obtained the no doubt coveted appointment of
brigadier's batman, for which he duly gave thanks to his tutelary
goddess.

Before passing on to the Roman cavalry regiments proper, we should
at least take note of this, what is somewhat grandiosely called 'legionary
cavalry', since the extent to which it used imported troop-horses and/or
local British remounts differs in no way from the same question as
applied to the auxiliary cavalry, except that in so far as it functioned as
cavalry at all it was in the role of 'light horse' rather than mounted
infantry or armoured cavalry. There never were more than four legions
in Britain at any one time, with perhaps an outside limit of four hundred
mounted men between them. It is reasonable to suppose them mounted

35

on light, rather fast horses. As they were constantly around his head-quarters, it would be natural for the legion commander to insist on good-looking ones, in order to increase his prestige in the eyes of the extremely horse-conscious natives (P12).

In its origin this little unit goes back to the days when the whole levy of Roman citizens, able and entitled to bear arms, was *the* legion. The sons of well-off families were allowed to perform their military service on horseback, and formed a troop by themselves. They were never as effective as the Roman foot; no Roman victory is attributable to the tactical intervention of this force; and in due course they were 'kicked upstairs'. Families who had once rendered this service became an order of lesser nobility known as *equites*, somewhat inaccurately called 'knights' in English cribs to the classics. But as the official hierarchy of the empire hardened into a system, the *equites* gave their name to a certain grade of officer, corresponding to what we now call 'field officers'. Commanders of legionary cohorts (*tribuni*), of auxiliary cohorts (*praefecti*) and of auxiliary cavalry regiments (*praefecti alae equitum*), and the senior staff officers of legions (*tribuni militum*), were all called equestrian officers: they are the majors, lieutenant-colonels and colonels of the Roman Army and they could be transferred from unit to unit, from arm to arm of the service, from province to province, and finally from the armed forces to the civil service. Both in a military and in a civil capacity they were accustomed to ride, but this is not why they are called equestrian. On tombstones, triumphal arches, etc., they are usually depicted at the head of their battalions riding pacing horses.

The career of the Elder Pliny is so typical that it will serve as a model for the life and death of a Roman of the equestrian class in the first century of our era. He entered the public service as a cavalry officer, stationed in Lower Germany, with one of the Tungrian or Batavian or Frisian regiments of horse. During this appointment he wrote a small-arms manual entitled *Javelin Drill for Mounted Troops*. In his middle years he served in the civil administration of Provence, of Spain and of Africa, with the rank of procurator. He died at the age of fifty-six, poisoned by fumes of the erupting Vesuvius which he inhaled in the course of carrying out his duties as commodore (*praefectus*) of a naval squadron based on Puteoli. This varied curriculum was punctuated by periods of retirement to the family estates at Como in Cisalpine Gaul: it was quite possible for equestrian officers to withdraw from the public service for quite long periods in this way without loss of seniority or, it seems, esteem.

Only a Roman could have led a life like this, and only a Roman could have written a book like his only surviving work, the great *Natural History*, which is an encyclopaedic mixture of observed fact and non-sensical literary borrowing. Some of its contents are relevant to the subject of our book, and in the section on horses we find, mixed in with old wives' tales about the impregnation of mares by the west wind, so naïve that we marvel any cavalry officer of experience could possibly credit them, a valuable note on the Spain of Pliny's day, which was one of the foremost provinces of the empire for horse breeding and especially military horse breeding. 'The Galician and Asturian tribes of the North', he says, 'breed a kind of horse which they call thieldones (or celdones) in their language. This smaller strain, which we call Asturcones, do not trot but have a special easy [*mollis*] pace produced by alternately moving both legs on the one side.' This is the first mention in history of the Spanish pacing gennet which was to enjoy great esteem in our country for the next sixteen hundred years or so.

We deal with the military side of the Roman occupation, as it affected our subject, before the civil, because it was the subject of the most considerable and detailed study of Romano-British horses that has ever been made, though nearly fifty years have now elapsed since it was completed. This was Professor Ewart's appendix to J. Curle's *A Roman Frontier Post* (1911). But also because something has been said in the last chapter of the primacy of Celtic, and especially Gallic, tradition in the Roman cavalry arm. Whereas in the legions, and in the infantry cohorts of the auxiliaries, words of command were always given in Latin regardless of the nationality of the troops, so that the most barbaric infantry soldier always understood the Latin for 'Left turn, right turn, quick march', etc., if he knew nothing else, such knowledge was useless in the cavalry. Arrian, in his book on the art of generalship, tells us that there was no Latin word for many technical expressions regarding the cavalry, especially for various formations and manœuvres, and that drill orders were given in Gallic or Ibero-Celtic throughout the service.

What this meant in terms of actual regiments is roughly this. By the end of the second century there were twenty-eight Roman cavalry units of Celtic origin, half of which had been first raised in Gallia Lugdunensis (Central France). The rest came from other parts of France, Belgium, northern Spain (Celtiberian), Britain and the western or Helvetian part of Switzerland, which provided one cavalry regiment from the canton Valais. Of the fourteen units from Gallia Lugdunensis, seven served in Britain at one time or another; they were:

Indiana	Sabiniana
Petriana	Classiana
Proculaiana	Agrippiana
II Sebosiana	

Petriana and Sabiniana were stationed on Hadrian's Wall, where there were also two Spanish units, the First and Second Asturians. The other two cavalry regiments on the Wall were the First Pannonians (Hungary) and the Sarmatians (Scythia). There was besides an independent squadron of Frisian cavalry called Prince Hnaufrid's Own, in the central sector, and on the left wing, at Burgh-by-Sands, another Frisian unit known as the Cuneus Frisonum Aballavensis, also identified at Papcastle near Cockermouth in Cumberland.[1]

One soldier whose tombstone we reproduce on P10 belonged to the First Thracian Cavalry, stationed at Colchester. There was one other Spanish cavalry unit in the province, the First Vettones, and another Gallic regiment from the modern departments of Vaucluse and Hautes Alpes called the Ala Vocontiorum.

It is this last which must claim most of our attention. It was stationed for a long time at Trimontium, now known as Newstead, near Melrose in Roxburghshire. There was a large camp here, big enough to accommodate a whole legion, first occupied during Agricola's Caledonian expedition in A.D. 79. The position commanded an important crossing of the Tweed, and the permanent fort which was built on the site of the camp was meant to contain a force equivalent to about two battalions. This fort was garrisoned by the Vocontii and one other unit. What the second unit was we do not know, but the horse lines certainly contained more animals than the 512 horses which were the establishment of the Ala Vocontiorum, but not nearly as many as the 1,024 which two cavalry regiments would require. The second unit was therefore most likely what was known as a *cohors millenaria equitata*, a mixed force much on the lines of the guides or scouts or frontier forces of later armies, consisting of 760 infantry and 240 cavalry, or more correctly mounted infantry.

From the very numerous horse bones on the site, Professor Ewart has shown the existence of six types of horse and pony besides intermediate types, the result of cross-breeding between these six. There was an 11-hand Shetland pony recognizable by its broad forehead, and another breed of pony, also northerly, between 11 and 12 hands, recognizable by its narrow, slightly dished face, which he calls *Celtic*. This had several characteristics now found in some Icelandic and Highland ponies; modern representatives of this strain are predominantly dun with eel stripe in colour and have a thick tuft of hairs high up on the dock, wider than the middle part of the tail. Both the foregoing were too small for riding and were probably used for transport, either in harness or in pack-trains. Then come two types the size of an Exmoor (12–13 hands), one with slender limbs and general 'Arab' conformation, such as ran wild all over western Europe in Pleistocene times, and the other more thickset and longer in the back, usually known as the *Forest* (not

---

[1] Ten different horsed units have been identified by name on Hadrian's Wall and between it and the Antonine Wall. This includes the Cohort of Syrian Archers from Homs, stationed at Carvoran. The designation 'cohort' normally implies that all the men in it were infantry, but *mounted* archers were an Arab speciality. As no other Roman unit consisting solely of bowmen is known, no precedent can be quoted, but if the Romans regarded the bow (as they did the sling) as a weapon that belonged 'by rights' to infantry, then they would quite likely call a unit of horse-archers 'cohort', just as in later times dragoons went in 'companies', not squadrons. In any case the Carvoran barracks had a shrine to Epona.

to be confused with New Forest) pony. There were also horses of around 14 hands, indistinguishable, so far as the skeleton goes, from the modern desert-bred Arab. Lastly there were some much heavier animals, with heads the size of 17-hand modern thoroughbreds, but standing only between 14 and 15 hands, coarse-limbed and with Roman noses, or, in some cases, a straight profile but a pronounced backward slope to the skull just above the eyes.[1] This type is called Siwalik after a range of hills in northern India where its bones are found in great profusion on prehistoric sites. It corresponds well to the description by Tacitus (Agricola's son-in-law) of German war-horses, which in sum he considered 'ugly and useless'.

Quite likely these last belonged to the *cohors equitatus*, the Caledonian Protectorate Levies or whatever they called themselves. Such units were always worse mounted than regular cavalry units; this information we owe to an unwonted burst of candour on the part of a Roman inspecting general, part of whose report on a similar unit in North Africa has been preserved. In it he says that the Guides did very well, *considering*, etc.

We leave to our readers the task of identifying one of these types on the tombstone of the cavalryman from Gloucester (P11) but would draw attention to the equestrian portrait of John Ball (P35), who appears to be riding, more than a thousand years later, something midway between the *Forest* and the Siwalik types as they are represented at Newstead. At Corbridge (Corstopitum), Northumberland, bones were found representing some of the same types, as follows: the 'Arab', the 'Exmoor' and the 'Forest'.

From the south of England, also in the early phase of purely military occupation, we have some concrete evidence at Colchester, which was a Belgic town called Camulodunum before the Romans came to Essex in A.D. 43 under Aulus Plautius. Horse bones are found in conjunction with Belgic coins dating back to A.D. 10. These are the same bones as occur at Glastonbury and at Newstead where they were assigned by Professor Ewart to the 11-hand *Celtic* type with fairly narrow, dished face. In this immediate pre-Roman period there are horseshoes from Colchester of the right size for these ponies, with six countersunk nail-heads arranged in the modern manner, but a wavy outline to the outer edge of the shoe produced by the manner of punching the nail-holes. The same ponies have left their bones in the first level of Roman occupation (a garrison and a settlement of time-expired soldiers), which came to an end when the colony was sacked and burned by Queen Boudicca in A.D. 65. In order to discourage further occupation Boudicca's braves dropped quarters of dead horse down the wells. But these bones in the wells are from 15-hand Siwalik horses, which must therefore have been among the very first Roman remounts in this country, or possibly

---

[1] The site also yielded the bones of a well-grown jackass, which must, in its brief and lonely lifetime, have been a strong contender for the title of the Most Northerly Donkey in the World.

introduced by the Belgae themselves in the later waves of their invasion, which was proceeding simultaneously with the first stages of the Roman conquest. On the other hand the auxiliary cavalry in Caesar's force, which did not remain in the country, consisted of Germans, and it is possible that Aulus Plautius brought a German cavalry regiment, whose title we do not know, mounted on horses from Lower Germany.

Only two cavalry regiments have been identified with the word for 'British' in their titles. They are Ala Prima Flavia Augusta Britannica in Hungary, and Ala Quinta Brittonum in Morocco. No trace of Alae Brittonum 2 to 4 has ever been found, and perhaps they never existed. Though British recruits with the right kind of equestrian tribal background were available, enough to form many regiments, it seems that these young men, at any rate from the northern tribes such as Brigantes, Parisii and Votadini, were accepted, along with the children of serving troopers, by the cavalry units stationed on the Scottish and Welsh marches. But there were mixed 'Guides' units in other parts of the empire containing a British element, and there was also the household cavalry, the mounted equivalent of the Praetorian Guard cohorts. These *equites singulares* were a true foreign legion, recruited from every tribe in the empire and from some outside it. Among the numerous altars at the regimental headquarters in Rome are some dedicated to Hercules (a classical disguise for some god, perhaps Thor, worshipped by German troopers), to Epona (inevitably) and to the Matres Campestres. The Campestres were deities of Celtic, specifically of Gallic, origin, and were a trinity like many Celtic gods.[1] But their cult was much more exclusive than that of Epona. Ostlers, donkeymen and muleteers were never admitted to it, nor soldiers of the administrative branch employed on stud farms, remount depots, etc. It was strictly for combatants only, but apart from that we do not know much about it. They had a temple in the barracks of the First Asturian Cavalry at Benwell, on the Wall.

Details of Roman saddlery and equipment from the early days of the occupation can best be seen in the remains from Hod Hill, a few miles north-west of Blandford in Dorset, a complete account of which was published by the British Museum while this book was in the press.

As long as the system of military organization set up in the early days of the empire lasted, the best chance of military advancement for a young Briton lay without question in the cavalry arm. Or indeed for any non-Roman. Roman authors have explicitly stated that even an Italian-born Roman citizen, without aristocratic connections, could not hope to reach the rank (or rather appointment) of *primus pilus* in a legion before the age of sixty; the *primus pilus* was only O.C. of the first company of

---

[1] They may in fact have been just Epona × 3, since most Celtic goddesses had triple aspects—as the Maiden, beautiful but austere, whose displeasure is death; as the Matron, beautiful and benevolent, a combined mother/mistress figure; and as the Hag, ancient, hideous and cruel, whose pleasure is death.

the first battalion, and beyond that lay only the *praefectura castrorum*, a sort of quartermastership equivalent to semi-retirement. (The extraordinary thing is that so many Roman officers *did* survive, fit for duty, up to the age of sixty.) On the other hand an illiterate Scythian or Batavian could enlist in an auxiliary regiment of horse at eighteen and might before the end of his twenty-five years' contract find himself a lieutenant-colonel commanding the regiment (*praefectus alae*).

Towards the beginning of the third century of our era Roman military ideas underwent a fundamental change, and the military system devised by Marius which had done such good service for so many generations was gradually replaced by another war establishment which recognized the legion and its relation to the supporting arms of cavalry and light-armed infantry, slingers, archers, etc., for the time-honoured anachronism which it had become.

In the first place, the nature of the military threat had changed. It was no longer a matter of protecting two relatively short land frontiers, the Welsh Marches and the Hadrian Line. Seaborne Saxons and Picts, and seaborne Scotti from Ireland and Galloway might fall on any point of the east and west coasts of Britain. For this reason it became necessary, while not reducing the frontier garrisons further than could be helped, to dispose the strategic reserve in greater depth southward than the old bases at Lincoln, Chester, Carlisle, York. For the same reason these strategic reserves had to be made more mobile. The legions retained their special entity and privileged position, but their establishment was greatly reduced and the proportion of cavalry, which now ceased to be a mere supporting arm, was increased; at the same time a new class of infantryman, called a *spatharius* because armed with the Gothic broadsword or *spatha*, came into prominence. In fact the *spatharius* differed but little from the Gaelic gallowglass with his claymore. Regiments now were called *numeri*, and the distinction between legions and auxiliaries became less important than that between both these classes and the new, less completely Romanized forces of *foederati* or 'allies' and *limitanei* or 'frontier guards'. Hengest and Horsa, who will appear in due course, were really *foederati* in the service of a Kentish king who regarded himself as a Roman. The *limitanei* were part-time territorials who were granted land while still serving, in contrast to the old type of legionary or auxiliary who was only given land as a gratuity on his discharge. They could therefore never be effectively used as a field army or *masse de manœuvre* even if they happened to be mounted. In their non-military capacity those *limitanei* settled in the south adopted the Mediterranean custom of living in a walled town and farming, either in person or with slaves or hired labour, holdings in the surrounding countryside. Over the years their morale sank lower and lower and they became lamentably Maginot minded. The end of Roman Colchester came, perhaps not by assault at all, but when the Saxons occupied the surrounding farmlands and the *limitanei* were starved out. Things had been different in the good old times of the Antonines when the soldiery lived in a walled camp from which the bazaar quarter was quite separate but which included a vast reserve of rations and fodder in the middle of the camp. Even behind their walls the *limitanei* were not too reliable, and in the end they failed to hold the quite considerable fortifications of Chichester and Pevensey against Saxon assault.

But in the north the *limitanei* appear to have been made of sterner stuff. They had never regarded the Wall as something to hide behind, but as essentially something to tangle the feet of the enemy (who was primarily a cattle raider and remained so to the end) while they hit him as hard as they could.

In the south the command was divided between the Count of the Saxon Shore, who controlled the ports and garrisons and fleet based on the east and south coasts, with an extensive coastguard and alarm signalling system, and the Duke of the Britains, who controlled the field army. Between them these two officers commanded a greater number of cavalry than of infantry. It is not quite clear how far their operational authority extended over the frontier garrisons. Possibly these depended in theory on the Duke of the Britains, more likely they formed two more independent commands, but in either case their fate is likely to have been something as follows.

Throughout the last two centuries of Roman occupation the bulk of recruits for the force on the Hadrian Line had been supplied by the British tribes living to north and south of it, so that the units in the right sector of the Hadrian Line, though still bearing such traditional regimental names as Asturienses, Vocontii, Sarmati, Petriana, Pannoni, etc., were in fact pretty solidly manned with Votadini, the sons and grandsons of Votadini who had themselves served in these units for many generations back. This does not imply any weakening of the military fibre. The machine was efficient enough to absorb much less suitable material than that. It was not by recruiting a few more thousand Germans for the legions (yes, even for the legions) that the Roman Army came by its inglorious end: it was by promoting half a dozen German generals too many.

The Roman army in Britain was not worn away by attrition at the frontiers. It collapsed because it was hollowed out from within. From time to time troops were withdrawn to meet yet another attack on Gaul by Germans from across the Rhine, and more frequently than that they were withdrawn to support some *coup d'état* by a general with political ambitions to set him up as Emperor of the West, or Princeps Galliarum, or more modestly, as Tyrant of Armorica or the like. But such actions are referred to always as the withdrawal of the legions, which is essentially what they were. Only the legions, which were often sent back again if the *putsch* did not come off, or again returned to duty by the successful *caudillo* if it did come off, took part in these adventures, together with such of the auxiliary troops as were normally brigaded with them. But the regiments on the Wall of Hadrian, and on the Welsh marches, do not seem to have been so closely linked to the legions at York and Chester and Caerleon whose tactical task was to support them. At most there was some occasional thinning out on the two frontiers, and the gaps were filled by new contracts with *foederati* and new establishments of *limitanei*. So that when the end came (and it came incredibly slowly and by degrees, so that men did not recognize it when the effective power of Rome really had departed never to return) it found these two forces more or less intact, more or less self-supporting, dependent on the supply bases in the south perhaps only for wine, for oil and for cash.

After an indeterminate period during which no rations, no orders, no pay, had reached the garrison of the Hadrian Line, it became clear to the commanders of the various units that the corps headquarters had melted away behind them, and that now they were on their own. Either some enemy had interposed himself between the garrison and the head-quarters at York, or that headquarters, and the Sixth Legion which was its strategic reserve, had been withdrawn, perhaps to support the political efforts of yet another general who fancied himself as an emperor-maker. The *tribuni* and *praefecti* of the right or Newcastle sector could not agree, in this contingency, as to which of them should take command. This is not surprising since the system of promotion in equestrian ranks of the Roman Army was intricate in the extreme, and depended on a system of cross-posting all over the empire, and of preferment alter-nately in the armed forces and the civil administration. Only the staff of the military secretary's branch, the *ab epistulis*, could tell at any given moment which of these officers was really senior and due for promotion next. They therefore went to Cunedda, King of the Votadini, and placed themselves under his command. Their action is not so shockingly un-Roman as it seems. Cunedda was not just another barbarian chief-tain; his forefathers and his tribe had been allies of the Roman people for many generations; his tenants had made a decent living selling pork and beef to Roman quartermasters, and horses to the Roman remounts department, for as long as anyone could remember. The daughters of his subjects had borne sons to auxiliary soldiers in the cantonments, and these sons had grown up to enlist as auxiliaries themselves, and when their time expired they had taken up farms on his tribal lands. Cunedda himself was probably an ex-officer of auxiliaries; his father and his grandfather, Paternus and Aeternus, had borne Roman names, and it was only a reaction of nationalist feeling, common in Britain about the end of the fourth century, that had led his parents to give him a British name (Kenneth).

Cunedda took command. After all, his own sons were probably serving in one or more of the regiments concerned. Living as he did in times when any chorus boy could be raised to the imperial throne by favour of the Praetorian Guard: when the current commander-in-chief of all Roman armies in the west was a Vandal named Stilicho, why should not a gentleman of ancient British stock and some military experience, backed by half a dozen regular colonels, assume at least some of the functions of the Dux Brittaniarum? Meanwhile his position, cut off from support in the south and with no warships of his own to cover his seaward flank, was untenable. If the whereabouts of the Dux Brittaniarum and his legion were unknown, there was, somewhere in the West Midlands, another Roman force under the command of the Comes Brittaniarum. This force was supposed to be coming to the aid of the King of the Ordovices, whose tribal levies were heavily engaged with Irish raiders on the coast of North Wales. The only chance of survival for the people of Cunedda lay in reaching some area where there were Romano-British forces still capable of resistance. He therefore evacuated his whole territory, which stretched from the Tyne to the Forth. Everything that could walk he set on foot. Everything portable he had loaded in wagons. Everything immovable he set on fire. Leaving behind them an empty land, the Votadini, escorted by the remnants of that army which had for so long been their protectors since the day when it had been their conqueror, trekked down across the devastated province of Brittania Prima, past the still derelict ruins of towns sacked in the great Pictish War a generation ago, into the province of Venedotia which the Welsh call Gwynnedd. There, with or without the help of the Count of the Britains, they did manage to drive out the Irish pirates. They settled on the holdings of Ordovices whom the Irish had slain, and became the Gododdin of Welsh legend. Their brood mares were turned out on the Welsh hills to replenish the depleted Ordovician stock. Medieval Welsh princes, in so far as they did not trace their descent from Irish invaders, traced it from Cunedda, Lord of the Cymry. So, probably, did Aurelius Ambrosianus (Emrys Wledig), called the Last of the Romans, and Uther Pendragon, and Arthur or Artorius, the equestrian hero with the Roman name, who so nearly saved—who perhaps after all did save —Britain from the dark night of barbarism.

Taliesin the bard was to sing of Cunedda thus:

> Cunedda ventured into dire conflict
> Into the scathe of a hundred conflicts before his shriving.
> He was prominent in the tumult with nine hundred horse.
> Among us he would freely distribute milch cows in summer;
> He would freely distribute war horses in winter.
> He would freely distribute sparkling wine and oil.
> He was a strenuous scion of a brave stock.
> A man did he appear—a lad of lion aspect.
> The son of Aeternus was a tremendous ruler.

Here we see some prudent strokes of policy for a Dark Age king. When the raiding season begins he distributes the milch cows among his subjects, making it harder to drive all away in one herd. When it is over and it is no longer necessary to keep all the squadrons mobilized, he disperses the war-horses on a work-for-keep basis among the mountain farmers, who have become a new kind of *limitanei*. We also see, from the reference to wine and oil, that somehow or other he managed to reopen communications with the south where these desirable things (indispensable things to anyone brought up in the Roman tradition) were produced. The reference to nine hundred horse might mean that he had once commanded one of the Roman milliary *alae*—nine hundred could reasonably be the effective fighting strength out of a paper establishment of 1,024.

It is nearly two hundred years after Cunedda's time before we hear the last of the Votadini. Their last sortie, against a more tenacious enemy than either the Picts or the Irish, was celebrated by Aneirin the bard, in his lament for the three hundred young horsemen of Manau Gododdin who perished in the assault on Catterick—all of them except the poet himself. They formed a special task-force, trained at the court of a North Welsh king called Mynyddawg for what was meant to be a decisive blow against the two small English kingdoms in Northumbria. If it had succeeded in taking Catterick, where the Great North Road crosses the Swale, communication between Deira (north and east Yorkshire) and Bernicia (Northumberland) would have been cut, while that between the chain of Welsh states, Elmet (west Yorkshire), Cumbria, Strathclyde, Rheged (Galloway) would have been maintained. Though the operation was carefully prepared and rehearsed for a whole year, it failed, and the Northumbrian counter-attack under Theodric of Bamburgh, called the Flamebearer, surrounded from the north and completely isolated the kingdom of Elmet, which itself was completely overwhelmed thirty years later, so that at last the English penetrated to the shores of the Irish Sea. Except for the systematic training and rehearsal the Votadini had lost all resemblance to Roman auxiliaries and had become again what they were in the beginning—the hereditary fighting caste of a wholly Celtic society. Yet the true requiem of the Romano-Celtic *equites* is this dirge of Aneirin for his companions, with their

> Instinct of man, with the years of youth,
> With courage for fighting.
> Fast long-maned stallions
> Under thighs of a fine youth
> With bright, blue-bladed swords.

Perhaps the Roman regiments on the left or Carlisle sector of the Hadrian Line faded away in a similar manner, becoming an hereditary military caste in the service of the King of the Novantae. At any rate, one of his descendants, Coroticus of Galloway, was addressed by St Patrick a hundred years after Cunedda's day as a fairly powerful Christian monarch controlling, apparently, Strathclyde and Cumberland, and preserving some Roman military traditions.

No aspect of life in what is called sub-Roman Britain can be discussed, however briefly, without some reference to the Arthurian problem. Least of all the horse-breeding aspect. In the days when

Arthur, 'rex quondam, rexque futurus'—the king that was and the king that shall be—was written off by the learned as just a glorious myth, conjured up by the imagination of the defeated Celts to comfort them through centuries of subjection, there was no need to consider what sort of horses King Arthur rode, nor why his favourite hound should have been called Kaball, which means 'the Pony'. But over the last hundred years the learned have had somewhat of a change of heart about King Arthur. Apart from the emotional need (if Arthur had never existed it would have been necessary for the Welsh to invent him, for the same reasons as the Romans invented Aeneas) there are certain historical facts which cannot be satisfactorily explained without postulating, about the year 500, a British military leader of more than ordinary ability, capable of halting the Saxon advance (which otherwise progresses quite steadily), according to both written and archaeological evidence, for a period of about two generations, so that the Saxon penetration of the area between Dorset and the Severn was postponed for half a century.

Historians more and more are coming to believe in such a leader, not perhaps a king but a mercenary general commanding the combined forces of many British kinglets, stiffened by a small *corps d'élite* owing allegiance only to himself—'Arthur's Men', who were the real-life originals of the legendary Knights of the Round Table. Knights postulate armour and lances. The use of the lance demands the existence of stirrups. Armour means big horses to carry it into battle. Arthur without the knights is unthinkable, not merely on account of poetic tradition,[1] but because of the way military technique was developing in Europe at that time. He could only have beaten the Saxons, in the 'nine pitched battles' of tradition, by borrowing Roman methods. Not from the original western Rome, which was now a pale impotent ghost, but from the eastern Rome that was still alive and fighting, with another thousand years of life before it. More than two centuries before the Romans left Britain, the legion, the heavy infantry brigade fighting in close order, had ceased to dominate the continental battlefield. More and more, supremacy was passing to mounted archers and various other forms of cavalry. The genius of Byzantium had evolved the cataphract, a mailed horseman armed primarily with a lance, by imitation of the Gothic horsemen who had caused such havoc at the battle of Adrianople. With these cataphracts large areas in the western Mediterranean were brought back

---

[1] 'Britain's overlord is never reckless.
He cast his thigh over the steeds of Mathon,
Of the Moelych breed; though so mettlesome,
Summer and winter they are quiet to handle
Because of the racecourse provided to train them
And the whipcord in disgrace to correct them.'

Taliesin on King Arthur.

'Him who gave me wine, beer and mead,
And big spirited horses in fine condition.'

Poet addressing patron.

under Roman rule by Count Belisarius, Justinian's brilliant commander-in-chief. The limiting factor was that there were only two kinds of horse suitable to carry a cataphract—neither was native to Asia Minor, where the chief Roman strength now lay: a huge Persian breed that had existed from the time of Xerxes, very expensive and difficult to procure, and the big cold-blooded Diluvial horses that the Goths had brought down with them from their long sojourn on the Baltic coast. The latter could now be obtained in fair numbers from Gothic breeders in Pannonia and Noricum, which correspond roughly to eastern Austria and western Hungary. (There is still a breed of heavy horse in Austria called a Noriker.) But Gothic kings preferred to horse their own followers with these, and hire out complete squadrons to serve as *foederati* in the Roman armies.

Assuming that Arthur lived and fought and died in Britain, or at the least that Ambrosius Aurelianus, an undoubted historical figure, did what Arthur is reputed to have done, how was he to horse the 'knights'? It is a long way from Britain to Noricum at the best of times, and in Arthur's time half a dozen minor wars were in full swing along the route. Neither Arthur nor his syndicate of princely employers can have been very flush of money. Imagine a Congolese agent of General Mobutu trying to buy tanks in the open market, say at Pittsburg, Pennsylvania, with a sackful of devalued Belgian francs and a handful of gold nuggets, and you will have some idea of Arthur's problem, even before he got his chargers on board at Boulogne or Nantes or Cherbourg.

We have seen that at least one Roman cavalry regiment on the Hadrian Line in North Britain had been mounted on cold-blooded horses more than fifteen hands high.[1] We do not know how much shipping was available when these regiments were withdrawn to the Continent. It may have been more expedient to sell them off to the Britons and scare up some remounts in Gaul, rather than waste time running a shuttle service with the available transports. After all *huit chevaux—quarante hommes* is a permanent equation not peculiar to the French State Railways, and it would take five times as many troopships *or* five times as long to ferry the horses as it would to ferry the troopers of the Ala Petriana. Suppose this had happened, the descendants of these horses by crossing with native mares must have dwindled considerably in size, but they would have imparted considerable substance, and the descendants of about a thousand troop-horses might well have been pretty numerous by A.D. 500, and perhaps about the size and build of a Fell pony. Perhaps a good Fell pony could do the trick if not kept in action too long. No British armour of Arthur's day has been found, but the original cataphracts wore, not chain mail, but scale mail—small metal plates sewn on to a buff jerkin. It was about as heavy, however, as the 'ring mail' of Anglo-Saxon heroes. A skilfully handled remount

[1] Taliesin says in *The Chair of Teyrnon*: '[Arthur] brought from the great wall Creamy horses used to the saddle.'

squadron of second horses, ridden by virtually unarmed 'squires', might have been able to keep an armoured squadron in action all day, for enough days on end to make mincemeat of a Saxon war-band which was not strong in missile weapons, was capable of only two tactical formations, those known as the 'boar' and the 'shield-ring', and consisted of chieftains in mail shirts armed with swords and a much larger number of commoners in helmets and leather jerkins with wooden shields and spears, axes and dirks *ad lib*. The trick would be to change horses when the enemy were in no position to interfere.

Perhaps then it could have been done with entirely native resources. But of these resources, the steeds of Arthur's men, we know absolutely nothing first hand. Burials of this particular period are comparatively scarce, and it is notoriously hard to say whether the dead man was British or English. Moreover, by definition, Arthur's men were Christians. Naked came they into this world, and naked they departed for the next. No longer, as in ancient Celtic tombs, were there grave-goods, including a bridle for the use of the deceased on the Ride of the Dead. As for the pagan Saxons, for many generations after the migration even the best of them were comparatively poor men, and nothing of any great practical value went into the grave with them. Even the seventh-century East Anglian cenotaph at Sutton Hoo, which belongs to a king and at first sight appears so magnificent, was contained in a ship no longer seaworthy and many of the objects in it are old and worn out. To our sorrow these objects do not include any horse-gear. (Does this bear out what we say about the first Saxon invaders, that they were men to whom there was no room for a horse on shipboard?)

> A grave for Kay, and a grave for Bedivere:
> But where is the grave of Arthur?

Where, for that matter, are the stirrups of Arthur's knights? No stirrup older than of the Viking Age has been found in this country.

The effect of Roman occupation on the peaceful use of the horse in Britain was wholly constructive.[1] In its early stages there was an enormous expansion of trade, at first along lines that were familiar to the British tribes but especially to the Belgae. Before the system of Roman trunk roads was completed there was a boom in pack traffic. Once a certain stage has been reached, not much development is possible in the pack business; it is just a question of horsemanship and loading technique; but pack-horses did require to be shod, if they were to ply on hard tracks, and that is why some of the Belgae used shoes before the Roman came. They could not build proper roads, but they could

---

[1] The largest horse represented in Roman-British art was engraved on a stone formerly built into York City Wall, led in hand by one of the Dioscuri. Even if Castor (or Pollux) is meant to be six feet tall (big for a Roman or a Briton) this horse is only fifteen hands high—but powerfully built.

build the line of single flags, about a foot wide, along which strings of pack animals could trudge. Such tracks, known as 'pack-trods', are still to be seen in the north of England today. Off the main roads, trade followed these tracks throughout the Roman period and for centuries after.

Along the roads marched the transport columns of the legions and their auxiliaries, and the convoys of merchants, Gaulish and Greek and Syrian, who followed in their wake. Some, but not all, of them, used bullock wagons, but some used horses and carts. These were not quite as efficient as some other Roman institutions. Owing to the absence throughout the ancient world of an effective rigid horse-collar, the tractive power of horses in draught was very limited. Maximum loads laid down by some Roman official for a two-wheeled (usually two-horsed) cart, was between two and four hundredweight, and even for a four-wheeled, four-horse wagon, less than ten hundredweight. Large draught horses were to be seen in small numbers in Gaul, like the ones drawing the omnibus or diligence in P13, but very few seem to have come to Britain.

The most startling development was in racing, a cheaper form of circuses for the multitude that involved no expenditure of dearly bought wild animals and gladiators. Moreover, the same horses could race again. The arena, without which no garrison town in the north and west and no commercial and administrative centre in the south was complete, was primarily a hippodrome or racecourse. The technique of chariot driving was a British speciality, preserved here much better than in Gaul, and British drivers and grooms were much in demand throughout the empire. Moreover, throughout the empire also, the size of chariot horses was very small: British ponies 12 or 13 hands high, despite what Hollywood tell us to the contrary, were the ideal chariot team, four abreast, very often over obstacles, as this picture from Arles shows us (P14a). A less elaborate and well-preserved mosaic from a Roman villa at Horkstow in Lincolnshire shows the same sort of event in progress here (P14b).

But the most lasting impression made by the Romans on the British horse trade was caused by the imperial posting service. This was copied from the system in Alexander the Great's dominions, in turn copied from the wonderful posting system of the Persian Empire, and it extended literally from one end of the Roman territory to the other. A special service, called *cursus publicus*, divided in sectors under prefects of equestrian rank who alternated this duty with command in the army, was concerned not only with the upkeep of roads but with the provision and maintenance of horses and vehicles. The latter were of two kinds, one an adaptation of the Celtic chariot, the other a sort of dog-cart, illustrated in P15. For those who could travel light enough, the same horses were available under saddle. But whether in harness or under the saddle, these horses paced when at their travelling gait or cruising speed.

The Roman (ultimately Greek) term for relay horses was *paraveredi*, from which is derived the French word *palefroi* and the English word palfrey, used to describe the typical travelling horse of the Middle Ages.

Horses were bred in Britain and Gaul for export in large numbers, and P16 is a picture from Gallia Narbonensis of a Roman horse-dealer on his way home with a draft which he may have bought in that province, but they are of a type common to both Gaul and Britain, and he may well have bought them this side of the Channel and shipped them from Portus Lemanis or Rutupiae.

The end of Roman rule in southern Britain is even more obscure, if anything, than in the north. It is as if we witnessed the decline of some old country house by stages, without actually witnessing the moment of crisis. When we last see Britannia Court occupied, about A.D. 410, many window-panes are broken and have been mended with board. Still, they *have* been mended. Smoke comes from some of the chimneys. None of the lawns has been mown short enough for a game of croquet, but still they *have* been mown—to make hay. We even catch a glimpse of the owner, Sir Constantine, moving rather stiffly about on the terrace. His clothes are shabby but he does not seem to be starving, and apparently there are still a few servants about the place.

The next time we see it, about 450, the roof is off the hall and the hearths are cold. There is a sort of trailer camp at the bottom of the garden, inhabited by a rabble of Low German spivs, fair-haired didde-cais attended by innumerable lurcher dogs and snotty-faced children. No doubt they have bought the old place for scrap. It seems we have missed the actual day when the old squire died, and the day when the bum-bailiffs moved in on the widowed Lady Constance. Nobody here-abouts seems to remember, or to think it very important, but we reckon it must have been some time about 430; after all, he had been failing for so long, and no heir. . . . When we look closer, we see, between the shacks and the benders and the caravans, tethered to the broken railings of the park, something that might well be old Sir Constantine's old mare. It can't be, of course. Why, she must have been dead these twenty years. But it might be her daughter. She looks rough but not uncared for. That is to say her mane and tail are in a state that old Coroticus the stud-groom would have described as bloody barbarous, but she is not actually lousy, her feet are not overgrown, and she appears well fed. What is more, she has a good-looking foal at foot. The walled espalier garden that was the pride and joy of Sir Constans, the late squire's father, is derelict and grown over with coarse grass. Half the gate is missing and its place is supplied by an old bedstead. In it are grazing a few well-grown yearlings and two-year-olds that also bear a striking resemblance to the old mare. Evidently the spivs know a good horse when they see one. This is not the end of Britannia Court, only a new and rather squalid beginning. *These* are the heirs, these snotty-faced, tow-haired children with their bottoms coming through the seat of their breeches. When he grows up (which will be distressingly early, according to the welfare experts) the eldest of them will marry the youngest grand-daughter of old Coroticus the stud-groom, but his mother will give it out that she is really the granddaughter (or maybe the daughter) of Sir Constantine himself, and in a few generations more everyone will come to believe it, for that is the way history goes. In another two hundred years the descendant of these two will be sitting in the high seat of the bare and black-raftered hangar that is his hall, while across the hearth a thirsty minstrel will be tuning his harp in honour of the current thane of Brettonhall, and of his descent in the tenth generation from Cad-wallon, a scion of the house of Woden, by his union with the Lady Constance the daughter of Constans the son of Constantius the son of Constantine the son of Augustus the son of Caesar the son of Romulus the great-grandson of Shem who was with Noah in the ark. . . . And a few quarts of mead later perhaps he will add some more verses in praise of the thane's horse Silvertop, the son of Goldenfell of the strain of Parafrithus by Caball by Incitatus who was descended in the tenth generation from Mearh the son of Eh who was with Noah in the ark. . . .

It is important to be quite clear about the light in which the Saxons and their kindred tribes regarded the Romans. They had absolutely no feeling of 'racial' superiority. Quite apart from the fact that most of the leading 'barbarian' figures of the early migration period had been in Roman employ at one time or another (people like Cerdic, St Germanus, Hengest, Alaric, Cunedda, all had much the same background) they had all evidence that the Romans were able to do things and obtain things that were quite beyond their own capacities. Their feeling towards the Romans was only of envy and admiration. The only things of their own which the English may have regarded as superior to the Roman equivalent are their law and their poetry, since in neither of these fields did they attempt to copy Roman models. But as late as the middle seventh century a rather second-rate Anglian king will have borne before him in battle an iron standard which is a crude copy of a Roman legionary *signum*. And it is an heirloom, probably having been in the family a century or more.

The Saxon poet who depended for a living on the bounty of an English war-leader sat down in the ruins of Aquae Sulis at Bath and wept because the noble men of old who built such things were no more. What to the English warrior was a precious weapon, a hard-edged sword wrought with magic runes, was often in fact a purely commercial Roman product, stamped with the maker's name but ornamented with the special flashy kind of hilt that was fashionable in west Baltic circles. What to the Romans was quite prosaically Chariot Route No. 1 was to the English Irmenstraet—the Way of the Noble Ones.

Although the characters of the heroic poems—the earlier English epics —were people who lived and died on the fringes of the Roman world like

Attila, Ermaneric, Theodoric, slipping now and then through the gap between the curtains that divided that world from the northern world of barbarism, the Old English minstrels were extremely shy of mentioning the Romans by name. They preferred to speak of 'ealde entas'—the ancient ones of more than human stature—though they knew well the Romans were not giants in any physical sense; or of 'Irmentheod'—the noble people—which makes us think of the Celtic euphemism 'the good people' for the fairies.

What sort of man then, in real life, was the 'noble person' in charge of the section, say between Barnet and Stamford, of Ermine Street, the highway whose Latin name we do not know? He was a very ordinary official of administrative grade, an equestrian procurator of roads and bridges, equivalent in status to a battalion commander in the army, a post which he had probably held at least once and might expect to hold again in some better regiment, if he did not get a posting as G.S.O.1. to a legion. But he was also in charge of government transport on that road, in particular of the relay horses which were its motive power and the legs of the imperial signals system. Suppose that his sector, if he was the occupant of the post, was not overwhelmed by a sudden incursion of Anglian raiders. Suppose that he did not give up his appointment because he found it impossible to work for the British kinglet to whom the last Roman provincial governor had handed over in a too-hasty process of 'Briticization'. Let us take the case where there was a planned withdrawal. Presumably the procurator would have orders to wind up his department and report to Mediolanum. What happened to the horses? Since the imperial lines of communication were being shortened there would be no point in withdrawing them to work in Gaul, where the local road system was adequately provided with post-horses. The sensible thing to do would be to sell them at best price to the local British landowners, Belgic nobles with Roman names who probably had a good eye for a *paraveredus* and whose sons fancied themselves as dashing drivers of the 'gig' type of chariot we have seen in Gaul. From them these horses would soon have passed, or their immediate progeny would have passed, into English hands—as booty, as hostages, as ransom or perhaps even in the normal way of trade or in payment for services rendered by English mercenaries in the service of British kinglets like Vortigern. Men like Hengest and Horsa would set a high value on the *paraveredi*, the noble horses that once had been the property of the Irmentheod.

CHAPTER FOUR

The English and the Vikings

I

'. . . and I leave to the monastery at Burton one
hundred wild horses and sixteen broken stallions as
well as all the remainder of my live and dead stock
except insofar as I have already bequeathed it elsewhere.'

Will of Wulfric, a Mercian thane, 1002.

THIS KIND of bequest is pretty general in the late tenth century. Thus
Aelfwold, Bishop of Crediton, in 1012, bequeathed 'to every man of my
household his mount which I have lent him, and five pounds of silver
to share between them'. Aelfwold also left a stud of 'wild horses'
running on the Buckland estates near Dartmoor, besides ten individual
bequests of saddle-horses, and to his lord the heriot of four horses with
armour which was appropriate to an earl or to a cleric of equivalent rank.

Nothing demonstrates better the association in the Anglo-Saxon mind
of horses with aristocracy than a verse in the Old English Rune Song, a
very ancient poem which was used for teaching the shape and phonetic
values of the magical runic characters to the very restricted class of
persons who would have to use them: ninety stanzas all on the principle
'A was an Archer who shot at a frog', etc. The rune which had the
phonetic value of modern E was written M, but the middle did not dip
so much: its appearance therefore suggested a horse, only slightly
sway-backed, and it was called 'Eh', which is a very archaic word for a
horse, a close relation of the Latin word *equus* and a still closer one of
the modern Gaelic *each*; later it came to be written *eoh* but it soon
dropped out of common speech: it is hard to see why, because it was

one of the very small group of words intelligible both to the English and the Britons.[1] However, by an early date its use was restricted to poetry and only the most grandiose sort of poetry at that. The stanza to memorize the rune Eh went like this: 'Eh byth for eorlum aethelinga wyn. . . .'

> The horse in the eyes of noblemen is the delight of princes,
> A stallion in the pride of his hoofs, when mounted heroes
> Bandy words about him, and always to the ambitious
> A source of comfort.

The rune R, which was given the name *rad*, meaning 'riding', shows that the English, in the dim primeval past at any rate, had not approached the horse, the noble *eh*, without some trepidation. The Rune Song says: '*Rad* seems easy to every warrior while he is indoors, but very courageous to him who travels the highway on the back of a stout horse.' Elsewhere in the same poem occur the words *mearh*, the masculine form corresponding to *miere* (mare), and another archaic word *wicg*, meaning horse, which soon disappears, and a metaphor in which the ship is called *brimhengest* (salt sea stallion) and its rudder *bridol*.

Probably, like *steda*, and for that matter *eoh*, *wicg* once had a precise meaning which it lost, and it gradually became just a poetic term for a riding horse. This precise meaning we shall never know. Its grammatical gender does not help: it was neuter, but no worth-while deductions can be made from this, since the Anglo-Saxon word for woman—*wif*—was also neuter. Its use to poets lay chiefly in the fact that as the only synonym for horse beginning with *w* it could be used in alliterative verses to fit in with a lot of epithets beginning *w*-: notably *wlonc*, which means 'proud'. As to its significance for us it would not be worth recording if one of its compounds had not survived for a little longer. A poem in the Exeter manuscript called 'The Accomplishments of Men' is really a list of technical skills; among verses describing carpenters, draughtsmen, shipwrights, poets, architects and others, there is one which goes

> Some men are clever with horses
> And wise in *wicgcraeft*.

This last word bears a superficial resemblance to our 'witchcraft', but is not its ancestor. The Anglo-Saxon words for sorcery were *wiccung* or *wiccecraeft*. Evidently *wicgcraeft* was veterinary science of some kind—most likely skill in foaling. Among the last generation of Suffolk horsemen a skilled but unlicensed (and often illiterate) horse-doctor was called a *witchman*, and though there has undoubtedly been some confusion with white witches, this Suffolk word is more likely descended from an Old English *wicgmon*, similar to *hengestmon* whose implications are discussed below. A surviving surname which may possibly go back

---

[1] 'Mearh', closely resembling Welsh 'march' = stallion, was another ancient word discarded by the English soon after the Settlement, except in poetry.

to it is Widgery, since Old English -cg was pronounced -dge as in bridge, etc.

That the Anglo-Saxon warrior-class, like the Celtic warrior-class, delighted in swift horses, is proved by certain passages in the Song of Beowulf, the great epic that describes events in southern Scandinavia, perhaps in the fifth century, but which took its final poetic form here in England some two centuries later. Here the warriors go to see the dark mere into which the defeated monster Grendel has dived after having his arm torn off by the hero Beowulf, and

> Thence old comrades again turned backward
> And many a youth, from the joyous journey—
> The brave from the mere on horses riding,
> The lads on shining steeds. . . .
> Now the bold warriors would let the chestnut horses
> Go at a gallop and contend in running
> Wherever they deemed that the ways were fair
> And known for their excellence. . . .
> At whiles in rivalry over the fallow fieldways
> They raced with their horses.

Exactly the same sort of impromptu trial is described in the sober Latin prose of the Northumbrian historian Bede: speaking of the retinue of John, Bishop of Hexham:

... The young men that were with him, and particularly those of the laity, began to entreat the bishop to give them leave to gallop, and make trial of the goodness of their horses. He at first refused, saying, 'it was an idle request'; but at last, being prevailed on by the unanimous desire of so many, 'Do so', said he, 'if you will, but let Herebald have no part in the trial.' I earnestly prayed that I might have leave to ride with the rest, for I relied on an excellent horse, which he had given me, but I could not obtain my request.

When they had several times galloped backwards and forwards, the bishop and I looking on, my wanton humour prevailed, and I could no longer refrain, but though he forbade me, I struck in among them, and began to ride at full speed; at which I heard him call after me, 'Alas! how much you grieve me by riding after that manner.' Though I heard him, I went on against his command; but immediately the fiery horse taking a great leap over a hollow place, I fell, and lost both sense and motion, as if I had been dead; for there was in that place a stone, level with the ground, covered with only a small turf, and no other stone to be found in all that plain; and it happened, as a punishment for my disobedience, either by chance, or by Divine Providence so ordering it, that my head and hand, which in falling I had clapped to my head, hit upon that stone, so that my thumb was broken and my skull cracked, and I lay, as I said, like one dead.

And because I could not move, they stretched a canopy for me to lie in. . . .

The narrator was actually Bede's highly respectable contemporary Herebald, abbot of Tynemouth, who had been in his day a very worldly young man indeed. His is the first account of a riding accident in England. There is also evidence in what seems to be an autobiographical passage from the poet Cynewulf of another sort of horse-race. It runs

> Before him the horse fled,
> Adorned with filigree trappings, along the measured miles.

This sounds much more like the ritual horse-race involving loose horses not ridden or driven, as in the Palio of Siena, that goes back to pagan cults like that of Mars at Rome, which included an annual chariot race and sacrifice. A feature of this ritual is special caparisons. Unfortunately it is as difficult to date Cynewulf as to place him in any particular region of England. Eighth century probably, Northumbria perhaps, is as near as the evidence will take us.

Among the gifts with which King Hrothgar rewarded Beowulf for his deeds were these:

> The Protector of Earls then bade eight [1] horses
> With gold-plated bridles be led into hall
> Under the barriers: on one of them was set
> A jewel-deckt saddle inlaid cunningly;
> That was the high king's seat of battle.

The gold-plated bridles must have been of the pattern with gilt-bronze on the cheek-pieces that we mention as found in Swedish Gotland. So far no jewel-studded saddles have come to light, but more and more archaeological discoveries go to prove that the descriptions of weapons and equipment in the Song of Beowulf are accurate and realistic pictures of royal wear-gear in the south Baltic area from about A.D. 400 onwards.

If the fifth-century leaders of the various war bands bound for Britain made little effort to bring horses with them, it was not because they contemplated with any pleasure the prospect of a life without horses. It is more likely that they had certain information that the British horses might be smaller than theirs but a good deal faster.

Among old-established continental breeds of horses in the lands whose shores face those of Britain, the Frisian bears, in the case of some individuals, a most striking resemblance to the Fell pony of the north-west. But the history of the Frisian people themselves is most closely linked with that of the English. Their language resembles, far more nearly than any other Germanic dialect, the speech of the Anglo-Saxons, and this is apparent not only in the oldest written vernacular records of the two nations but in the similarity of the rustic speech of Friesland and some English dialects of our time, in so far as both have not been swept away by the levelling wind of radio and television. The Frisian territory, even within historical time, once occupied a greater portion of dry land than it does now, and the immersion of their farmlands between what are now the Frisian Islands and the mainland was one of the chief causes which led to the Migration of Peoples in the Baltic-North Sea-Channel coast area. Not that the Frisians minded getting their feet wet;

---

[1] The number of eight horses is perhaps not arbitrarily chosen. According to the Laws of Canute the heriot of an earl was eight horses and their gear. Heriot was the fee in kind which had to be given up to his overlord by every heir before his succession to an hereditary dignity became lawful. Perhaps by conferring this exact fee in the first place, Hrothgar was in effect raising Beowulf to the earldom.

they were a first-class maritime nation and were only supplanted in their naval and mercantile ascendancy by the Norwegians and Danes at the beginning of the Viking Age (say A.D. 800).

Before that they had played some part which is now hard to determine in the settlement of Britain by the Angelcyn. Characteristic Frisian patterns of jewellery turn up in the oldest English grave sites of the Migration Age, and in the oldest English place names of the Settlement period there occur personal names of Frisian type. It is possible that in some measure the Frisian merchant seamen contracted with Angle and Saxon adventurers to ferry their possessions to Britain once they had won a foothold, and that some of them took land along with their clients. The Frisians of the fifth and sixth centuries appear to have been the only North Sea tribe possessing cargo ships that would transport—let us say—live horses.

The most striking evidence for the interweaving of the destiny of the Frisians and the Angelcyn is in the fragment of a poem interpolated into the text of *Beowulf*, and usually called 'The Fight at Finnsburg'. Finn was a king of the Frisians; his name is one of the few that are common to Scandinavian, West Germanic and even Irish families of the heroic age. At one point in this fragment of an epic the Frisians are actually called 'Jutes', which is the more usually accepted name for that section of the Angelcyn which settled in Kent, Wight and the New Forest. Their opponents in this particular fight are variously called Danes and 'Half-Danes' and their leaders appear to be connected by marriage to the royal house of Frisia. Their chief at the moment when the poem opens is called Hnaef but he is killed in action and the command taken over by his kinsman Hengest.

Scholars nowadays tend to think that this Hengest is a real historical character and identical with the brother of Horsa who was employed as a *foederatus* by Vortigern, the post-Roman British king. No character with the name Horsa appears in this fragment, but one of the warriors on Hengest's side bears the name Eaha. This rarely found name bears the same relation to the ancient English word *eoh*—steed—as Horsa does to the word *hors*. Eaha means '(Somebody) of the Horses'.

There is one more link, much nearer the home of the Fell pony. In the last stages of Roman rule, not many generations before the action of the Finnsburgh poem, the garrison of Housesteads (Borcovicum), which was the central fort of the Hadrian Line, consisted of one cohort of auxiliary infantry supported by an independent squadron of federate cavalry, known as the Cuneus Frisiorum. The commander who first brought this band into Roman employ was called either Hnaufrid or Hnaefrid, compound of the name Hnaef.

Historians, supported by archaeologists, have long since discarded the legend of total genocide by the English or even of a wholesale westward retreat by the Britons. There was at most a shifting of political power and of social priorities; even intermarriage between British and English princely families, notably of course in Vortigern's kingdom of Kent. The West Saxon hero Cerdic, ancestor of the kings of Wessex and hence of the present royal family, bears a recognizably Romano-British name— Coroticus or Caradoc. And the Northumbrian poet Caedmon also bore a Celtic name. Caedmon was by his original calling a cowherd, which is significant. It seems that though the English were superior to the Britons in agriculture proper—they had a much better plough—and as woodsmen, being much handier with the axe, and better builders in timber—in animal husbandry they were slightly inferior. It is easier for a conqueror to take over the management of herds than the cultivation of fields from the vanquished, but in the long run less profitable if the conqueror has not such a good way with a cow. The English had come to stay and it was to the long run that they looked. They employed British shepherds and flockmasters, as is proved by the fact that to this day shepherds in the north country count sheep by means of what sounds like a nursery rigmarole, 'Yain, tain, tethera, pethera, pimp . . . ' but is really an only slightly garbled version of the Welsh numerals up to twenty. The Celtic arithmetical system was based on a unit of twenty, unlike the Germanic one, which worked on the dozen, the long hundred and the gross.

Along with the Celtic stockmen there were grooms of British birth, at least in the royal West Saxon household. In the laws of Ine, King of Wessex, who vanished from history in 726, there is a passage assessing the fine to be paid for manslaughter according to the social grade of the victim. Among these grades is listed the 'Welsh horse-thane', which has caused a good deal of dispute among the experts. The most puzzling feature is that the fine is so large that it cannot possibly be meant to atone for the slaying of a mere stable-hand. It puts the horse-thane well and truly in the officer class, whether 'Welsh' means 'British' or just 'foreign'. But homely occupations can in a few generations give their name to important titles, as witness the Constable and the Marshal, those high functionaries of the Frankish Empire whose titles meant originally no more than 'companion of the stables' and 'servant of the mares'. Perhaps as the West Saxon stud was built up from the ruin of the years of conquest so its British head lads rose in the social scale, until by the time of Ine they spoke English as well as the next man and ranked above many Saxon families. Yet they were still thought of as 'the Welsh horse-thanes' as if their skill at their calling were indeed a heritage of their Celtic descent. But the Celtic studsman, unlike the shepherd, has not bequeathed many technical expressions to us—only one short word that we associate almost at once with British native ponies: dun.[1] This word occurred in late Anglo-Saxon, but is not to be found in the dialects of the continental Saxons at any period, nor in any other Teutonic language. It means grey in general, but not the grey of horses: it is the

---

[1] Welsh *dwn*, Gaelic *duinn*.

Celtic word for the horse-colour which the Germans (and perhaps Hengest and Horsa too) call 'wolf-grey'.

This is perhaps all the 'hard' or positive evidence we shall ever have that the Anglo-Saxons took over the British horse-stock with at the most an insignificant admixture of imports. But there is a striking lack of evidence to the contrary!

In the south-Scandinavian–Baltic area, where the ancestors of the English had been spending the last few centuries, there had been ponies but also larger animals. A typical jointed snaffle from Valstenarum, on the Swedish island of Gotland, found in a grave of the late Iron Age, has a mouthpiece five inches wide, which is consistent with a stature of between fifteen and sixteen hands. The rings of this snaffle were bronze, and the reins were not directly sewn on to the rings but on to clasps of gilded bronze, showing that the horse which it fitted was used on important occasions. Another bronze bit with jointed mouthpiece was found on a site with much closer association to the migration of the English tribes. This was actually in the Nydam boat, a vessel discovered in Slesvig nearly a hundred years ago, which is thought to be the identical type of boat in which Hengest, Horsa, Cerdic and their contemporaries actually made the crossing of the North Sea. This boat differs in important details from Roman ships and from the superb Scandinavian ships of the Viking Age. In the first place it had no keel. It had a very narrow beam, some ten feet, in proportion to its total length of seventy-five feet, and was only four feet deep at the waist. Stability, even in calm weather, cannot have been its most striking feature. Moreover, the sides, instead of 'tumbling home' as the sides of the Viking ships did at the waist, were prolonged in a very shallow curve, so that it would have shipped a great deal of water over the gunwale. As three of the bits were found actually in the skulls [1] of horses inside the boat, it is tempting, but would be very misleading, to jump to certain 'obvious' conclusions. This is not a transport overwhelmed by some mysterious disaster on the very point of setting sail for Britain (it had no mast or sail, anyhow). It had been deliberately sunk in the shallow water of a bog, and many of the weapons in the boat had been ritually damaged to make them useless to anyone who might try to salvage them. This was in fact an elaborate burial which combined some features of the Scandinavian ship-cenotaph with the horse-graves of the Scythians. The beach on which the Nydam chieftain was to disembark and mount his horse was not the earthly shore of Britain but the shore of the next world. His boat would have been quite unsuitable for transporting live horses.

One of the few certainties about the Anglo-Saxon conquest is the complete decline and disappearance of the chariot in this period. It had ceased to have any military significance at the time of the Antonine campaigns in Caledonia, but had survived in the Roman province and

---

[1] The headless skeleton of one horse lay *outside* the boat. It was 12 hands 3 inches high. The bit is the headpiece to this chapter.

in the neighbouring Celtic kingdoms for various civilian purposes. Now it vanishes utterly. In the whole of his *History of the English Church and People*, Bede, writing about three centuries after the end of Roman rule, has no mention of chariots. Once, in his *Life of St Cuthbert*, he mentions a 'chariot' (*currus*) which is obviously not a war-chariot but some kind of travelling carriage, belonging to the wife of King Egfrid of Northumbria. It was in use in the far north-west of the English territory, significantly enough at the site of the Roman city of Carlisle, on the marches of the old territory of the Brigantes and the Novantae.

There is no direct evidence that the Saxons and their kindred brought any horses with them, and they had little need to do so. It was not their custom to fight on horseback, and most of their immediate objectives, the places which they knew of that were really worth looting, even if they lay inland, were easily accessible by ship up the rivers. Most tidal estuaries in fifth-century Britain extended much farther inland than they do now. If all went well in the assault phases, horses would be added unto them in due course, for they knew there were plenty of horses in Britain. If it did not, then horses would not help them. Far better to use the available cargo space for more ammunition than for a lot of four-legged gluttons for fresh water that would be sure to rock the boat, probably on a lee shore in dirty weather. Victory and Welsh steeds, or a quick cutting of losses and a retreat by the way they had come.

There is one possible exception, that of the Jutish royal family in Kent. Hengest and Horsa did not arrive prepared to fight their way inland. They had been summoned as the allies, or rather the mercenaries or *foederati*, of the Kentish king Vortigern. They could take their time, they had Frisian connections, they could even hire one of the deep-draught merchant ships that were still to be had, in ever-decreasing numbers, in a few ports on both sides of the Channel, for their journey would be made under practically peace-time conditions. Now in some way, the details of which are not at all clear to us, these famous brothers were connected with a cult of white horses. The arms of the county of Kent to this day are a white horse. So were the arms of the North German duchy of Brunswick, which was also later to provide some kings of Britain. As long ago as the times of Tacitus some North German tribes, the Ingaevones or devotees of the god Ingvi-Frey, had practised a rite of divination which was carried out by a sacred white stallion executing a sort of bending-race between two rows of stakes. We shall see what Hengest means presently. Hengest had a son, Aesc, and his descendants were called Aescingas, not Hengestingas, which shows that Hengest was a name used only for ritual purposes, which his Christian descendants did not care for. Probably Horsa had another name too. There is reason to believe that the sacred white horses were in fact the ancestors of the Hanoverian Cream, which is not a large breed of horse, but this reason is part of another story. If Hengest and Horsa intended to stay in Britain they would have gone to any reasonable length to bring with them a breeding nucleus of the sacred cream stud, for it was primarily on their guardianship of this totem that their hold over the Jutish tribesmen rested. The Jutes were not a race but more of a religious confederation, and a living symbol of unity was more important to them than it was to groups bound together by a common ancestry.

The name Horsa does not mean 'mare' as so many history books so confidently declare. If it were the nominative case, the final 'a' would mean, not a feminine noun as in some other languages, but what is known in Germanic philology as a 'weak masculine'. But it is not the nominative case. It is the ordinary genitive plural of the Old English word *hors* which stands for the equine species in general but the adult male in particular. The name of this hero was really 'Somebody of the Horses'. What proper name stood in the place of 'Somebody' we shall never know but probably it was a word so expressive of heathen abominations that it was taboo to the Christian clerics Gildas, Nennius and the rest, and they refused to write it down. If it be objected that the by-name 'of the Horses' sounds much more Celtic than Germanic, like Niall of the Nine Hostages for instance, then we can only agree; it is just one more example of the blending of Celtic and Teutonic tradition, custom and genealogy that becomes more obvious the further we look into the history and archaeology of the Dark Ages.

At the other end of South Britain from Kent there lived, about this time, a king of Cornwall called Mark, internationally known, through the Arthurian cycle, as the husband of Iseult and the uncle of Tristan. Cornwall in the fifth century was much bigger than it is now: since the kingdom of Wessex was only in its beginnings, and torn moreover by an internecine feud between the Jutes of Wight and the New Forest and the Saxon dynasty of Cerdic, it had made little headway against the Britons of the west and controlled only Hampshire, South Berkshire and part of Wiltshire, so that the king of Cornwall reigned also over Devon, Dorset and most of Somerset. In those years which we call the Dark Ages because they are at once the twilight of the Roman world and the grey dawn of western Christendom, we should consider Mark as a very suitable name for a Celtic king with Roman and Christian antecedents; his godparents might have had in mind either one of the emperors called Marcus or else Mark the Evangelist. It comes therefore as a shock to find that his name in Welsh is March ap Meirchion—meaning Stallion, Son of the Horses. This is explained by a Welsh legend about the same king, to the effect that he had human form, but the ears of a black horse; that he always wore long hair, and a hat, and that the barbers who periodically cut his hair had no sooner swept up the clippings than they were assassinated. This story makes sense if we assume that March was not only a king, nominally Christian, but also the scion of an ancient British house who were also hereditary priests of some Celtic horse-cult like that of Rudiobus or Epona. The ears which legend fixed permanently to his skull belonged in reality to a ritual horse-mask which he wore only at the seasonal festivals of the cult, as the priestess of the Mare-headed Demeter had done long ago in Thessaly. The 'barbers' must have been tonsured Christian clerics, perpetually threatening to denounce in public the king's association with the ancient gods—which everyone else knew about but sensibly forbore to mention—and periodically being silenced by assassination.

We should find this theme repeated many times if the recorded history of this period were less fragmentary. It is still echoed in the Highland name borne by many people today in this country and in Canada: MacEachern, and some variant spellings. It means 'Son of the Lord of Horses'. Traditionally MacEacherns come from Kintyre and adjacent parts of Argyllshire. About the middle of the Roman occupation, when Roman penetration to the north had reached its zenith and the auxiliaries were holding the Antonine Line from the Forth to the Clyde, Kintyre was occupied by a tribe of Picts called Epidii. This is a tribal name on the ancient totemistic pattern, and may be interpreted 'Children of the Horse' or 'Foals of Epona' according to choice. At the period when Ptolemy reported their presence the Epidii were in close contact with the Romans since the coast of Ayrshire opposite their peninsula was well inside the Roman territory. But more significant than that is the fact that west and east of the Kintyre peninsula lay islands which in medieval times and later than that have been renowned for horse-breeding; of these islands, Jura, Islay and Arran, we shall hear more later.

The antiquary Kemble suggested that the genealogy of the early kings of Kent, tracing back Hengest to Woden, is really a confusion of human with equine pedigrees, and that some of the names in it really belong to the Jutish royal stud: as if, after some cosmic calamity, a historian should write of the early twentieth century: 'And the next ruler of all the Britons was The Tetrarch, whose mentor in youth was Attiperse the Wizard of Druids Lodge who lived to be nine hundred years old. Now the father of The Tetrarch was The Byerley Turk and his mother was Queen Victoria: he was born in the year of the Great Plague and therefore was known as the Spotted Wonder . . .' But we do not think even Gildas was ever as muddled as that. We may still hope that one day archaeology will tell us more about the horse-cult of the Jutes.

If therefore we are led to assume, from a complete lack of evidence as to the importation of horses by the Angles, Saxons and Jutes, that they resolved to make do with local British stock from the start, we have other and much more positive evidence that the first generations of the Angelcyn addressed themselves at once with ferocious energy to the serious business of horse-breeding.

If we look at the one-inch Ordnance map of almost any part of England we shall learn far more about the settlement of the Anglo-Saxons than we could ever learn from what survives of written history and from the physical remains that archaeologists can definitely relate to the early generations of English occupation. This is because, by and large, it was the Britons who named the rivers, the mountains and the forests of England, but the English who named or renamed the inhabited places. And except where Anglo-Saxon names were displaced by Scandinavian or Norman place names, it is the former which we still use today in a more or less modified form.

The table on pages 64–5 contains a column of place names embodying words to do with horses, particularly with horse-breeding, and a parallel column of surnames derived from the same horse-element. The names in the left column have been chosen somewhat arbitrarily from a huge mass of similar names. There is no human activity to which the English place names refer more constantly than horse-breeding, and the names of this group greatly outnumber even the very numerous pig-farming group, the Swindons and Sowdens and the like. The names that appear in this list were all conferred between the middle fifth century and the middle eleventh century: mostly in the first rather than the second half of this period; and all of them have been written down either in Domesday Book or some other document of equal antiquity.

The three commonest words for the adult male horse, entire, in Old English were: (1) *Steda*, fairly evenly distributed over the country in names like Stedham. (2) *Hengest*, much more thickly distributed, to all appearance. But in fact during the early period there was also a personal name Hengist, of which the most distingished was that Kentish king whose brother was called Horsa. Thus Hengistbury, overlooking the entrance to Christchurch harbour opposite the New Forest, may mean Stallion Castle but much more likely the Castle of Hengist. On the other hand Hinksey, Hinxton, Hingstondown, Hinxworth are certain to mean places (one island and three enclosures) where stallions were kept. (3) *Stanhors*, much less common in place names than the other two, but fairly frequent as a field name in the north of England. For instance a Stony Horse Close in Wensleydale is not noticeably more stony than the Horse Close almost next to it.

The Norse word for a stallion, closely related to *hengest*, was *hestr*, and in the north, where the Anglo-Saxon names are overlaid with Scandinavian ones, we have such forms as Hest Bank in the Lake District, Hestam, formerly Hestholm = stallion's islet, off Lewis in the Hebrides, and Hesterheugh near Yetholm in Scotland.

A variety of north-country names like Hesketh, such as Hesketh Hall in the North Riding of Yorkshire, are derived from the Old Norse word for a racecourse, *hesta-skeith*. The Vikings dearly loved racing or indeed any kind of contest that could be betted on. Of all the impressions that the veterans of the Varangian Guard brought back from Constantinople, the largest city in the world and the greatest repository of what was left of the art and culture of antiquity, the most vivid was the spectacle of large sums of money changing hands as the result of races in the Hippodrome. We have an account of a race in the Saga of King Sigurd

[*Continued on page 66*

64

with element *fola*

PLACE NAMES	SURNAMES
Follifoot (YWR), Foulridge (La), Fowberry (Nhb), Fullamoor (D).	None recorded?

with element *mare*

Marden (K).	None recorded, *because they are all in the form* stot, stod?

with element *hors*

Horseupclough (Be),Horsenden (Bk), Horsepath (O), Horseforth (YWR), Horsey (Nf), Horsham (Sx), Horsington (So), Horsley (Db), Horsted (Sx)	Horsman, Horsecroft, Horscraft

with element *colt*

Colton (St)	Coltman, Colter, Coltard

with element *stod*

Studfall (Lympne, K), Stotfold (Bd), Stottesdon (Sa), Stotscales (farm in Dentdale)	Stott (byname), Stodhart, Studdart, Studdy, Studman, Studdert

with element *estalun*

Stalling Busk (YNR), OF *estalun*— ON *buski*. One would say an impossible combination!	Stallon (slanderous byname)

with element $\begin{cases} \text{OE } hengest \\ \text{ON } hestr \end{cases}$

Hinksey (Brk), Hinxhill (K), Hinxton (Ca), Hinxworth (Hrt), Henstridge (Su), Hingston Down (Co), Hinchliffe (?), and Hest Bank (Cu), Hest Fell (Cu)	Hensman, Henchman, Hinksman, Hinckesman (Henson), means literally stud groom, personal attendant on stallion, hence later use meaning pimp, procurer

with element *hross* (ON)

Rossthwaite (Cu), Rosedale (YNR), Rosgill (We), Rosley (Cu), Ross Hall (Sa) (Rossendale (La)?)	

with element *cart*

Cartwey (Bk)	Carter

PLACE NAMES	SURNAMES

with element *waegn*

| Wainfleet (Li), Wanstead (Ess) | Wainer, Wenman |

with element *palfrey*

| | Palfreyman, Parfrement |

with element *capul* = pack-horse

| Capplerigs (Cu), How Caple (He) | Cappleman |

with element *rouncy* = cob

| | Runciman |

with element *steda*

| | Stead, Steed(s), Steadman, Stedmond |

with elements *start, amble*

| | Startup, Ambler |

with element *wicg* = horse

| Wedge Hill? (Do), Wedge Rock (IoW), Broadwood Widger (D), Wiggamore (D) | Widgery |

with element *mul* = mule

| Mowlish (D), Moulton (Che, Li, Nf, Np), Moulsoe (Bk), Moulescoombe (Sx) | Mul, character in *Anglo-Saxon Chronicle*, son of a Welsh girl by a West Saxon prince |

with element *esol* = donkey

| Ellesborough (Esselberge in 1195) (Bk) | Esla (not after 1066: cf. Horsa) |

with element *wraen* = stallion

| Wrantage (Do), Wrenhill (Ches) | Possibly some names now written Wrenn, etc., are from a nickname similar to those derived from *estalun* above |

with element ? ? ? ? See p. 192

| None | Powney. Not uncommon. No place name of this form exists. No work of reference attempts to explain the derivation of this surname |

the Pilgrim which does not throw a very favourable light on the speed of Swedish horses. It was between Magnus, the Norwegian Crown Prince, and a cousin of his called Harald Gille Krist, whose mother was Irish and who had been brought up in Ireland and wore Irish brogues and a kilt. Harald raced on foot while Magnus rode a horse from Gotland. We have mentioned Gotland before. Harald won three heats running, but it is only fair to add that when the matter was brought to the attention of King Sigurd he bitterly reproached Magnus for entering any such contest with such a hangover as he must have had that morning.

The Anglo-Saxons had two words for mare. The first, *miere* or *myre*, is so similar to the word *mere*, a boundary, which can occur in any place name, that it is almost impossible to sort out which is which in combinations like Maresfield in Sussex, which does not mean what you think it ought to mean. The other word, *stod*, is the feminine counterpart of *steda*, a couple like fox and vixen, foal and filly, where the difference in gender is expressed by altering the value of the middle vowel. The collective noun for a bunch of mares was *gestod*, but the *ge-* was dropped at the slightest provocation. There is a great number of names with this element; four different Studleys (glade where mares pasture); Studland in Dorset; Studham; Studdal in Kent which was once *Stod-weald*—'the wood of mares', showing that it was not only in clearings but right among the timber that brood mares were turned out. Another numerous group of forms like Stotfold is from *stod* and *fald* = enclosure. But this name would seem to occur always on or near the site of a Roman transit camp. These were all laid out to standard pattern, varying only according to the size of the drafts they were meant to accommodate. Studfall Castle (which is not a castle) in Kent is a fair example of the transit camp to accommodate one cohort on its way to or from the harbour of Portus Lemanis (Hythe), from which the troopships normally sailed. With their regular rectangular shape, bounded by a double ditch and a bank which only needed crowning with thorns to make it both wolf-proof and stallion-proof, it was the ideal place to keep mares, especially at night. Moreover these sites having been chosen by Roman army engineers were all naturally well drained, and just underneath the turf which had grown over them after a few decades of disuse they had one priceless asset—a gridiron pattern of hard roadway in between the lines of cantonments. Now a decent road surface was something that no Englishman was to be able to build for many centuries to come, and the avenues of the old marching camps were the ideal place to trot up a horse for the benefit of the customer or under the orders of the horse-leech. Even after the barrack hutments had all fallen in ruins, the Anglo-Saxon horse-breeder got his money's worth out of the old studfolds.

It may be appropriate to mention here a Gaelic place name, Garrion-haugh near Cambusnethan, recorded in a document of 1126 and meaning *the pasture for garrons or working ponies.*

We have few place names containing tne English word *Stall* = stable, but the surname Staller in pre-Norman times meant either the owner of a stable (not a man who worked there) or a rather important official of the royal household equivalent to the Norman Constable (*comes stabuli*) or the Frankish Marshal: he was responsible for the royal horses but it was definitely a clean-boots job.

Both the Old English word *hors* and the Old Norse equivalent *hros* meant equine in general but also stallion in particular. Names containing this element are evenly distributed over the country but usually in such a way that it is not possible to determine in which sense the word is being used. The form Ross- or Ros- occurs more frequently in the north, as one would expect, and especially in the north-west, in Cumberland and Westmorland, in Lancashire and in Yorkshire west of the Pennine watershed. Rossthwaite in Borrowdale is almost the exact equivalent of the south-country Horsley (*hros*, + *thveit* = *glade*). Sometimes we have a combination in one name of English and Norse elements, as in the Dentdale farm (now abandoned) of Stotscales, from *stod* in conjunction with the Norwegian *skáli* = shed or booth: a shelter for brood mares.

Another equestrian type of place name peculiar to the north-west is that which contains the element *capul* as in Capel Crag, Cappleback, Capplerigg, etc. This is from the Old Norse word *kapall* in various combinations. In this language the word was a fairly general term for horse without any special implication as to sex or age, and it was derived from an Old Irish word *capall* or a Manx word *kapyl*. While a few of the Norse immigrants to Cumberland came direct from Norway the majority had reached it by way of Ireland or the Hebrides or the Isle of Man, sometimes involving a sojourn of several generations—time enough to pick up a lot of Gaelic habits and ways of speech. Ultimately the word is derived from the Latin *caballus* and·is a relic of the Roman occupation of Britain and the auxiliary cavalry: it was the word they used for a troop-horse as distinct from an officer's charger (*equus*) or a transport horse (*jumentum*). The medium between the Latin and Norse forms must be the Manx or the Old Irish one, since the Welsh word derived from *caballus* is *ceffyl*, which would have produced a different form when borrowed into Norse. Now the Romans never conquered and never tried to conquer Ireland and no Roman soldier ever set foot there on duty. But I will suggest that they sometimes did so on leave. Though none of the auxiliary units is actually called Hibernian or anything of the kind it is well known that after the first century or so the auxiliary regiments ceased to be recruited in the country from which they took their title, and it is entirely in keeping with Irish tradition that individual Irishmen or groups of Irishmen should have crossed the sea to take service in the Roman cavalry. And when they came home on leave or time-expired, what more natural than that they should impress the boys in the shebeen at the crossroads with a smattering of camp

Latin? The word has stuck, and it is used in Irish today as a general term for a horse, with a diminutive, *capaillín*, meaning pony. In modern Gaelic of Scotland it means a barren mare, as it does also in modern Icelandic. This last fact, coupled with the total absence of the word from modern Norwegian, goes to show that it was something the Norse picked up in Ireland, since many Norse settlers in Iceland had previously tried their luck in Ireland, and indeed there were a fair number of native Irish servants in the households of the early settlers. But the Norse in Cumberland had plenty of other words for a horse, and it seems likely that when they said *kapall* they meant 'the sort of horse we used to see when we lived in Wexford', etc.

If that is so, it is the one exception to the general conclusion that we can draw, on linguistic grounds at any rate, about the horses of the Anglo-Saxon period. The Old English, and indeed the Old Norse, vocabulary was complete and copious when it came to describing the age and sex of a horse. But it had little scope when it came to describing various sizes and shapes and uses of the horse. The logical explanation of this can only be that by and large the English had only one type available—the one they had inherited from the British.

Notice how often the word for horse of some kind occurs with some element meaning hill or ridge or spur of high land, especially where it is a case of mares or young stock, as in Fowlridge. Evidently 'high and dry' was the Anglo-Saxon motto when it came to siting a breeding establishment. A typical site is mentioned in the will of Prince Athelstan Ethelredsson, who died in 1015: 'and to my hunter of the red deer I leave the stud which is on *Colingahrycge* [Coldridge in Wiltshire]'.

The word 'colt' is also a frequent element in English place names of a respectable antiquity, most commonly in the form Colton, Coulton, Coltham; but it seems probable that in some districts and at some time the words 'colt' and 'foal' have changed places, so that we should not too hastily scoff at Americans when they say 'colt' meaning foal of either sex. John of Trevisa (Anglo-Cornish, *d*. 1412) has this definition: 'A colte is a mere sone and hath that name while he souketh,' but goes on to say 'the sely hors colt is foled in divers happe and fortune', and concludes a chapter in his translation of a book called *On the Properties of Things* with these words: 'And now at last take heed of your hors colt for going and paas, hard or soft, esy or unesy, what he useth in youth unnethe he may leve it in elde.' The moral is that as the twig is bent so will the tree grow, but the implication is that he would call foals either horse colts or mare colts, according to sex. The expression 'mare colt' instead of 'filly' is fairly common on Exmoor even now (1962) and must once have been current throughout southern England, as it occurs frequently in Kentish farm inventories of the 1580's.

On the other hand the unknown authors of both *Gawain and the Green Knight* (Cheshire) and *King Horn* (Lincolnshire), both written in John of Trevisa's lifetime, use 'fole' meaning a horse in the prime of life: but always in an adventurous or 'noble' context, where another author might use 'steed'. Again in Lincolnshire, Richard Welby of Molton, near Spalding, made a will in 1465 leaving a special bequest of 'my bay fole that goeth in the marsches' without mentioning the mare, as if it was at least weaned. So that when a place name, at any rate in the north midland area, contains the element 'Fol-', perhaps it does not imply quite such a nursery as we think. A complication is that in the Scandinavian languages and especially in Icelandic, which is the nearest allied to the form of Norse once spoken in England, foal does mean only the very young animal, the sucker; and in the northern half of England such names are far more likely to be derived from the Norse *foli* than from the Saxon word *fola*. Perhaps the explanation of the 'heroic' use of the word 'fole', speaking of an animal of some distinction, is the intention to emphasize that it was well bred. Just as the word 'Childe' is used to mean 'hero' in the human sphere, or as minstrels spoke of Beowulf simply as 'the son of Ecgtheow', they may have referred to a noble horse as 'the foal of . . . ', some celebrated sire.

We have evidence from the late Anglo-Saxon period that it was the custom to let the foals run after the dam until the next foaling season came round, instead of weaning them for sale at autumn fairs. This is evident from the will of Wulfgeat of Dunnington, near Shifnal in Shropshire (just across the River Severn from the Long Mynd where the famous Church Stretton herd of hill ponies has run time out of mind). Wulfgeat drew up this will in 1005, and in it he bequeathed to the king his lord, besides the customary heriot of two stallions with shields and weapons, ten mares and ten colts. Also to Bruna his executor six mares and six colts for his trouble. Now as no man can foresee the season of his death any more than the day or the hour, it must follow from these bequests that the management of Wulfgeat's stud was such as to provide sixteen such units of 'mare-with-foal' at any time of the year—either this season's foal or last season's!

The name Follifoot is supposed to be connected with the custom of horse-fighting for sizable wagers, introduced by the Vikings. It may be so, but if so it is almost the only evidence we have that this custom was practised in England. Of the numerous organized horse-fights described in the sagas all, so far as I know, took place in Iceland, although the heroes of these stories, even when they are Icelanders, were mostly travelled men, and the scenes of action are quite as likely to be Caithness or Yorkshire or Wexford, Bergen or Rouen, or even Sicily or Constantinople for that matter. Though the custom may well have originated, on a small scale, in Norway, it seems to have become an Icelandic speciality, possibly connected with the cult of Frey, which in the last phase of northern paganism was much more popular in Iceland than elsewhere, but more likely connected with the complete absence of game animals larger than the hare or predators larger than the Arctic fox from the Icelandic fauna. Settlers, accustomed in the old country to hunting the wolf and the bear, the stag, the boar and the elk, may have found things a little dull when they had time to spare from shepherding or fishing, and hankered after some more dangerous occupation than hawking for wild geese and ptarmigan. There was always the blood feud, of course, but that was apt to come expensive and usually at some stage led to some very tedious litigation at the Althing. Apart from that there was a murderous form of ice-hockey which could not be played all the year round—and the horse-fights. This was dangerous enough for the owners, who went into the ring with their stud-horses as seconds to give tactical assistance: they were not supposed to touch their opponent's horse, but were just as likely to get savaged as their horse was. But England, especially Northumbria, was still full of large game in the Viking Age, and we need not suppose that *aficionados* of the fighting stallion were any more numerous in the old Danelaw than the English cockfighting 'fancy' at the present day, or any less eccentric.

The surnames are appreciably later in date than the place names, since most English parishes and a huge number of farms acquired their present name not later than the eleventh century, whereas surnames were not generally inherited until about 1250. After then, John, son of John the Smith, was also called John Smith, whatever his calling. But before that he would be called either John Smithson, or if he had some physical peculiarity, such as a harelip, let us say, John Scarth (from *Skarthi* = harelip), and *his* sons would be called either Johnson, Scarthison or something quite different again.

Notice how numerous are the words for horse attendant, evidently showing how specialized their functions must have been. Palfreyman, 'groom of the pacing ponies'; Runciman, 'groom of the cobs'; Hinksman, 'stallion leader' (we still have him); Cappleman, 'groom of the *caples*', who are dealt with elsewhere in this book. Stothard and Colthard and similar names probably do not denote skilled occupations but a more lowly class of employment; the herding of brood-mares and colts on unfenced commons was not an occupation for grown men of normal physique, though it had to be done. '*Haltr rithr hrossi*', says an old Norse proverb, 'the lame can ride, and a handless man herd stock'. If anything went seriously wrong the maimed or half-witted or very young herd was expected to fetch Ralph Studman or Howard Coltman, a real specialist who would deal with the matter. Studman and Stedman and Coltman are three different kinds of stud groom, charged with the care of brood-mares, stallions and young stock respectively. Horseman is probably not an all-rounder but another stallion-man. Or it may refer to the bearer's feudal commitments, when he was required to attend the muster of militia mounted and equipped with the expensive panoply of a man-at-arms. But for this he would require a stallion anyway.

Some light on the conditions under which horses were kept in Anglo-Saxon England, on the eve of the Viking invasion, is cast by the report of two Italian bishops, George and Theophylact, who were sent by Pope

Hadrian to attend the Synod of Chelsea in 786. This was a summit conference, both ecclesiastical and lay, between King Offa of Mercia, then the dominant power in the island, and Cynewulf, King of Wessex, the second biggest state, each with their bishops. Of the midland English George and Theophylact reported 'also many of them eat horses, which no Christian does in the East'. This was something of an understatement, since the eating of horseflesh was in fact forbidden by canon law throughout Christendom, partly in imitation of Mosaic Law but partly because eating horseflesh was characteristic of many heathen cults of late Roman times. The fact that it took place in England at all, or openly enough for a foreign mission to notice it, is surprising at this date. Horseflesh was not part of the normal diet of the English, it is not mentioned along with other staple foods and its price is not quoted along with that of other commodities in market charters, etc. Plenty of documents exist assessing rent and tithes in terms of sides of bacon and quarters of beef, but nobody paid his rent or any part thereof in horsemeat. Famine and similar disastrous situations apart, horsemeat was only consumed as part of the ritual of certain pagan cults, some of British, some of Anglo-Saxon origin. But paganism had officially come to an end, more than a century earlier, with the death in battle of Penda, the heathen King of the Midlands. The next wave of heathen invaders were not to appear in any strength for another twenty years, and their advance guard, the three shiploads of Norwegian pirates who murdered the harbour-master of Poole when he came down to collect their mooring fees, did not appear until the very year after the Synod of Chelsea. What this remark by the papal emissaries must necessarily imply is that the sacrificial banquet of horseflesh, as a feature of the cult of one of the numerous pagan horse deities, was still practised in central and southern England by people who were nominally Christians, subjects of Offa, who was a highly civilized prince and treated on equal terms with the Emperor Charlemagne.

But there were other, everyday Mercian practices of which the good bishops equally disapproved. 'They also by an evil custom mutilate their horses, slit their nostrils, fasten their ears together so as to make them deaf, and dock their tails.' All these customs brought the disfavour of the Church because they were associated with the ritual mutilation, both of worshippers and their animals, which formed part of the rites, again, of certain heathen cults in various parts of the world. In point of fact we have no picture, throughout the Anglo-Saxon period, of a docked horse in this country, or of a horse with its ears fastened together. The slitting of nostrils is not a thing that would show up very clearly in a small miniature, but it may well have been the practice to cut slits or notches in the nasal cartilage, as in the ear, as a mark of ownership. We shall come to the details of ear-marking much later in this history. If tails were not docked, they were almost certainly cut in characteristic ways when breeding stock was running on the commons; partly again to denote ownership, as the tails of New Forest ponies are now cut in four different ways to show which agister is responsible for them, but also for another practical reason, well known on Exmoor, where many farmers cut all tails off by the hocks, and then a quarter out of that, at the beginning of winter, because in a really bad blizzard a full tail, always turned to the prevailing wind, can fill up solid with snow, with fatal results. Thus after the Great Blizzard of 1881, a fine stallion was found dead on Winsford Hill, from exhaustion caused by a two-hundredweight snowball which had formed on his tail. 'Fastening the ears together' probably really means sewing up one ear, which was a quack-surgical, and quite useless, treatment for the 'staggers' still practised in much later times.

It is easy to come away with the impression that hunting played a less important part in the life of the country in Anglo-Saxon times than it did after the Conquest; but this is a false impression, created by the legal evidence. Norman forest laws, which governed all aspects of hunting, were at once more severe and more complicated than Anglo-Saxon laws on the same subject, which therefore tends to bring them more into the foreground of the picture so far as written evidence is concerned. In Anglo-Saxon documents there is much less prominence accorded to what is forbidden than to what is permitted or enjoined in this respect. Nearly all important grants of land made by Anglo-Saxon kings, whether West Saxon, Mercian, East Anglian or Kentish, refer to the custom of *faestingmen*: either it applies, or does not apply, to the estates in question. *Faestingmen* was a customary duty that went with the occupation of the land; it was the obligation to feed and lodge the king's horses, his hawks and his hounds, and the men in charge of them, for a certain period every year, and it could vary from compulsory puppy-walking, such as farmers undertake voluntarily for M.F.H.s nowadays, to lodging two falconers and their hawks for a week or so, or stabling the king's hunters which preceded the court on its progress from one royal manor to another.

Moreover, despite wars and invasions the population of the country as a whole was increasing all the time, and a corresponding inroad being made upon the waste. As more and more land was taken in for cultivation or pasture, both kings and their subjects became more and more explicit in asserting their rights over what remained of the wilderness, either as rough grazing or as a game preserve or as a source of timber, and there is a greater profusion of documents stating who is allowed to hunt where. We mention the subject at this point, because it was Knut, the most popular and successful of the Danish kings in England, who codified the laws about hunting.

II

Bjørn sent for the stud of horses that were near the out-barn, for they were being fed hay while the hard weather lasted. The stallion was by the well-known sire Hvíting ('Son of the White One') and was himself white, but the mares with him were chestnut. There was another of Hvíting's colts, also white, in Thórarinsdal, but the mares with him were black. Bjørn had the stud led out before Thorstein, and said he wished to make him a present of them. . . .

Saga of Bjørn the Hitdale Champion, early eleventh century.

The Scandinavians of the migration period were, if possible, even more horse-conscious than the Anglo-Saxons, and like nearly all the Indo-Europeans they associated horsemanship with noble birth. In the very early Norse poem known as the *Song of Rig* the origins of social classes are explained in a parable about the journey of the god Heimdall; at the end of each day's march he stops at a different house and begets a son; one becoming a serf, one a churl, one an earl. Though all these grew up as different as chalk from cheese, and though all their descendants took after them, yet all were the sons of the same god. The moral is that though social differences may be rigidly observed, and may be justified in order to make society work at all, yet each of us has a certain inalienable human dignity befitting the sons of a god. You may well ask how a crowd of pagan barbarians can have arrived at this highly philosophical view of human destiny; but it is not our business to answer, but only to point out the role that horses played, theoretically, in the old Scandinavian social hierarchy.

The original Serf (þrael) excelled at the ordinary tasks of day-labourers—hedging, ditching, muck-spreading, tending swine and goats. The original Churl (Karl) could make agricultural implements, break in oxen and work them in the plough and wagon. But Earl (Jarl), the third son of Heimdall, as soon as he could walk, learnt

> to ride the horse, to loose the hounds,
> to draw the sword and to swim the stream.

When he grew up he gave his followers

> treasures and jewels and mares with well-sprung ribs.

Now the sons of Earl were twelve, of whom the youngest was called King (Konr)—

> games they learned, and sports and swimming,
> taming horses, round shields bending . . .
> but King the youngest alone knew runes.

One day when King was going through a wood, shooting birds, a crow sitting on a branch said to him:

> 'Why wilt thou thus kill us birds, young King?
> It would be more fitting for thee to ride on horses . . .'

Shortly after this point the poem breaks off.

It will be more significant for our purpose to quote from the very early poems like this which were composed in Scandinavia and show the customs and ideas prevalent before the Vikings set out for Britain, than from the much richer prose literature composed in Iceland, since the latter was the work of men who had had much contact with Britain and Ireland, or of their descendants, and contains many elements that are not pure Norse: just as the Icelandic pony is not pure Norse. The scholar Finnur Jónsson was of opinion that all these archaic poems were of Norwegian origin though actually written down in Iceland. Such a poem is the *Words of the High One*, or the *Wisdom of Odin*. It is an extraordinary mixture of mystical and practical elements, and among the latter are shrewd pieces of advice about the conduct of private life and of public business. There are straightforward commercial maxims about such things as the advantage of buying anything in the rough and selling it in a finished state:

> Buy a mare when she is thin and a sword when it is rusty.

Likewise advice to young men on such important matters as drinking and courtship:

> Like to the love of women in whose thoughts are lies
> Is the driving unshod over slippery ice
> Of a two-year-old colt, badly broken and fresh.

The adjective used for 'fresh' is *teitr*, meaning 'gay' when applied to humans (or, in certain contexts, 'fighting drunk'), and it is the origin of the word *tit*, which north-country readers will recognize at sight but which we will explain more fully when we come to consider the galloway. In a passage which teaches not to be ashamed of poverty, riding a bad horse is taken as a symbol of poverty, like old clothes:

> Thou shalt not shame thee for shoes or breeks
> Nor yet for a sorry jade.

(*Jade* is itself derived from a Norse word *jalda*, meaning a mare too old to foal again.) We shall see later that Chaucer has a striking passage in which he echoes this thought, probably quite unconscious of the source from which this bit of traditional wisdom was derived.

Such then were the equestrian ideas of the Vikings. What physical contribution did they bring to the development of horse-breeding in Britain? In the way of saddlery and equipment, a great deal. So far as archaeology can tell, they introduced the stirrup to Britain. Opposite is some Viking horse gear, nearly all of Scythian design. The characteristic shape of the stirrups, a flattened loop, is a copy in metal of the thick hide loops which the Scythians used, and the leathers hung on a proper tree of modern type but not of English origin, a product of the typical Norwegian speciality of birchwood carving. Also in birchwood is a characteristic Norwegian type of draught collar, superior to the English model.

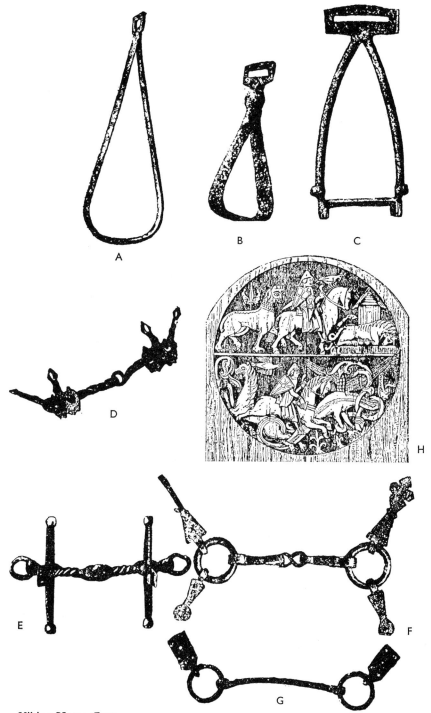

Viking Horse Gear.

A, B, C. Different models of stirrup iron, all found in Scandinavia but all deriving ultimately from Scythian stirrups, loop of multiple rawhide.

Bits. (But see Appendix III, p. 291.)

D. Jointed twisted mouthpiece, $4\frac{1}{2}$ inches, V cheek pieces.

E. 'Liverpool' type, under $4\frac{1}{2}$ inches.

F. Plain snaffle, nearly $5\frac{1}{2}$ inches.

G. Jointed snaffle, La Tène pattern common also to England and Ireland, over 5 inches, gilt clasps for cheek straps.

H. Stirrups and bit in use, from carving on ancient church door in Iceland.

If the Vikings wished to bring horses with them, the means were at their disposal. On the opening pages of this story we saw heavy horses being unloaded from Norman ships. But these Norman ships were in no way different—certainly not superior in carrying capacity—from the Norse *drekki* or warship. The structural defects of the old Nydam boat had long since been eliminated. There was a proper keel, stouter riveting, proper floorboards laid over the bottom strakes of the hull. Most of these improvements had had to be made before the long ships could carry a mast and sail, but beyond that point there had been further modifications of the general design, all making for greater stability and seaworthiness and for a greater proportion of *usable* space within the hull. But if the *drekki* could carry half a dozen horses in the waist there were other means by which larger numbers could be carried, as they were carried to Iceland according to the saga accounts of its settlement. The Vikings had at least four types of cargo ship available—the cog, the buss, the *knarr* and the *byrthingr*. Unlike the galleys these were designed primarily for sailing, and the first-named type carried no oars at all. Horses in the cargo of a galley inevitably meant that several oars normally rowed through ports in the waist of the ship could not be worked.

Of the Scandinavian migration routes sketched out on Map 2 the first Norwegian wave is the most significant for our purpose. The first landfall along it, Shetland, was settled by the Norse long before they had been heard of in the rest of Britain—perhaps as early as A.D. 700. At this time the archipelago was empty, or nearly empty, of human inhabitants, though in pre-Roman times it had been quite populous (the same is true

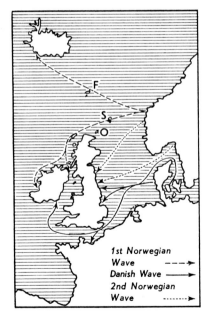

1st Norwegian Wave - - - →
Danish Wave ——→
2nd Norwegian Wave ········→

Map 2

Three-waves from the North Sea

This is a simplification. In fact the repercussions of the first Norwegian wave went on after the others had come to a halt. So far as England is concerned, they took the form of migration into Cumberland and Westmorland from Ireland and Man. But in Scotland they took the form of direct interference by the Norwegian crown into Hebridean affairs until the battle of Largs, 1263. There was movement also from Scotland and Ireland to Iceland, and from Orkney and Shetland and East Anglia to Normandy.

KEY

F = Faeroes   S = Shetlands
O = Orkneys

of Orkney). But ever since Britain had been geologically sundered from the Continent, ponies of Shetland type had run wild on the moors of Caithness as well as in Orkney and Shetland. Neolithic people at Rinyo in Orkney and Sumburgh in Shetland had eaten them. Iron Age people in Sumburgh had worked them in harness. Now perhaps they were all running wild again in the Shetlands; perhaps a few of them were being worked by the even fewer Celtic fishermen and hermits on islets called Papa This and Papay That. The first Norsemen in Shetland were fishermen also, and had no need to bring horses with them. The shelties were perfectly adequate for carrying nets and creels and other gear down to, and, with luck, fish up from, the landing-places. They could also help to drag the boats up the slipway when it came time to lay them up for the winter, and to drag the occasional stranded pilot-whale up the same slipway in readiness for a glorious greasy orgy. In the next phase the islands figured as a base for pirates driven out of Norway by the increasing central power of the Yngling dynasty of Vestfold. It must have been like some of the West Indian islands in the seventeenth century— anarchy with a rival gang in every other creek, armed neutrality being the usual form except when the temptation to a little hi-jacking became too strong. These people had little use for horses in their base either, since all the work they did there was unloading goods from one ship into another.

In the middle of the ninth century King Harald Hairfair and his followers, having mopped up all opposition at home in Norway, decided to clean up that nest of pirates, Shetland, and brought the islands under Norwegian rule administered through the Earl of Orkney. A brother of the first Earl of Orkney was the first Duke of Normandy, known in French as Rollon or Rou, but to the Norse themselves as Walking Rolf. The chieftains to whom Harald granted land in Orkney and Shetland had little use for riding horses, since most of their estates lay on more than one island, and it was easier to get about their property by boat than any other way. The Shetland pony still sufficed for the modest crofting that was all the Norse agricultural activity in the islands amounted to, as well as for the perpetual chore of carrying peat necessary to keep the winter fires burning in an increasingly treeless landscape. There was therefore no incentive to bring horses from Norway to Shetland. Nevertheless archaeologists have revealed a slight increase in size of horses at Sumburgh, between early Iron Age and Viking times. The horses buried at First Century level were under ten hands, like the modern show Shetland. Those at the Viking Age level were slightly over eleven hands.

Now for the first time merchants settled in Shetland. They learnt from Harald's men, who had learnt from the pirates, that conditions were very different in the lands farther to the south and west. In the Western Isles, horses were much less numerous than in Shetland, and on the mainland of Scotland south of Caithness the only horses were much bigger than shelties and less economical to keep, not being satisfied with a winter diet of cods' heads and seaweed. A trade in the small ponies to the West Highlands and Islands thus grew up, and from early times we hear of the sheltie in the Hebrides side by side with the 'native' ponies of those parts which the Picts had used in their raids across the Wall. There was besides no indigenous breed of horses either in Faeroe or Iceland, and exporters from Shetland could undersell Norwegian horse shippers there because the sea voyage was appreciably shorter. To this day Icelandic and Faeroese ponies show certain Shetland characteristics, and in the language of Man, which was once one kingdom with the Hebrides, a small pony is still called a sheltie while any other horse is called a chabyl.

The next sphere of Norwegian expansion was the North Scottish mainland, western Highlands and Galloway. The latter name means the Land of the *Gall-Gaedhil*, the renegade Christian Gaels who had joined the heathen Norsemen (*Lachlannach*) in their piracies. Here at last was something like dry land, which needed a sizeable horse to move about on. It was worth while sending home for some of those horses which had been the pride of every Norwegian noble clan.

From lack of positive evidence we must conclude that nothing much in the way of *selective* stock-breeding was done by the English. But Scandinavia was a different matter. Every one of the major deities of pagan Scandinavia had some species of animal sacred to him or her. Thus the goat to Thor, the cat to Freyja, etc. Every temple or sacred grove was surrounded by a stockaded enclosure in which a small herd of the sacred animals grazed. The majority of these sacred herds were of horses, since the horse was the attribute of more than one pagan god— Odin, Frey, Heimdall among others. It seems that these sacred horses and mares were originally selected primarily for their looks, since they were apt to bear names such as Gullinfaxi (Golden Mane), which suggest some flashy colour scheme like palomino. Although there were such things as public temples, the majority were private property of chieftains who were also, *ex-officio*, *godir* or priests of whatever god inhabited the temple. The *godir* therefore who served equestrian gods always had a small surplus of good-class horses to dispose of, and the stud itself was an heirloom together with the hereditary priesthood-cum-chieftainship. Selection was practised not so much by castration of sub-standard males but by culling at the seasonal sacrifices and by the fact that religious awe reinforced normal sanctions. Thus if one's colt broke into the temple paddock and violated the sacred mares, the owner was guilty not only of civil trespass but of blasphemy. There is an anecdote of the early Christian king of Norway, Olaf Tryggvason, whose missionary methods were violent, and, in the opinion of his subjects, ill-mannered, desecrating the sanctuary of a heathen god: this he did, not only by breaking the idols and their sacred vessels, but by getting on the sacred stallion and riding him away, while his courtiers did the same to the sacred mares.

This shows once more that the sacred breeding stock *was* broken to ride and drive—but they only actually worked in religious processions. Conversion must have brought a sharp decline in the quality of horse-stock: but as immigration to Britain ceased before this date, we need take no account of it (P24*a*).

The wars in Caithness and Sutherland, which ended in the defeat of the Picts, between Sigurd son of Eystein Big-Mouth with his ally Thorstein the Red of Dublin and the Pictish king Maelbricta the Tusk, seem to have been conducted mainly on horseback, according to Orkneyinga Saga. It seems unlikely that Shetland ponies were used for this purpose. The saga also says that Earl Sigurd died and was buried somewhere in Strath Oykel. The phrase used, 'set in howe', implies full-dress inhumation in a round barrow, which is likely since Sigurd was a pagan. In that case he would almost certainly have been buried with one or more horses and their saddlery. The Oykel is not a long river, nor are its banks heavily cultivated. It should not be difficult by air survey to identify Sigurd's howe, and its excavation might tell us a lot about the Caithness horses of the ninth century. But much is to be deduced from the inscribed crosses of north-east Scotland which date from this era. P17, P54 are traced from these.

What horses were available from the temple studs in Norway? First of all a big horse, so big that it must have carried much Diluvial blood, and of which we have good pictorial evidence.

P24*a* shows some specimens from a tapestry woven about 820 and used to decorate the cabin wall of the funeral ship of Queen Asa of Vestfold. This grave also contained an ornate ceremonial wagon. The horses are admittedly larger than life, but the artist must have had some breed of big horses in mind.

Secondly, the Vestfjord pony, or Fjording, often called in England the Norwegian pony *tout court*. This is a stocky type with a good small head, now uniformly dun in colour, and almost always a golden dun with a characteristic upright mane, an eel stripe and a not very full tail; the long hairs are straight. The mane hairs of the Highland and Western Isles pony today are still straight, the tail hairs less so and more abundant than in the Vestfjord, and of 116 pedigree Highland ponies registered in 1959, 67 were dun of various shades. In conformation the Highlander strikingly resembles the Vestfjord, whose chief habitat in Norway is the province of Hordaland. It was from Hordaland (Haerethaland) that the first Norwegian raiders to be definitely identified by British chroniclers came.

Thirdly, the Gudbrandsdal pony, also stocky, today a good deal taller than the Vestfjord, having abundant slightly wavy mane and tail. The chief colours are black, brown, bay. In conformation it much closer approaches the Fell and the Dales of modern times than the Highlander. The almost uniform colour of the Fell is black, and black, bay and brown predominate among the Dales. It may or may not be pure coincidence that the colloquial name for the Gudbrandsdal breed in modern Norwegian is *Dølehest*—Horse of the Dales (P24*b*).

The ship-grave of Queen Asa contained, as well as the wagon, two sledges. These had elaborately carved bodies on solid runners, without shafts. The attachments for the swingle-trees, however, show that although they were comparatively small vehicles, they were each intended to be drawn by a pair—hence a pair of ponies.[1]

But before leaving the far north let us spare a moment to consider Walking Rolf and his nickname. The sagas explain it by saying that he was so tall that he could never find a horse to carry him and had to walk everywhere. This is indeed a tall story if taken to apply either to Norway or to Normandy. But in relation to Rolf's stay with his brother in Shetland it would make sense.

This first wave passed on from Galloway and Cumbria to Man and Ireland. Man is a comparatively small island and from a military point of view there is no reason why the Vikings should have needed horses to get possession of it, no part of the island lying more than a day's march from the sea. As for Ireland, although practically every port except Galway city owes its foundation to the Norsemen or Ostmen, as they came to be known, and although both Norwegians and Danes often played a decisive part in the civil wars which culminated in the battle of Clontarf in 1014, they did so mainly by their very possession and control of these harbours and consequently of foreign trade, leaving campaigns 'up the country' to the care of whatever Irish king happened to be their ally (sometimes their employer) at the time. As for actual Scandinavian settlement, more than in any other European country it was confined to the sea-coast. The innermost Norse place name is Leixlip on the Liffey. It means 'the salmon leap' and it is symbolical. At the point where navigation ceases and the salmon have to leap to get up the rapids, there the Norse interest in the country also ceases. It was not to such narrow bridgeheads as these that the Vikings brought their own horses.

Viking art is extraordinarily rich and has a great delight in animal forms, including the form of the horse. But like Celtic and early Anglo-Saxon art it is decorative rather than representational. Like them it derives ultimately from the art of the Scythians, those nomads of the Eurasian plain who lived on and by and almost for the horse. We reproduce some examples which we think most significant of pictures made by Vikings both in Norway and in the lands which they occupied, but it must always be borne in mind that the uppermost thought in the artist's mind is not the realistic portrayal of the subject but the design it will make on the space to be decorated. Realism as we know it is something that came in from the Mediterranean, and if what the Viking

---

[1] Recent researches and measurements of horse bones by Dr Nobis of Kiel (see page 82) indicate an average height of fourteen hands at Oseberg and Gokstad ship-graves, but a great variety of conformation, especially about the head.

artist wanted was a serpentine form, then he would not hesitate to give his horse the contours of a snake. Nevertheless the consistent tendency to draw horses long in the back is probably due to the fact that the models were also somewhat long in the back.

The second Viking wave came from Denmark, and eastern England took the brunt of it. It passed round the south coast, turned up towards the south and east coasts of Ireland and was smartly repelled there by the Norwegians—the White Strangers—who had just managed to get there first. When we read of Danish attacks on East Anglia, Lincolnshire and the coast of Yorkshire in the Anglo-Saxon records we commonly find that the first act of the Danes after building a fort at their landing-place was to seize as many horses from the surrounding country as they could lay hands on before fanning out on raids into the interior. The native horse of Denmark at this time was a large Diluvial type unlike the ponies of Norway. Part of this Danish wave joined the Norwegians in the settlement of Normandy and they may have brought some of the heavy horses which were among the ancestors of William the Conqueror's Great Horses. The only survival of the Old Danish word *hest* = horse, in ordinary speech as opposed to place names, is in the special vocabulary of Suffolk horsemen; the 'owd bors' used to talk of the 'Forehust' or trace-horse. In no other part of England is this word still in use.

The third Viking wave came not only from the western Norwegian fjords, but also from both sides of the great bay, Viken, into which Oslo fjord runs. It broke almost entirely on the coastline of Lincolnshire and Yorkshire, where it overlaid the existing Danish settlements. Its last force was spent in the battles of Gate Fulford and Stamford Bridge in the East Riding, only a month before Hastings.

There is considerable written evidence for an extensive horse trade between various parts of the British Isles not politically united in the eleventh century. For instance in the Annals of Ulster for 1029, the ransom demanded by Mathgamain O'Regan, King of Brega, who had been lucky enough to kidnap Prince Olaf, son of the Danish King of Waterford, included 1,200 cows, 120 Welsh (Bretnac) horses, 60 ounces of gold, etc. It looks as if the total consisted of the same sum repeated in different denominations, a form of parallelism very characteristic of Old Irish literary style: if this is so then one Welsh horse equals ten Irish cows or half an ounce of gold. We shall see later something more of the relative values of cows and horses in Ireland.

Throughout the first three quarters of the Viking Age there stood a town called in Danish Hedeby but in English aet Haethum, near the present Slesvik. It was the greatest commercial centre of the Baltic-North Sea area; King Alfred's friends, the merchant seamen Wulfstan and Othere, had done a lot of business there. In the year 1050 Hedeby was burnt to the ground and never rebuilt. This happened during the war between King Sweyn Estrithson of Denmark and Harald Hardraada the King of Norway who nearly became King of England sixteen years later: of this event the court minstrel of King Harald (who did the burning) remarks complacently:

> Hedeby was burned
> From end to end.
> A strong deed I think
> It can be called.

There could be two opinions about that. But the sudden end of such a thriving port at least provides a fixed point by which to date at the latest any object found on the site, which has been the subject of exhaustive investigation both of Danish and by German archaeologists. Dr G. Nobis of Kiel has made a special study of all the domestic animal remains from Hedeby, among which bones of nine individual horses could be identified and measured. The range of stature (all were adult) was narrow—between 13 hands 2 inches and 14 hands 2 inches. But from the contours of the skull and jaws their appearance must have varied considerably, from Roman-nosed 'cold-blood' types to those with the straight profile and concave lower jaw that we associate with oriental breeds. The obvious employment for horses on such a commercial site at this date is of course as pack animals.

While it would be an overstatement to say that Arab merchants frequented the port at any time, they were occasionally to be found there, and one of them, Ibrahim al Tartushi, a subject of the Emir of Cordova, recorded his impressions of the place almost exactly a hundred years before the great fire. He says that it was remarkably well provided with fresh water but that the inhabitants made very little use of it for washing purposes. He cannot have been impressed with the Danish horses, for he does not mention them, but his silence in this respect is significant, for on the subject of religion he says that some of the townspeople were Christians but the majority were pagans, and that the latter sacrificed various animals to their gods. He specifies under this head sheep, goats, cattle and swine, from which we may deduce that the characteristic Scandinavian cults of Odin and Frey which entailed horse sacrifices were not practised at Hedeby.

In the last decade of the tenth century it seemed to the English that the worst times of the great Danish invasion against which Alfred had fought had come again, with new refinements of misery. The most deadly combination that was possible in all the western world came into play against the luckless King Ethelred Evil Council: the Norwegian Vikings, who could in normal times be played off against the Danes, allied themselves, under the leadership of Olaf Tryggvason, with the Danish army of Sveinn Forkbeard; as if that were not enough the king, unteachable by experience, placed a proven coward and traitor, the Ealdorman Aelfric of Hampshire, in command of the West Saxon militia, who were repeatedly let down and abandoned by him in impossible tactical situations. The Danish army, supported by the Norwegian fleet, passed up and down the country at will, exacting such tribute as they wished 'in burning, harrying and slaughter, both along the coast and in Essex, Kent, Sussex and Hampshire. Finally they got themselves horses and rode far and wide and continued to do unspeakable damage', says the chronicle. Enormous sums of tribute were exacted in return for promises of immunity which no one but the king believed genuine; ten thousand, sixteen thousand, twenty-four thousand and thirty-six thousand pounds of silver were paid at intervals of about two years. Comparison with our currency is somewhat meaningless, but these sums together represented the value of more than a quarter of a million cows—many times the total stock of horned cattle in the country.

No wonder that many looked forward with relief rather than with dread to the end of the world, which was expected in the year of the first millennium. But the fatal date brought, not merciful oblivion, but a new character to play her baleful part, as the king's bride, against this sinister backdrop of murder and rape, arson and blackmail. This was the Lady Emma, daughter of Richard Duke of Normandy, England's *femme fatale* if ever there was one. She despised her husband (a widower at thirty-six, he had sired twelve children by his first wife) and hated her own children. She survived Ethelred and five of his successors, while all the time her secret sympathy was only for the cause of her nephew William of Normandy.

Yet in those dark hours the arts in England flourished as never before. For the first time English masons built to the design of English architects stone churches that would stand comparison with continental models. Minstrels could still compose poems in the ancient heroic mode, undimmed by more than four centuries of use, that can still move us by their evocation of loyalty and valour, even though their inspiration was now only the story of some hopeless defensive battle such as the last fight of Alderman Byrhnoth at Maldon:

> 'Do you hear, herald of pirates, what this people says?
> They will give you for tribute the points of their spears,
> And the bitter edge of the swords our heirlooms . . .'

Strangely in the desolate garden of England came the flowering of the most characteristic pre-Conquest English art, that of miniature painting. About the year 1000, the Psalms of David were copied in the scriptorium of St Augustine's Abbey at Canterbury, embellished, sometimes to the extent of half a page, with exquisite pen-drawings in coloured inks which for lightness and grace and a pervading sense of motion are equalled only by Chinese brush-drawings. The vivid images of the Psalms are interpreted in equally vivid pictures in which the human figure is only about two inches high—sieges of walled towns, deer sweeping through the forest, men ploughing, hunting, hawking, feasting, sailing in ships, men riding and leading horses. Although horses are mentioned only five times in the Psalms that was not often enough for the Master of Canterbury. We reproduce some of his equestrian scenes here (P20–22). All his animals are ponies, by our standards. By comparison with the human figure they seem to range in size from about 12 hands 2 inches upwards. There are warriors riding out to battle, a hawking scene with magnificent hounds like Irish wolfhounds, a fight between horsemen armed with javelins, and finally horses by themselves, turned out to grass and gambolling with delight. The saddles look remarkably modern, much more so than the Norman war-saddles of the next century; but even at this late date there are no stirrups. These are the best, indeed almost the only realistic pictures of English horses in the years between the departure of the Romans and the arrival of the Normans; it is our good fortune that they are also as romantic and pleasing as this.

The heroic way of life in England, and the supremacy of the warriors such as we see in these Canterbury pictures, were part of an unbroken tradition stretching back to the Bronze Age, and it ended on the field of Hastings. Its best epitaph is in these lines from the Song of Beowulf that was still being sung on the eve of Hastings, describing the typical Bronze Age cremation of the hero:

> Then round the bale-fire rode the valiant sons of princes,
> Twelve earls uttering their grief and mourning the king,
> Composing elegies in praise of the hero.

CHAPTER FIVE

The Early Middle Ages

'I offer him to you as a gift: take him, my lord.'
Then the King said: 'I do not wish it so:
If I take your horse from you he will not have so fine a master.
Such a horse as this needs such a rider as you
For routing Moors in the field and pursuing them after the battle:
May the Creator not bless whoever would take your horse from you,
Since by means of your horse and you we all have received honour.'
Then they parted and the court rode on.

Poema del Mio Cid, tr. W. S. Merwin.

E luegos partío la cort—the court rode on. It was always riding on, in all the kingdoms of western Europe, alike in England and Scotland, in France, in Spain, in Norway and in the innumerable principalities and duchies between the Po and the Scheldt that since Charlemagne's time had been called the Holy Roman Empire of the German Nation. Only in the true Roman Empire, that of the East, was there a city large enough to support the court all the year round and a system of transport efficient enough to bring to the capital all the goods that the court would consume, and an economy advanced enough to convert into cash that part of the royal revenues that was not needed for the current maintenance of the court and the upkeep of the armed forces. Even the Pope, like the secular sovereigns, did not sit permanently in the Holy City but progressed round his temporal dominions. That pattern of society, or at least of its upper strata, was almost uniform throughout the western world. At the head was a royal family descended from one or other of the chiefs of the Germanic tribes who had broken in on the Roman Empire half a thousand years before. Below him were on the one hand a greater nobility, all of whom could speak French more or less and many of whom knew no other language: equal with them an order of prelates whose official and liturgical language was Latin; below them again a secular clergy somewhat closer to the soil, a monastic clergy which was the last repository of Latin culture, and a fighting lesser nobility or gentry whose estates, called knights' fees, were the units of agrarian economy, and whose equipment and tactics in war were

85

practically identical with those of Duke William's chivalry at Hastings. When at the end of the eleventh century there came the armed clash of Islam and Christianity, the Arabs pretended not to be able to distinguish between these armoured riders of the Great Horse, and called them all indifferently Feranghi—'Franks'. And when the emperor at Byzantium saw fit to command the Hetairarch to raise yet another force of heavy cavalry, equipped with the characteristic Norman armament, this corps was called the Francopouli—'the little Franks'—though its ranks might be filled with Lombards or Bavarians or Englishmen.

In England, although there was a new military system and a complete gallery of new faces among the provincial landowners, the court functioned much as it had done under the later Anglo-Saxon and Danish kings. It came to rest three times a year, for the crown-wearings at Westminster, Winchester and Gloucester, for a period of weeks, just as Edward the Confessor's household had done: but for the rest of the year it was on progress, and the English monarchy cannot truly be said to have had a settled home in and about London until the advent of the Tudors.

The landed magnates by the terms of their oath of fealty were obliged to accompany the sovereign on some part of his progress about the kingdom, the lesser barons to escort their liege lords from one part of their scattered domains to another, and the knights in their turn to follow the barons to whom they had done homage from one knight's fee to the next. The duties of a knight consisted of three kinds of service: that in the field, for forty days in peace or sixty days in war, known as scutage or shield-carrying; garrison duty, or castle-guard, variously as required; and escort duty, called in French *Chevalchée* and in Latin *equitatio*—literally 'riding'. If the first meant necessarily a capital investment in war-horses and a steady expenditure on their upkeep, the last meant a similar investment in lighter saddle-horses for the progress as well as a suitable train of draught- and pack-horses.

This custom of progress round the estates was dictated by the simple economic fact that it was cheaper, when rents were paid almost entirely in kind, and that kind predominantly in foodstuffs, to bring the eaters of the landlord's bread to the source of supply rather than to transport the bulky rents and taxes to the capital, or, in the case of tenants-in-chief, to what was called the Head of the Honour, the principal manor of the pluralist landowner where his own court was held. At the summit there was also a political consideration; in an age of general illiteracy there was no way of impressing the sovereign's personality on the mass of the subjects except by the king showing his face regularly in as many parts of the kingdom as possible. For this latter reason, the need for a type of horse that would enable the monarch to present an impressive figure to his subjects, not too unlike his equestrian portrait seen on the obverse of his Great Seal and some of his coins, was felt early, and met by the Courser of State. The Chamberlain and his colleague the Master

[*continued on page* 91

1

2

FIGURE OF A HORSE
FOUND AT BOURNE, LINCS.
Purchased 1924.

3

4

5

6

7

8

9

12

11

10

12 A

13

14A

14B

15

16

17

18

19

20

21

22

23

24 A

24 B

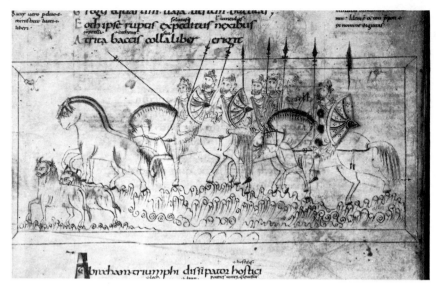

25

26

27

28

29

ssaum fieri de pano qualibet anno post
to hoc decos & decim sportem pondey illius
amnu auus medius talis est Q.D patti

30

31

iudicia tua domine
Quoniam tu dominus altissir
super omnem terram: nimis era
tus es super omnes deos

32

nasti in terra sanctuarium eius.
ruristi omnes sepes eius: posu

33

34

35

36

37

38

39

40

FEELDE

LE

41

NOTES ON THE PLATES

1. The Galway Curragh. A splendid sea-boat. This design was the master-piece of early Bronze Age naval architecture. Now made with a canvas skin, it was until recently covered with horse-hide like the Greenland 'umiak'. Like it too, the curragh will carry pigs or goats or sheep or calves with their legs tied, but not adult cattle or horses. (Cf. 17, page 29.) *Photo by Irish Tourist Board.*

2. Bronze statuette from Lincolnshire—early Roman-British period. *British Museum.*

3. Bronze statuette from Gaul, early Gallo-Roman period, found at Châlons-sur-Marne in the territory of the Catuvellauni, a Belgic tribe. *Photo by Jean Roubier.*

4. Bronze group of Epona, mare and foal from Alise Ste Reine. *Musée d'Antiquités Nationales.*

5. The 'Forest' Ponies on the Mildenhall Salver. *British Museum. Photo by Jean Roubier.*

6. Bronze terminal in form of horse-mask, from chariot-pole found at Stanwick, N. Yorks, but belonging to a chariot of type associated with the Belgic Parisii of Holderness. *British Museum.*

7. Slab carved with image of Epona from southern Gaul. Pre-Roman. *Photo by Jean Roubier.*

8. Plaque with image of Epona from military chapel in the Rhineland. *Photo by Jean Roubier.*

9. Carved limestone image of Epona from Alise Ste Reine. *Photo by Jean Roubier.*

10. Roman auxiliary's tombstone. Longinus, corporal of horse, I Thracian cavalry, Colchester. Died between A.D. 43 and 49, aged forty, with fifteen years' service. *Colchester Museum.*

11. Roman auxiliary's tombstone. Rufus Sita, trooper in mounted squadron of VI Thracian mixed battalion, Gloucester. Aged forty, with twenty-two years' service. First century A.D. *Gloucester City Museum.*

12. Mounted section of Roman legion in action against the Caledonians, about A.D. 150. Slab erected by Legio II Augusta at Bridgeness on the Forth. *National Museum of Scotland.*

12A. Roman general and staff, mounted. The so-called Sarcophagus of St Helena at Rome. *Photo by the Papal Office of Works.*

13. The Roman Public Conveyance. The fore-runner of the diligence or the omnibus, drawn by a pair of unusually large horses in southern Gaul. *Photo by Jean Roubier.*

14. The Hippodrome—Races in Progress.

    (*a*) On a carved lintel at Avignon. *Photo by Jean Roubier.*

    (*b*) On a mosaic floor, formerly at Horkstow in Lincolnshire. *British Museum.*

15. Roman Post Chaise from Gaul (Arles). Of a pattern identical with that used in Britain. In some of the Mediterranean provinces mules were used, but in Britain and the northern part of Gaul invariably horses. *Photo by Jean Roubier.*

16. Roman horse-dealer, Gallic groom, and stock-in-trade. It took thirty days to walk laden pack-horses from the western Channel ports to Marseilles, according to Pytheas. Presumably it would take quite as long to walk soft green young stock a similar distance. Therefore if such horses were bought in Britain and shipped to Gaul they would have to fetch a stiff price in the south to justify all the outlay in time and work, even if the groom was an unpaid slave. *Photo by Jean Roubier.*

17. Tombstone of a Dark Age Prince. In Scotland beyond the borders of the Roman Empire, and also beyond the range of subsequent English conquest. The cross incorporated in the design indicates the deceased was at least nominally Christian, but other elements in the design, as often in these monuments, are of pagan origin. Below the mounted figure are engraved the details of the farrier's honourable calling, but these themselves are the badge of more than one heathen god. *Photo by D. M. Goodall.*

18. Gallic shrine to clan ancestors. Freize from lintel at Roquepertuse. *Photo by Jean Roubier.*

19. Carved panel from the Frank's casket. Northumbrian work of the early Christian period. Actually shows a burial in pagan style, but without cremation. The hero has already been buried (right, inside the round barrow), the horse is outside, with the mourners. It may be awaiting sacrifice. *British Museum.*

20. Horses on the Hills, from Canterbury Psalter. *British Museum.*

21 and 22. Mounted warriors from Canterbury Psalter. *British Museum.*

23. Twelfth-century Chess Knight. Found on the seashore of the Isle of Lewis, walrus ivory, apparently of Norwegian workmanship. The armament and saddlery are a compromise between the Norman and the Viking styles. In general, the arms and armour are of a pattern hopelessly obsolete in twelfth-century England or France. The bridle, instead of the universal Franco-Norman curb, has a simple snaffle as used in Saxon England and Roman and Celtic Britain. The horse has been dwarfed by the design of all the chess figures, because every piece had to be bottom-heavy to enable it to fit into the travelling casket, and to be used for games on the cabin table while the longship rolled and pitched. Even discounting this element, the size and shape of the piece has something to do with living models in the Hebrides. *British Museum.*

24*a* Enormous Horses in a Religious Process. On a tapestry panel which adorned the cabin of the ship in which a Norwegian queen was buried at

Oseberg; if, as is reasonable to suppose, the old lady did the embroidery herself when a girl, then the date is near enough A.D. 800. The other half of the panel shows the same sort of horses drawing ceremonial cult-wagons, but singly and not in pairs. A similar cult-wagon was actually found in pieces in the ship, but it had a pole for two horses. The horses actually buried with the ship averaged 14 hands. Were the animals in this picture pure fantasy? *Skibets Museet, Oslo.*

24*b* The two surviving Norwegian breeds. Left Fjordings. Right Gud-brandsdal. (Dølehest).

25 and 26. English Illuminated Manuscript, probably also copied at Canter-bury, about the year 1000, of a text of the *Psychomachia* of Prudentius. Costume and other details that were used to illustrate the English text are, as was customary, modelled after the style of the artist's time. The pictures show people of forceful and violent character, which in the experi-ence of most Englishmen at that period means Danes by land or Nor-wegians by sea. So this is what the great Danish army looked like when not wearing armour or helmets. The horses, even allowing for some eccen-tricities on the part of the artist, are plainly of different type from those drawn in the Canterbury Psalter. Probably they represent local animals looted from Suffolk and Essex, but just possibly Danish-bred and im-ported deliberately for military purposes. *British Museum.*

27. Mounted Warrior on Tapestry from Church at Baldishol in Norway. About contemporary with 23 and, like it, slightly behind the fashion in arms and armour by French or Norman standards. Head of horse like a caricature of the Arab type. It might mean that such horses had been imported to Norway as early as this, but much more likely, since the Norwegians were the most widely travelled of Europeans, that the artist had seen such a horse, either in the course of an expedition to 'the land of Blue Men' (the Barbary coast), or else during service in the Varangian Guard, the crack corps of northern mercenaries maintained by the emperors of Constantinople. *Photo Oslo, Kunstindustrimuseet.*

28. The Three Types on which the Military End of the Feudal System depended, from the Fifteenth-century Manuscript of Lydgate's Siege of Thebes. The pattern was the same for the whole period from the eleventh century onwards. Left, the knight on the destrier, centre the squire on his rouncy, leading, in his left hand, the palfrey which the knight rides when not armed and ready for battle. *British Museum.*

29. King John Hunting. He normally used palfreys, but this is probably what would be called a courser in medieval terms. *British Museum.*

30. The capul as draught-horse. Marginal drawing from the Assize of Bread for the City of London, showing the fraudulent baker being 'drawn on a hurdle' by two horses with rigid collars, which are already of a pattern almost identical with that used today. This is not really a hurdle, but the universal 'traha' or wheel-less dray, used for carting muck, building materials, etc. At this date a pair of ordinary draught-horses could manage one of these, but at least four would be needed for the four-wheeled wagon. Late thirteenth century. *Corporation of London Library.*

31. The rouncy as war-horse. Model, dateable from the style of helmet as close to 1300. Tail missing. This was an aquamanile or table water-jug. It represents a knight whose war-horse (destrier) has become a casualty, and who has therefore put his 'great saddle' on the rouncy which normally the squire rides. One can see the saddle comes too far back on the loins ever to have been made for this horse; also by the spread of its legs that its weight-carrying powers are being heavily taxed, but it has the typical hindquarters of the rouncy (compare also P73 and P74 below), which will enable it to do the job for a short spell. *British Museum*.

32 and 33. The capul as draught-horse. Normally only two were required for the country cart of this pattern (East Anglia or Lincolnshire here), of which we see varieties from the Highlands (P57 and text figure 29) and the West Lowlands (text figure 30), as well as the Pennines (P62) more than four centuries later. In all these models the rails were the permanent part of the sides; there were removable wicker-work linings derived ultimately from the wicker sides of the Iron Age chariot. *Luttrell Psalter, c.* 1340, *British Museum*.

34. King Arthur MacMorogh coming down the mountain to confer with the English commanders. *British Museum*.

35. The capul as saddle-horse. John Ball at the head of the rebel army in 1381. *British Museum MS. Royal* 18E. *i. Froissart's 'Chronique'. Photo by Christopher Trent*.

36. Palfrey used for hawking.

37. Palfreys nominally being used for hawking. *British Museum carved ivory mirror-backs, fourteenth century*.

38. The capul as pack-horse. Bringing seed corn to sowers in the field. *Queen Mary's Psalter. British Museum*.

39. The harrow-puller (*hercarius*). Compare with the cart-horses on the same farm (Ps 32, 33) and with the harrow-puller in text figure 4. Again, the collar is completely 'modern'. *British Museum*.

40. Tinkers leaving Aberdeen, about 1630. On the right is a substantial burgess, perhaps a senior member of the university, whose horse may be compared with the tinkers' ponies. This is the earliest known picture of tinkers. Note the shaven but undocked tail of the pony ridden by the tinker's wife. Pack-saddles are put on over a straw mat, held in place by straw breast-ropes. *Painting in possession of Marischal College, Aberdeen*.

41. The 'parcel of woodland in Stocks Close', showing ponies grazing, 1607. *Wiltshire. Plan in Public Record Office*.

continued from page 86]

of the Horse were always on the look-out for the sort of well-schooled stallion that would fulfil this role. If only on account of the required size, the native pony could never play the part of Courser of State, but the peripatetic court employed large numbers of native horses in what Hollywood calls the supporting cast.

The knight and his destrier, as the basic fighting unit of the medieval army, needed a minimum of three other horses to keep them in action day after day, even through the six-week campaign which was the medieval strategist's ideal operation. Preferably there should be a second destrier, because the Great Horse, despite its other virtues, was rather soft. In any case it was meant to be ridden only in action. But a second destrier meant a second squire, which came expensive unless the knight had a second son who must be provided for anyhow. There must be a palfrey for the knight to ride when not in action and a cob or rouncy (*runcinus* in Latin) for the squire to ride while leading the destrier. Also a pack-horse to carry the knight's armour. When chivalry reached the pitch of elaboration where the destrier too wore armour, then there must be two armour-carrying pack-horses who could be put to a small wagon when the axis of advance (or retreat) lay along a carriage-road. The rouncy had to travel at a trot, if only because the war-horse which the squire led was a natural trotter, this gait being inherent in the large Diluvial breeds. The palfrey on the other hand paced or ambled, and could thus be supplied from any of the native breeds which were predominantly non-trotting by nature. If a foal out of a palfrey mare grew up with trotting propensities, it would be schooled in hobbles until it did pace.

The palfrey goes back in name and in blood to the Roman occupation. The word is derived from the Graeco-Latin word *paraveredus*—relay-horse. These were the horses which maintained the Roman posting service, conveying the imperial messengers from one end of the empire to another if need be. The Romans had no stirrups and their language in its classical form had no single word to mean 'trot'. The travelling horse of the Middle Ages was like the Roman post-horse, a pacer—'gaited' in the American sense.

Many sporting knights liked to beguile the tedium of the approach march by flying a hawk at game-birds or coursing a hare along the route. This could be done on a palfrey (it *must not* be done on the destrier if he was to be kept fresh for action) but those who could afford it added to their string a courser, which was a hunter; coursers might be bred anyhow but they must have a turn of speed, and the best of them were used for racing. The motive was not entirely sporting; as in medieval civil life, so in the military sphere, the pot was a strong incentive. The officers' mess would be poorly furnished if it relied entirely on the salt beef and oatmeal which was all the quartermaster had in his wains. The senior ranks of a medieval host were no different from a tinker going along the country roads of Ireland, with his lurcher continually foraging on the flanks. Wellington's officers hunting in the Peninsula were quite in the medieval tradition.

This feature is well seen in the Bayeux Tapestry. Right up to the 'moment of truth' at Senlac, Norman barons and bishops are depicted with falcons on their fists. But the palfreys and cobs are conspicuously absent from the tapestry. This too is a touch of realism. The composition of the Norman army for the Hastings campaign was highly unusual. Out of a total strength of between six and seven thousand, almost half were cavalry. This is because only Phase I of William's plan was carried out. He was able to mobilize, with enormous effort, little more than seven hundred warships and ships of burden fit to carry horses. Into them, in the first lift, he put all his knights and their destriers, his Genoese archers and the best of his fully armed foot. This assault wave was only meant to seize a bridgehead while the ships went back to pick up the support wave. In the latter were included the rouncies, palfreys with their squires, some light infantry and as many pack-horses as would fill the ships: not enough, but it was hoped to supply the balance of pack-horses from what is politely called 'local requisitioning' in England. Without the support wave the Normans could not advance more than a day's march inland; but no sooner had the ships got back to Normandy than the wind went round to the north, and the second wave was delayed for many days. In fact it did not land until after the battle. If William had not managed to crush all resistance by the evening of 14th October, he might as well never have given battle at all, because he would have been unable to advance farther, nor would his knights have been able to fight with much chance of success on the morning of the 15th without fresh horses. In the event, there was no battle on the second day, and no pursuit, because there was no significant English force left to pursue. By such a narrow margin was England lost and won.

If it appears at times that there is an undue emphasis on the linguistic factor in these notes, we must beg the reader's pardon: but it is only by understanding the technical vocabulary of the horseman of bygone generations that the modern reader can really get inside his skin. That is why we quote so many passages in the original language, though always with a translation; there are available many modernizations and paraphrases of great elegance (notably for Chaucer) but often when it comes to horses and the lore that surrounds them, the paraphraser's skill deserts him and he translates with a modern word which does not at all imply the sort of horse that the old author meant. For instance your modern poet will often say 'steed', meaning no more than a vaguely admirable rating for a horse. But *steed, stede, steid, steade* and their ancestor *steda* had very precise meanings which changed, but still remained precise, as time passed over the islands.

Once the Norman power was established the English abandoned their use of the word *steda* to mean any male horse entire, and fixed its use to mean the Norman war-horse or *destrier* (latinized as *dextrarius*)—the stallion *par excellence*. The Normans expressed the old use of the word *steda* by *estalun*—the one horse so valuable that it must be housed in a stable—*estal*—no matter what else had to run out. To express stallion in its capacity as breeding sire the English now fell back on *stānhors*, later stone-horse, and *stōdhors*, later stud-horse, contracted still later in America into 'stud'. *Hengest* fell entirely out of use except in the combination henchman. But 'horse' by itself continued to have a principally masculine connotation, more among some parts of the islands than in others; this very evening I had a long conversation with an Anglo-Irish dealer concerning a certain 'full-horse'. My full-horse was a Connemara colt rising three.

Turning to practice as opposed to words, there now began a grading of horses by size, for use. The larger horses were used for riding. The largest of all for the riding of knights. The smallest for draught, the worst for use on the land and the middle size for pack transport. Pack-men avoided the smaller ponies because many of their routes lay along narrow tracks where the tops of the heather, bushes, projecting rocks and the like would scrape the bottom of the load and damage it if the horse could not carry it high enough. On the other hand too tall a horse is tiresome to load and unload, especially if there is only one 'lademan' to many horses. Unless we bear this scale constantly in mind for the whole period from the Norman Conquest to the middle seventeenth century, we are liable to get an entirely wrong idea of the appearance and function of some old author's cart-horse or hack or hobby or nag.

Great play has been made with the fact that in the Domesday Survey certain townships bordering on Exmoor contained animals called 'equi silvatici'. Certainly the second of these words is derived from *silva*- a wood, and in the distant past had meant 'living in the woods'. But long before the end of the Roman era the word had lost this precise meaning; it is the ancestor of the Italian *selvaggio* and the French *sauvage* and the English *savage*. (The earlier sense of the English *savage* is not so much ferocious as shy and untamed). *Silvaticus* was not used by eleventh-century Norman clerks as meaning any kind of specifically 'woodland' or 'forest' beast. Speaking among themselves they would describe these as 'des bois' or writing it down in an official document, 'de boscis'. *Equi silvatici* does not mean that in early Norman times Englishmen recognized a special 'forest horse' either in Professor Ewart's sense or in the modern New Forest sense. Moreover, such animals are represented in other sections of Domesday Book, far away from Exmoor and Dartmoor and the New Forest. There is little doubt that if the survey had included the upper reaches of the Yorkshire and Durham dales, Cumberland and Westmorland, it would have recorded even greater numbers of *equi silvatici*. But the inhabitants of those parts had an acute distaste for government surveyors, and if any of them had showed himself west of a line drawn from Richmond to Ripon, he would have been stuck full of arrows before he could say Jehannot Fitzrobin. These chapters of Domesday Book therefore remained a blank.

It is as well to recall the manner in which this great register was compiled. The commissioners and their clerks met, in every township, the principal landlord or his bailiff, the parish priest and a deputation of the oldest tenants. Between them they stated the bounds of the township, the acreage of its ploughland, the rent it had been worth in Edward the Confessor's time (that was what the old men were there for) and what rent the lord expected to get for it in 1086. Also what stock was running on the common. The commissioners and their clerks had no English. Neither, very often, had the landlord or his reeve, who spoke to the commissioners in French. The parish priest translated the evidence of the old tenants into Latin, in which language the clerks wrote down a complete economic picture of the township. The clerks wrote down *silvaticus* every time the village elders said 'wild'. This word had the same form in eleventh-century English as it has now, and it had the same meaning then and now when it was used by the same sort of people.

Scientific gentlemen are very fond of lecturing us for promiscuous use of the word 'wild' in connection with horses. First, because of the long-standing legal distinction between animals *ferae naturae* and domestic animals. The former are, legally speaking, no man's property as long as they are alive; while the latter are chattels, which is the same word as cattle (Old French *chaptel*). But the 'nature' invoked in this distinction is a scholastic and artificial concept which no natural scientist of our day believes in for a moment. However, from a legal point of view, every horse in Britain now has an owner and has had, for many generations. It is not game, though I fear the time may come when it will be regarded as vermin, and not only by that very vocal section of the population which now regards huntsmen as vermin. Studies summarized in such works as that of Bengt Lundholm on the domestication of the horse in Scandinavia and in the more recent account, by Dr Erna Mohr of Hamburg, of the wild Mongolian (Prjevalsky's) herds and those of their descendants which have been in captivity for the last sixty years, show that there are only two significant physical changes which infallibly denote domestication at some time and which the horse does not lose even many generations after reversion to a feral state. These do not include, as was once widely believed, changes of coat colour. White or white markings are not an infallible sign of domestication. This fact became evident as soon as the piebald 'Shetland' ponies of the palaeolithic cave paintings came to light.

The two infallible signs, induced alike by true domestication and by captivity in zoos, are first a shrinking and sharpening of the muzzle, at first affecting only the flesh and skin but after further generations extending actually to the shape of the skull. Second, a rapid advance in sexual maturity. The initial draft of Mongolian horses were captured as foals, and arrived at zoos in Russia and points west as yearlings. None of them produced offspring until over six years old. Not only did the fillies not come in season but the testicles of the colts did not fully descend until all growth in stature had ceased and both sexes had a 'full mouth'. But with each successive generation of Mongolian horses, so far as it could be observed in the zoos at Prague, Munich, Berlin, Hamburg, Woburn Park, sexual maturity came earlier and earlier. Judged by these two standards, no British breed of hill ponies has 'wild' characteristics. None of them has the characteristic swelling muzzle of the wild Mongolian, of the Tarpan or of their near relatives as portrayed in the cave paintings (perhaps because once dependence on the sense of smell becomes less absolute a form of atrophy takes place which can never be put into reverse?).

As to the second point, it is a common experience among moorland herds in southern England and Wales that two-year-old fillies drop foals, usually in the spring following a summer of exceptional grazing. Occasionally these foals are live births following full-term pregnancy, more commonly they are abortions, sometimes in the late autumn. Abundant grazing on hill pastures usually means a dry hot summer. If the autumn and winter following are equally dry, as in 1959–60, the winter keep is correspondingly poor. Poverty makes mares slip their foals. The early born fillies, eighteen months old in their second September, come in season in the late summer, and are covered, as often as not, by equally forward two-year-old colts, full of grass and gallantry. Such conditions can occur in 'nature'. It is true that in the truly wild herds the mature stallions keep the colts away from the females, and themselves probably cannot be bothered with precocious fillies when there are plenty of mares in the prime of life to choose from. But not much more so than under hill-grazing 'domestic' conditions. It would seem that in the truly wild herds there was a self-adjusting mechanism which ensured that females which were themselves immature should not be further burdened with a foal, born or unborn. If these were unable to keep up with the main body on the seasonal migration that would endanger the safety of the herd as a whole, since the instinct of the boss stallion is to round up the stragglers, cost what it may, come blizzard or wolves or men. And if there is such a thing as 'nature' it exerts its influence for the preservation of the herd as such, not of individuals.

Such cases are less often reported in the Highlands, in Shetland, on the fells and in the dales. There the 'wild' order of things seems to obtain more consistently. But this is probably due to the influence of climate, which is not a question of absolute temperature, but of the combination cold-plus-damp, two factors that, in combination, have a retarding effect, and did not occur together in the central grasslands of the Eurasian land-mass where the last truly wild herds of horses survived into modern times.

Nevertheless there are Englishmen, not unacquainted with horse-breeding, who say 'wild' and know what they mean when they say it. They mean what Wulfric of Mercia meant, when he made his will in 1002, by his 'hundrath wildra horsa'. Simply the breeding stock which he had running out, perhaps on the Peak. Some of them no doubt had never had a rope on them; others had no doubt been broken at one time or another; perhaps most of them, once caught up, would lead in a halter. But he was not using them for work *now*, nor did he intend to do so in the near future; in contrast to his 'xvi tame hengestas', some of which no doubt were the sires of those very 'wild' foals, but all of which were now carrying Wulfric's house-carles about their business of peace or war.

Thus when an Exmoor farmer says to me 'that's a tame foal', pointing to some little tacker in the centre of a milling mob in the yard, I know he means he has been kept in the in-fields with his dam for some reason or another, and perhaps even handled a little. But he is blood-brother to the other unhandled stock of the same herd, and another season may be running out on the moor with them. Since English is my native tongue, as it was of Wulfric the Thane, who wrote as good English as most zoologists, I prefer his usage. 'When I use a word', said Humpty-Dumpty, 'it means what I want it to mean.' Well, not quite: but so long as one knows what one means. . . .

Just how long the herds of truly wild horses survived in Britain is a question that can never be answered now. But there is one piece of evidence that may be significant. During the Pictish War of A.D. 367, when the barbarians outflanked the Hadrian Line by sea and overran nearly the whole of Britain, a wealthy Roman family at Mildenhall in Suffolk buried their household treasures, including a valuable service of silver plate, before seeking refuge in the nearest walled town. For some reason they never returned to dig it up. It was later recovered, almost complete, and is now to be seen magnificently displayed in the British Museum. Though the technique of silver-smithing is Roman it need not necessarily have been made in Rome, or even in Gaul, for before the Pictish War there were craftsmen in Britain capable of producing work of this standard. If it was made overseas, it was probably made to the order of the customer, in the design dictated by him. Most of the larger pieces show mythological scenes and animal friezes in relief, but one flanged dish (No. 9 in the catalogue) shows two ponies of *Forest* type, one standing and one lying, under some trees. Neither wears a halter. This in itself is not significant: but the context is. All the other animals on this dish are *wild* animals; deer, boar, elk and so on. In fact the design represents the larger wild fauna of north-west Europe—it could be the larger wild fauna of Britain in the fourth century (P5).

In 1171, almost exactly a hundred years after the Conquest, William Fitzstephen, a monk known to some authorities as Stephanides but probably to most of his contemporary Londoners as Stephenson, wrote an account of the city called *Descriptio Civitatis Londiniae*. It is full of interest from many points of view but chiefly for its vivid but tantalizing short sketch of the Friday horse-market at Smithfield. (We shall have cause to visit Smithfield again later in this book.) Unfortunately he wrote in Latin; one would give much to know what words he would have used from his native vocabulary to describe some of the horses in the following passage, which has been so often quoted with partial and arbitrary curtailment, and translated to suit the preconceived ideas of the quoter, that we think it best to print the greater part just as it stands, giving our own gloss with which those of our readers who have some Latin are at liberty to agree or disagree, always bearing in mind that the usages of the twelfth century are not the usages of classical Latin.

Feria est ibi celebre spectaculum nobilium equorum venalium.
There is a fair where the sight of well-bred horses for sale is well known.

Spectaturi vel empturi veniunt qui in urbe adsunt comites barones,
Either to look on or to buy everyone who is in town comes—earls, barons,

milites civites plurimi.
knights and many burgesses.

Juvat videre gradarios succussatura nitente suaviter ambulantes pedibus.
It is a joy to see the palfreys with a flashing action smoothly ambling,

Lateraliter simul erectis quasi a subalternis et demissis.
raising and setting down their feet as it were, both on one side alternately.

Hinc equos qui armigeris magis conveniunt, durius incidentes sed expedite tamen,
Here horses more suitable for squires with rougher but fast gait

qui quasi a contradictoribus pedes simul elevant et deponunt.
which is it were raise and put down opposite legs at the same time.

Hinc nobiles juniores pullos qui nondum freno bene asseuti altius incidunt
Here well-bred younger colts not yet well accustomed to the bridle rear up

et mollia crura reponunt.
but go softly.

Hinc summarios membris solidis et vegetis.
Here are pack-horses with stout and nimble legs.

Hinc dextrarios pretiosos elegantis formae staturae honestae micantes auribus
Here are expensive chargers of handsome conformation and impressive height

cervicis arduis clunibus obesis.
switching their ears and arching their necks: they have massive quarters.

In horum incessu spectant emptores primis passum suaviorem
When these are run up the prospective buyers first watch the slower paces and then

postea motum citatiorem qui est quasi a contrariis pedibus anterioribus
the faster ones in which the forefeet are alternately raised and set down and

simul solo amotis et admotis et posterioribus similiter
then the hind-feet likewise

. . . clamor attolitur, vulgares equos in partem ire praecipitur.
. . . a shout goes up to take the common horses aside.

Stant ibi aptae aratris, trahis et bigis equae. Quarumdam ventres foetibus
Here are mares for ploughing or draught in sled or double harness cart.

tument. Alias editi foetibus obeunt pulli lasciviores, sequela inseparabilis.
Some of them are heavy in foal. Yet others have brought forth foals
which frisk about, their progeny not yet weanable.

It will be seen that the market falls into five main parts described
above, for

(1) Gradarii or 'pacers', the palfreys, amblers, street nags or what you will,
that are to be the constant companions of our journeys for so many years
to come.
(2) A category for which no convenient Latin word occurs and which has to
be paraphrased as 'horse suitable for squires'. It is a cob, as we shall see
in a moment, and it trots.
(3) Good quality young stock of all kinds.
(4) Pack-horses.
(5) War-horses, called by a latinized form of the French term 'destrier'—the
horses of the right hand, because when not in action they were led by a
mounted squire on the off-side of his cob, while the knight took things
easy on his palfrey. All destriers trotted: it was in their blood to do so, as
it is in the blood of many breeds whose original home was in marsh land.
Because it was inconvenient to lead a trotting horse from a pacing horse
the squires were mounted on trotting cobs, and for no other reason.

There was a sixth section for brood and draught mares, and foals.

It will be seen that out of the above six categories, only the fifth and
part of the third consisted of imported stock or the progeny of animals
imported during the last hundred years. Possibly some of the pacers
were of partly oriental breeding, but it is not very likely that palfreys of
such quality would ever descend in the social scale as far as Smithfield
Market.

The section on the mare-market is tantalizing. From the gender of the
Latin words used it might seem to imply that in the twelfth century only
mares were used for all harness work. Probably this was nearly but not
quite true. It is noticeable that in this section the brood mares do not
seem to be sorted out from the working mares, and under certain
circumstances medieval farmers probably worked their brood mares
right up to the time of foaling. It is less harmful for a pregnant mare to
work in harness rather than under the saddle or in a pack-train, especially if only in traces, not shafts. The sledge (*traha*) of course had no
shafts. What is surprising is to see the plough (*aratrum*) mentioned at all
in connection with horses. But in so far as the English ploughed with
horses at all they evidently used mares at this date. Geldings were

practically unknown. Probably the horse-plough was only used in a few parts of the country where for one reason or another the oxen were unsuitable or not available. King Alfred had remarked with some surprise in one of his geography books that his friend Ottar the Norwegian ploughed with horses when at home in Lofoten. The earliest horse-ploughs must therefore have been introduced either to Northumbria or the Danelaw. Certainly horse-ploughing was not a Saxon or Norman custom in the eleventh century.

In the year 1188 the crusades were going very badly. Saladin, the Kurdish general, recaptured Jerusalem, which had been in Frankish hands for nearly a hundred years. As part of an international recruiting drive the aged Baldwin, Archbishop of Canterbury, set out on a tour of Wales to preach the crusade. In his train went Giraldus Cambrensis, alias Gerald de Barri, Archdeacon of Brecon, a prolific author of travel books. The fruit of this journey was his famous *Itinerary through Wales* and his *Description of Wales*. He reports that in Gower he heard of a local boy who had been carried away by 'little men of pygmy stature' and spent several years in their underground home, eventually returning to his own family. This is a frequently recurring theme of folk-lore, both Celtic and Germanic, and is not, in its origin at least, pure fantasy. It could be that in remote pockets of the forests and the mountains there remained some dwarfish survivors of the pre-Celtic population who lived, unabsorbed, a secret life which was a continuance into historic times of the Neolithic pastoral culture, in their round, turf-roofed pit-dwellings, and that they occasionally kidnapped children of the dominant races. The interesting thing about Gerald's boy from Gower is that his Little People had 'horses adapted to their size'. Perhaps they were people of flesh and blood, and perhaps their horses wore the three-inch bits of very Early Bronze Age workmanship that have been found, among other sites, in Wales.

In the central district of Wales called Powys, south of Lake Bala, Gerald found 'most excellent studs put apart for breeding, and deriving their origin from some fine Spanish horses, which Robert de Belesme, Count of Shrewsbury, brought into this country; on which account the horses sent from hence are remarkable for their majestic proportion and astonishing fleetness'. Robert de Belesme was the son of Roger de Montgomeri, Count of Arundel and Shrewsbury, who commanded the central 'battaile' of the Norman cavalry at Hastings. Our illustration shows Spanish war-horses of the eleventh century, the kind of horses ridden by the Cid Campeador and his companions. As will be seen, they are of the same general type as the Norman or Frankish destrier, but rather better looking. They are just the kind of animal that a Norman baron would consider worth importing even at considerable expense. They were the ancestors of the famous Andalusian breed, which in turn was the ancestor of the modern Lipizzaner, by way of the Neapolitan;

but they also managed, by their union with Welsh mountain mares, to engender the Welsh cob, which under the name 'Powis horse' was to provide so many remounts for English armies from the thirteenth century onwards. Astonishing fleetness and majestic proportions are of course both relative: the former by contrast with the lumbering Norman destrier, and the latter by contrast with the Welsh pony. But then, under-statement was never one of Gerald's literary faults. Here be it said that in some connections, such as natural history, Geraldus is a formidable liar. But he was also a political realist who regarded war as the chief instrument of politics. And in matters of military significance such as archery and horse-breeding his observations are strictly objective and he can be regarded as a first-class witness. In the *Description of Wales* he remarks that the 'higher class go to battle mounted on swift and well-bred steeds' and that when the tactical situation demanded it they did not scruple to dismount and fight on foot; a lesson which no Norman officer ever learnt. Further, the Welsh warrior caste were 'wholly employed in the care of their horses and equipment'. At the end of the *Description* he says that during the reigns of the first three Norman kings the Welsh nation were taught the use of arms and the management of horses by the English and Normans. On the face of it this statement is manifest nonsense: what it means is that during this period the Welsh aristocracy learnt, by imitating Norman knights and English quislings, the use of 'Frankish' armaments and the management of horses like those imported by Robert de Belesme, for horses of this type had not been seen in Wales since King Arthur's time (P73).

But Gerald was not only an archdeacon and a writer of guide-books. He was a real-life agent of that bugbear of continental staff officers, *Der Bridisch Indelligenz Zerviz*. Prior to the Welsh propaganda crusade he had been employed as a Norman spy in Ireland; and his *Topography of Ireland* and *How to Conquer Ireland* were written for the benefit of Henry II's high command. We are fortunate in that one of the earlier manuscript copies of this former work, which the author revised at least once, is illuminated with contemporary marginal drawings illustrating the text in considerable detail. We reproduce below (P75) a picture of twelfth-century Irish horses drawn from this source, which says, of Irish horses in general, that the riders 'also use woollen trousers that are at the same time stockings, and these are mostly dyed. When they are riding they do not use saddles, leggings or spurs. But they drive on and guide their horses by means of a stick with a crook at its upper end which they hold in their hand.' (Ordinary hunting-crop?) 'They use halters which are at once both bit and bridle, and do not prevent the horse from grazing as other bridles do.' The last sentence might be taken to mean something like what Americans call a hackamore bridle, or some sort of dropped noseband, except that archaeology shows a perfectly regular series of snaffle-bits from Ireland going back from medieval times to the La Tène Iron Age period and perhaps earlier.

Probably what Geraldus means is just a snaffle. The new kind of curb, with long cheek-pieces that would in fact prevent a horse from grazing, had been in use in France and Britain for the last hundred years, while the Irish, who never adopted any British or continental fashion for the first two hundred years or so of its existence, were still using the snaffle, which, whether of Bronze Age or twentieth-century design, does not interfere much with grazing. He added that the Irish went 'naked and without armour into action'; 'naked' may simply mean without the leather hauberk which it was necessary to wear between one's skin and a mail-shirt, but it may just possibly be meant literally, since it was part of the ritual of Bronze Age chariot fighting, as we see at Troy and Mycenae, for the heroes to go into action nude, but wearing a helmet and carrying a shield (P75). Later on we shall see, at a period about two hundred years after the *Topography* was written, an Irish king campaigning in armour of a type that was already slightly old-fashioned in Geraldus's day.

Throughout this period mention of palfreys is very frequent in legal documents concerning the region now known as the home of the Dales and Fell breeds. It would appear that palfreys were bred extensively in the Honour of Richmond (a vast complex of estates between the Tees and the Nidd, held by the descendants of Count Alan the Red of Brittany, a companion of the Conqueror), in Furness and Cartmel in Lancashire, and in the Eden valley of Westmorland. Thus in the very year of Magna Carta the Abbot of Furness, having offered ten palfreys by way of rent to a landowner in Borrowdale, actually paid 50 marks, which at five marks a head is a fair price for a palfrey (£3 6s. 8d.) then.

Constitutiones de Foresta

This is the document which mentions animals which are at large in forests but are *not* beasts of venery or of the chase nor yet vermin.

It purports to be by Canute but is in fact a forgery, though an ancient and interesting one. In fact practically the whole of Canute's forest law is contained in par. 80 of his Civil Code and is of a noble simplicity. It says:

'And I will that every free man shall be entitled to hunt over his own land whether it be fields or woodland: and all I ask is that no man shall hunt over *my* land, wherever I have given orders for it to be preserved.'

Neither the English nor the Danes recognized any special set of laws concerning game. Forest Law was an invention of the Normans, or rather a Norman adaptation of Frankish custom. The written code laid down by William I on this subject has been lost, but a hundred years after the Doomsday survey some Norman official drew up a revised code for the approval of Henry II, some time between 1177 and 1184. Because the memory of Canute was still respected by the native English, both in the north and in the south, the preamble invokes his authority for this elaborate set of regulations, which set up four separate grades of officials and laid down a savage scale of penalties beginning with blinding and castration. 'Sunt et qualia quamplurima animalia quae quanquam infra septa forestae vivant et oneri et curae mediocrium subjacent forestae tamen nequaquam censeri possunt: qualia sunt equi bubali vaccae et similia.' That is: 'There are also many animals which although they live within the pale of the forest and are under the charge and care of the *mediocris* yet cannot by any means be reckoned as *of* the forest: such are horses, *bubali*, cows, etc.'

The *mediocris* was the middle grade of forest officer set up by this decree. He was of a rank that the English would have called thane, second class (not a King's thane), as is shown by his heriot of one entire horse with one lance and shield plus £3 in cash. Plainly, a sort of agister. *Equi* means the same sort of horses as would be running on a common.

Bubali. Cannot mean a truly wild ox, since it is deliberately classed with other privately owned animals. I think it is *Bos primigenius*, the aurochs, which most authorities think was domesticated here in Neolithic times and still kept by the more backward stockbreeders down to the Middle Ages when its descendants merged into the bigger draught/beef breeds of true domestic cattle (*Bos longifrons*.)

The whole question of royal forests profoundly affected stockbreeders in the first half of the Middle Ages, less so in the second half. It was not so much that keeping stock in the forest meant working in a different landscape—the difference between forest and non-forest was one of degree rather than kind. What mattered was, in the forest the different system of law tilted the scale in favour of the wild game and against the *animalia nequaquam forestae* mentioned in the above passage. For instance, all medieval pastoral farmers used to help out their forage supplies through the winter by means of 'browse'; that is, they would lop the leaf-bearing branches of trees such as the elm when the leaves were fully grown and dry these like hay; as a winter feed this provided bulk if nothing else. But in a strictly preserved royal forest the chief duty of the verderer (an official who still survives and flourishes in Hampshire, though now he exercises his authority on behalf of the commoner rather than of the Crown) was to see that this 'vert' or browse was reserved for the king's deer. Moreover horses and horned cattle were barred from forest grazing during the winter haining, and again in early summer during the fence-month when the does dropped their fawns. Swine might run in the royal forest only during a certain season known as the pannage months. Though villeins on royal forests did have certain inalienable rights they were very restricted, and probably fewer horses were bred there than on commons in other parts of the country. Later on, as the enclosures gained ground in other parts of the country, the scale tilted the other way, so that only in royal forests did the small commoner enjoy his rights of pannage, turbary, marl, fuel wood and the rest, which formerly had been available on all the common lands of England. For almost a hundred and fifty years after the Conquest the whole of Devon and Cornwall, outside certain townships and liberties, was royal forest. In 1204 financial difficulties constrained King John to sell out, and the whole area *except* Exmoor and Dartmoor was disafforested in consideration of 5,000 marks for Devon and 2,000 marks and twenty palfreys for Cornwall. The palfreys at current prices would be worth 100 marks the score, or £3 6s. 8d. a head. When more than six hundred years later the Crown parted with the last of its forest rights on Exmoor, the wheel had come full circle and the moor had become almost the last refuge of the 'rough' horse breeder in the west country.

During the reigns of the Norman kings a custom grew up in Richmondshire which helps to form a picture of the progress of horse-breeding in that area, which is roughly the western half of the North Riding. Holders of knights' fees, in middle age, began to donate the title to land, or the use of land, to the abbeys. This knightly class were mostly of Breton origin, their ancestors having followed Count Alan of Brittany in the train of the Conqueror, and they held their land from the Earls of Richmond, who were called either Alan or Conan in a rather bewildering succession. Constable Burton in Swaledale is so called because it belonged to Roald, Constable of the Honour of Richmond. Constable means 'comes stabuili' or companion of the stables, and the first Constable of the Honour of Richmond had the oversight of all Count Alan's horses. In the Manor of Constable Burton was a farm still called Studdah which was originally *stod-hagi*, or 'the hedge around the mares': obviously connected with the duties of the Constable. In this predominantly Norse-speaking region, the *stod-hagi* may well have been, in its time, the temple precinct of some Norse god.

The great abbeys came more and more to dominate the agrarian economy of the North Riding—Fountains, Rievaulx, Jervaulx, Mount Grace, Easby—but especially the Cistercian houses, mostly founded in the twelfth century. The cession to the abbey by the knight usually took the form of an exchange of gifts, so that it was not quite a free gift nor yet an absolute sale. What the abbey gave back was more of a substantial luck-penny. Thus between 1146 and 1171 Ralph FitzGichel and Lesley his wife gave to Fountains four acres and a perch at Swainsland and Osmundeshenge and got back some cash and a palfrey worth 20s. which is about 1½ marks. Between 1180 and 1190 Robert Warin gave the same foundation two acres of meadow land and the monks gave his wife the Lady Sigge a palfrey valued at one silver mark. It would be obviously discourteous for the monks to acknowledge such donations with a palfrey that was not at least of respectable quality, so we must assume a steep rise in the price of the article before King John's reign, since in 1200 Alan de Lucenbi had to give a palfrey worth 10 marks as a 'fine' on entering into his inheritance. Some idea of the amount of stock kept by abbeys is evident from a gift to Easby Abbey by Picot de Lascelles in 1179; it took the form of grazing rights on the Lascelles hill-pasture, not only for sheep but for forty 'equae de haraz' or brood mares. It is worth noting that the biggest Cistercian house in the South of England was Beaulieu in the New Forest. We need not wonder that Chaucer's monk later on had such an eye for good palfrey.

Baile Suthain Sith Eamna

In the Irish manuscript known as the Book of Fermoy we have a picture, no doubt slightly idealized, of the Hebrides as they were in the thirteenth century. It is a poem addressed to an unknown prince who would be known in Scottish annals as the Lord of the Isles, but in Norway as the King of Sudryar (the South Isles) and Man. The manuscript is much later than the original (*c.* 1300) composition of the poem, which refers constantly to the ancestors of the prince, some of whom have Gaelic and some Norse names. It is interesting that the Irish poet still thought of the Hebrides as a place where there were horses fit for a prince to ride. Here are some random lines from it:

> In bright Emhain of the fresh grass
> Many the men on whom a noble eye looks,
> Many the vehement rider of a dun steed (eich duinn) . . .
> O man of the white steed . . .
> Fierce on thy part were the heavy blows . . .
> Pursue thy raids on a worthy steed
> For a foolish steed carries one away . . .
> Evil for us that the Dubh-Soingbenn
> Is no more in the brilliant stud of Fingal.

'Bright Emhain' is the Isle of Arran. Dubh-Soingbenn was a black horse belonging to the legendary hero Cuchulain. The 'fresh grass' is the celebrated grazing lands of the Hebridean machair. The poet thinks of Arran as still well-wooded, with many apple and yew trees. Dun in the Celtic world was still reckoned a 'noble' horse-colour, whereas in England by this time it was thought of as the colour of tough, dependable but very plebeian farm-horses.

The medieval image of a Highland or Hebridean chieftain by land is always a warrior on horseback, which seems strange to us, thinking backwards. This is because there stand between them and us some of the most formidable, and certainly the most spectacular, infantry regiments the world has ever seen. But the tradition of the Highland infantryman goes back to the bands of gallowglasses, *gall óglaich*, professional swordsmen who played a decisive part in the civil wars of Ulster in the sixteenth century; their weapon was the claymore, not the modern basket-hilted sidearm but the original two-handed *glaibh mór*—the 'big sword', which was unmanageable on horseback and at one time was chariot-borne, as we saw in the chapter on Roman Britain.

All wars since writing was invented have had one factor in common, that is that they have kept a multitude of clerks innocently employed in the base areas making out interminable indents and requisitions. The wars of Edward I were no exception but for the fact that, out of the mountains of 'bumf' that they engendered, a roll of parchment has been preserved that is of the utmost relevance to our story. It belongs to 'the Wardrobe', that is the expense accounts of the king's household, which in that day was a sizable part of the national budget; the household cavalry was paid, fed, horsed and equipped out of 'Wardrobe' funds, so naturally it contains a list of horses serving in the Falkirk campaign of 1298. It details 800 horses with the name of the knight or squire to whom each horse was 'on charge'. Each horse has its 'appreciation' or estimated value set against it—not what it had cost the Wardrobe to buy but what the clerks estimated it would cost to replace.

The entries are of four kinds, two of them describing horses of the kind Fitzstephen saw being sold at Smithfield more than a century earlier. Those of type (1) list war-horses suitable for knights—*dextrarii* or destriers. Those of type (2) use the word Fitzstephen was fumbling for when he described the horses suitable for squires, *runcini*, 'rouncies' —a hard-trotting cob. Those of type (3) list animals of a sort not available to English kings in Fitzstephen's day but now coming into their own: *equi powis*, 'Powys horses'—none other than Welsh cobs. They too are all ridden by squires. Entries of type (4) say simply 'horse' and they may mean either destrier or cob. For instance, Sir John Calthorpe serving as a knight must have had a destrier, though an indifferent one since it is valued at only sixteen marks, whereas Baudet the Fleming serving as a squire must have had a cob though it is assessed at £15. Only these four terms are used, presumably because they were the only types recognized by the remount service, just as there are still only three kinds of tree in the Army—pine-trees, poplar-trees and bushy-topped trees.

Since this is a Scottish campaign most of the *runcini* in the companion list of 564 *equi forinseci*—i.e. those not belonging to the household cavalry but to the feudal levy, must have been of north country origin, but they are described and 'appreciated' in exactly the same way. Evidently the valuing was done by different assessors, some of whom used pounds sterling as the unit, some used the mark (two-thirds of a pound) and some reckoned in shillings. In the translations of the entries we have reduced all alike to pounds, shillings and pence. Here are nine of these entries, each with at least one detail different from the others:

FALKIRK ROLL OF HORSES

(2) Thomas de la Mare, valettus Johannis de Staudon, habet unum runcinum falvum cum lista nigra precii x mar

Thomas de la Mare, squire to John Staudon, has a yellow dun cob with a black eel stripe value £6 13s. 4d.

(3) Robertus de Bosco, valettus Domini Henrici Cantoke habet unum equum powis precii xii mar.

Robert du Bois, squire to Sir Henry Cantoke, has a Welsh cob value £8.

(1) Dominus Petrus de Chauvent habet unum dextrarium falvum precii xx mar.

Sir Peter de Chauvent has a yellow dun destrier value £13 6s. 8d.

(3) Dominus R. filius Pagani habet unum dextrarium sorum bauzain cum stella in fronte precii C mar.

Sir R. Fitzpayne has a chestnut destrier with white feet and star, value £66.

(3) Robinettus filius Pagani habet unum equum powis vairon precii xxv mar.

Robin Fitzpayne has a Welsh cob, black with white spots value £16 13s. 4d.

(1) Dominus Henricus de Bello Monte habet unum dextrarium brunum badium precii xl mar.

Sir Henry de Beaumont has a bay-brown destier value £26 13s. 4d.

(4) Dominus Johanes de Caltop, miles Domini Adami de Walles habet unum equum doyne precii xvi mar.

Sir John Calthorpe, knight in the service of Lord Adam de Welles, has a dun horse value £10 13s. 4d.

(4) Baudectus le Flemenge valletus Domini Reymundi de Sancto Quintino habet unum equum morellum precii xv lib.

Baudet the Fleming, squire to the Sieur Raymond de St Quentin, has a 'mulberry' horse value £15.

(2) Hugo de Mytton de comitatu Ebor habet unum runcinum nigrum liardum precii Cs.

Hugh of Mytton from Yorkshire has a blue roan cob value £5.

Every now and then there is a marginal note which is an interesting reminder of the crusades, the last of which was not long over. It will record that on such and such a date such and such a cob (Welsh or English) was sent back *ad carvannum*—to the supply train. This word is the Arabic *kairawan*, or caravan.

The Latin of this document is extremely dog. Sometimes it breaks down into French or English when the clerk did not know the Latin for something like 'dun' or 'white socks'.

Careful study of the colours mentioned fails to bring out any definite pattern—that is, there is no colour which is confined to or predominant among either the destriers or the rouncies, though the only blanket-spotted Appaloosa in the whole list is a Welsh cob, and a most expensive one probably on account of its colour. But then, Robin Fitzpayne, though serving as a squire and not yet knighted himself, was the younger brother of Sir R. Fitzpayne, Knt, who precedes him in the list, and would be likely to draw a better sort of remount than one less well connected. The Sieur de St Quentin was a French vassal of the English crown.

There are fifteen basic coat colours named, many of which are used in combination, as 'liardus'—roan, which occurs as 'niger liardus', 'roughe liardus' and so on. They are:

albus	white	piole	pied
grigius	grey	pommele	dappled
ferrandus	iron grey	roughe	red bay
badius	bay	badius clarus	light bay
brunus	brown	sorus	chestnut
doyn	(mouse?) dun	varius (vairon)	blanket-spotted
(favus) falvus	yellow dun	morellus	'mulberry';
liardus	roan		impossible to gloss by
niger	black		now, but probably either liver chestnut, strawberry roan or dark bay.[1]

All the horses are overvalued by comparison with open market prices of the day. This is because the war had been going on for some time and prices had risen slightly, but chiefly because some items have the marginal note 'interfectus apud Foukirk'—killed at Falkirk, and the clerks of the Wardrobe would have to indent for the price of a replacement. Like all officials everywhere at all times they believed in leaving themselves a comfortable margin for contingencies. In fact, recorded market prices for the south of England in 1299 show good-class palfreys sold at £4 13s. 4d., £5 and £6 6s. 8d. Then and for a long time to come the value of palfreys was much higher than that of *runcini*. In 1295, before this war, a typical 'bailiff's horse', i.e. cob, had sold for £1 4s. 10d.

In theory the horse establishment of a medieval army, excluding the transport services, was three Little Horses to one Great Horse. This ratio was more or less true for the household cavalry, the regulars of those days, but in fact the feudal levy of Edward I was much more heavily diluted with Little Horses, which of course were drawn overwhelmingly from native pony stock. The feudal levy of the northern shires and North Wales, which turned out for the Falkirk campaign of 1298, comprised 564 horses—what you might call the first line yeomanry. Of these only eleven are marked in the rolls as *dextrarii*. But a further ninety-four, which are shown as 'equi', belong to vassals who were serving as knights, and must therefore really have been destriers. Only one in every five was therefore a Great Horse. There were twenty-three *equi powis*—Welsh cobs—and the remaining 436 animals are shown as *runcini*—rouncies—that is cobs and ponies of English origin. A typical 'lance' from this unit is that of Sir William de Echingham: 'habet unum dextrarium nigrum cum stella in fronte et tres pedibus albis precii 50 marc'; his young brother Robert served as his squire on a bay rouncy and there were four men-at-arms with one chestnut, one light bay and two bay rouncies. Presumably one of these 'valetti' was Robert's batman. But Edward I was a savagely efficient commander. It is not

---

[1] *Morello* in modern Italian means black when applied to cherries or horses. But 'black/niger' is already accounted for in this list.

conceivable that he would have tolerated 564 mounted men drawing pay, rations and forage of whom only 105 were the effective fighting strength. We cannot escape the conclusion that the 'battaile' of the levies consisted of a front rank of 105 knights or men-at-arms equipped as knights and something like two supporting ranks mounted on 210 of the more substantial *runcini*, and wearing half-armour, with lances. That still left 249 armour-carriers—*armigeri*—and second horsemen. The 436 *runcini* were of all imaginable—and some almost unimaginable—colours. Though they must have been a fair sample of the ancestors of the Dales and Fell breeds of modern times, no firm conclusion as to the predominant colour of northern horses suitable to carry a squire can be drawn from this motley roll-call. Some conclusion *can* be drawn as to relative value. Here, as in the case of the household cavalry, a good *runcinus* is assessed as high as or a little higher than an indifferent *dextrarius*. The marginal line comes at about 25 marks or £16. Among northern cobs there seems to be a predominance of dapple grey (*ferrandum pommele*) and a fair sprinkling of blacks. One of the Powys cobs was white, one had an eel stripe, one was dun with a white star. The colour of six of them was not mentioned at all, and the remainder are all described as *pommele* (dappled). This can only mean that there was a colour regarded as typically Powys, so that all the clerk need record was 'Powys' and whether the colour was dappled or solid or had an eel stripe. The colour that best fulfils these conditions is chestnut or golden dun.

In the *Annals of Ulster*, January 1270, occurs this passage:

'The defeat of Ath-in-chip was inflicted by Aedh, son of Phelim O'Connor and the men of Connacht on the Earl Walter de Burgh and the other foreigners of Ireland. And there were abandoned one hundred horses with their saddles and armour [*luirecaib*].'

The foreigners of Ireland are of course the Anglo-Normans of the Pale. This is the first mention in these islands of armoured horses, and it marks the stage at which the native breeds were finally excluded (if they had not been excluded before) from the front rank of heavy cavalry, since not even the Powys rouncy could carry an armoured man, his weapons and its own armour.

Right at the end of this period occurred one of the most spectacular encounters between a fully armed knight on a destrier and another, without his lance, sword or shield, and mounted only on a palfrey. The man on the palfrey won. The story has often been rehashed but we do not think anyone can beat John Barbour's treatment of it, based on the eyewitness accounts of men who were old when the poet was young.

King Robert the Bruce is making his dispositions on the field of Bannockburn, just as we saw Harold Godwinsson doing at Hastings, only Robert is not making the too-common mistake of using a Great Horse for this purpose. It is fatal, when assigning their positions to men who will fight on foot, to do so on a tall horse, because you will get a

totally different idea of the ground in front of them from theirs. In the
case of archers it is particularly misleading since their actual field of fire
will be much more restricted than what the general can see from his
destrier. This principle remains true in the twentieth as in the thirteenth
century, as anyone who has shared our experience as a subordinate
commander of anti-tank guns, being told where to bring our weapons
into action by a battalion commander *standing up in a jeep*, will agree.
Experienced commanders therefore rode a palfrey for this purpose, as
it would bring their eye nearer to the level of the infantryman's, and it
was easier to get on and off. Any well-made palfrey would stand to be
mounted, but the best destrier in Europe might well need three men to
hold him. (It is not without significance that Napoleon used a 14-hand
Arab for this job.)

> His battaille gert he well array
> He deployed his formations skilfully
>
> He rade upon ane gray palfray
> He rode on a grey palfrey
>
> Litill and ioly . . .
> Small and good-looking
>
> Schir Henry of Boune, the worthy . . .
> Sir Henry de Boune, the respected knight . . .
>
> Come on a steid, a merk-schot neir [1]
> Rode up on his war-horse to within a mark-shot [1]
>
> He thought that he suld weill lichtly
> He thought he could quite easily
>
> Win him, and haf hym at his will,
> Beat him and have him at his mercy
>
> Sen he him horsit saw so ill. . . .
> Since he saw him so poorly mounted
>
> Than sprent they sammyn intil a lyne;
> Then they squared off so as to meet head-on
>
> Schir Henry missit the noble kyng;
> Sir Henry missed the noble king
>
> And he, that in his sterapis stude
> Who, standing up in his stirrups
>
> With ax that wes bath hard and gude
> With his axe that was both tough and good
>
> With so gret mayne wrought him ane dint
> Dealt him a blow with such strength
>
> That nouthir hat ne helm might stynt
> That neither hat nor helmet could withstand
>
> The hevy dusche that he hym gaf
> The hard clout he gave him
>
> That he the hed til harnys claf.
> So that he split the skull down to the [neck] armour

[1] A hundred and fifty yards.

The hand-ax-shaft fruschit in twa
The shaft of the hand-axe was shivered in two

And he doune til the erd can ga
And Sir Henry fell to the earth

All flatlyngis. . . .
Flat on his face. . . .

From Barbour's account of this battle and its prelude we can also see just what a vast number of *vulgares equi*, or country-bred horses, were required to keep the heavy chivalry in action. His estimate of the English strength is:

Ane hundredth thousand men and ma:
And fourty thousand war of tha
Armyt on hors bath hed and hand
And yheit of they were thre thousand
With helit hors in plate and mailye
Til mak the front of the batailhye.
And fifty thousand archerys
He had, forouten hoblerys. . . .
Of cartis als that yheid thame by
Four scor were chargit with fcwale.

Let us forget the palpable exaggerations, and remember that Hall, the English chronicler, also estimated the Scottish host at Flodden at a round hundred thousand. It seems to have been the done thing to put the enemy strength at this figure if (*a*) they outnumbered your side and (*b*) your side won. Never mind if the total number of knights' fees in England in Edward I's day was only five thousand, and so could not possibly have mobilized forty thousand men 'armyt on hors'; and concentrate on the figure of three thousand 'with helit horse'. *Helit* means masked, and this is the first mention in Britain of armour for horses as well as for men. Most authorities accept this figure of three thousand to form the front rank of the English army. It was not custo-mary to form up the 'batailhye' more than ten ranks deep, so that thirty thousand is the outside limit, and even that, at six troopers per knight's fee, is stretching the resources rather far. It would mean, without allowing for any interval between the three main 'batailyes' in which it was customary to deploy an army, that the front of the cavalry forma-tions alone was 4,500 yards or two and a half miles—a vast array for those days. Thirty thousand Great Horses would be a sizeable proportion of the destrier population of England: it *might* have been got together. But the knight himself on his destrier was only the core of a little unit known as a 'lance' which consisted of anything from two to four *vulgares equi* and three men. There was the palfrey or courser on which the knight rode unarmed when not in contact with the enemy, the hack on which the squire rode leading the destrier, and the pack-horse which carried the knight's armour (alternatively the pair of horses in a cart for this purpose). The only possible economy was to have a lightweight page to ride the destrier and at the same time lead the pack-horse; but it would take a good page to do this if the destrier was really in fighting form. Say three light horses to a lance, that would make ninety thousand alone. All, with the possible exception of some coursers ridden by knights and barons, country-bred. Half Barbour's total consists of archers (it seems there were no pikemen) on foot, and there were forty thousand armoured horse according to him. That leaves ten thousand to be accounted for, and they are the hobilars kept separate in the total from the archers. In this case hobilar means mounted archer, and they would need ten thousand 'hobbies' to mount them. (We will consider the exact meaning of hobby later.) It would not be impossible to provide ten thousand suitable remounts for hobilars from the combined resources of northern England and North Wales, but it would be quite impossible to mobilize sixty thousand archers, whether riding or on foot. Probably the figure for hobilars is right but the figure for dismounted archers too high. The proportion of mounted to dismounted troops overall in this English army is unusually high, but it was usually greater in expeditionary forces to Scotland than to the Continent, as the question of loading the horses into shipping did not arise. There remain the transport horses proper, the eighty carts full of firewood and at least four times as many with rations, ammunition, tentage and the like, probably drawn by pairs of what we should call ponies. And the long strings of packhorses in charge of 'layd-men', apart from those belonging to the knights.

The Exchequer Rolls for the Realm of Scotland have been printed and are full of details, especially prices, about horses. Unfortunately the rolls for the years of Falkirk and Bannockburn are not preserved, but in the first quarter of the fourteenth century they included the Wardrobe accounts which were considerable but not so large a part of the state's economy as the English Wardrobe funds. They record a horse bought for the king from the Seneschal of Darneley for £10; probably a good palfrey, if we allow for the fact that the unfavourable Scots-Stirling rate had not yet set in. This was in 1342. In 1329 we have receipts for 8*d.* for the skin of a dead draught-horse (*affer*, a Latin word more in use in Scotland than in England). A pack-saddle for 7*s.* and a pack-horse to carry it for 24*s.* closely comparable with English prices at the same date. Some pack-horses came much cheaper. The King of Scots bought five of them for 37*s.* the lot in 1326. This last entry, with similar ones, constitutes a trap for the unwary. They figure in the rolls as 'equi cariagii', which might raise a flutter of interest among harness-fans. But we may be quite certain there was no such thing as a carriage in Scotland in 1326. In the professional dog-Latin of exchequer clerks at that time, *cariagium* meant freight. These horses were in fact used to transport lime in panniers—*pro calce cariando*. An account of daily travelling expenses for a king's messenger is interesting; though it does not record prices, this particular journey was to Islay to fetch horses from a stud there. This is the next island to Jura, which is mentioned as a horse-breeding centre in the reign of Mary Stuart.

Of the Scottish light horsemen, as the English borderers too often saw them, Sir John Froissart, private secretary to Edward III's queen, who had also been at the court of David II of Scotland, speaks with authority.

'When they invaded England, they were all usually on horseback, except the camp followers; they brought no transport, neither did they encumber themselves with any provisions. Under the flap of his saddle each man had a broad plate of metal; and behind his saddle a little bag of oatmeal, so that when occasion needed, cakes were made of the oatmeal, and baked upon the plates; for the most part, however, they ate the parboiled flesh of the cattle they lifted, and drank water.' We may assume that they did not take the water neat.

The Scots were not all horsed alike. Froissart says ' . . . sont les chevaliers et écuyers bien montes sur de bons gros roncins et les aultres communs gens du pays sur petites haquenees.' When the first English translation of Froissart appeared in 1520 Lord Berners rendered the last sentence thus ' . . . the common people on littel hakanays *and geldings*'. By Henry VIII's time, for some reason which does not now appear obvious, the idea of a hackney or light trotting horse automatically suggested a gelding to the English mind.

CHAPTER SIX

Later Middle Ages

I preye yow heretely, telle us somwhat elles
For sikerly, nere clinking of your belles
That on your bridel hang one evry syde
By hevene king that for us all dyde
I should er this have fallen down for slepe;
Sir, say somewhat of hunting I yow prey.
Wordes of the Host to the Monk.

WE HAVE seen portrayed in the Canterbury Psalter some typical (perhaps rather better than typical) horses of pre-Conquest times. In the year of Chaucer's birth Sir Geoffrey Luttrell of Ingham in Lincolnshire ordered an illuminated psalter which took as subjects for the marginal illustrations scenes from the daily life and work of Sir Geoffrey's own manor of Ingham. These have been used again and again to illustrate the social history of the fourteenth century, but we make no apology for reproducing some of them once more, beginning with a familiar picture that might have been drawn to illustrate one of Chaucer's tales itself, except that Chaucer's cart was loaded with hay and this one with sheaves of corn. Here is the passage:

And right at the entryng of the townes ende,
To which this sumnour shoop hym for to wende, *intended to go*
They saugh a cart that charged was with hey, *saw*
Which that a cartere droof forth in his wey.
Deep was the wey, for which the carte stood.
The cartere smoot, and cryde as he were wood,
'Hayt, Brok! hayt, Scot! what spare ye for the stones?
The feend,' quod he, 'yow feeche, body and bones,
As ferforthly as evere were ye foled,
So muche wo as I have with yow tholed! *suffered*
The devel have al, bothe hors and cart and hey!'
 This somonour seyde, 'Heere shal we have a pley.'
And neer the feend he drought, as noght ne were,
Ful prively, and rowned in his ere: *whispered*
'Herkne, my brother, herkne, by thy feith!
Herestow nat how that the cartere seith?
Hent it anon, for he hath yeve it thee, *seize; given*
Bothe hey and cart, and eek his caples thre.'

'Nay,' quod the devel, 'God woot, never a deel!'   *not at all*
It is nat his entente, trust me weel.
Axe hym thyself, if thou nat trowest me;   *ask*
Or elles stynt a while, and thou shalt see.'   *stop*
   This cartere thakketh his hors upon the croupe   *pats*
And they bigonne to drawen and to stoupe.   *bent forward*
'Heyt! now,' quod he, 'ther Jhesu Crist yow blesse,
And al his handwerk, bothe moore and lesse!
That was wel twight, myn owene lyard boy.
I pray God save thee, and Seinte Loy!
Now is my cart out of the slow, pardee!'

and here is the picture (P32). In modern books it often bears the caption 'Harvest cart going up hill', but this is not so. The horses are only drawn so because the space they have to fill is L-shaped. Their legs are bent because, as Chaucer says, 'they bigonne to drawen and to stoupe'. The last word denotes the characteristic flexing of the knees with which the well-trained draught horse brings his weight into the collar to overcome initial inertia of the load. One can see it is just starting, because one of the labourers is still pitching up the last sheaf. Perhaps it was the last load of the day and the carter was impatient to be out of the field.

In a companion picture, a burlesque of the same subject, we see a cart under way, driven by a monkey but drawn by the same team (P33). The monkey gives no scale by which to measure the horses, but the harvesters in the first picture do. The team of blue roan, yellow-dun and black are only ponies in stature, though cobbishly built. Here (P39) is a less pleasing specimen, a bay 'hercarius' or harrow-horse, which may be profitably compared with the horse in the harrow of the eleventh century on page 3. At the other end of the farmer's year, here is a horse of the same period bringing bags of seed-corn into the field for the sowers (P38). Comparison with human figures in the Luttrell Psalter is very instructive, since one page shows Sir Geoffrey himself setting out for the wars, and unless all the Luttrells were dwarfs his destrier must have been a good seventeen hands high. But none of the farm-horses can have been much above thirteen hands high on the Ingham estate.

An episode in the French wars of Edward III illustrates very well the disparity of esteem in which the hackney and courser were held at that time and for long after. In 1356 the English had the luck to capture King John of France on the field of battle. This was the situation that every medieval political leader dreamed about. It was literally the situation which the inventors of the game of chess had in mind when defining the term 'checkmate'. But actually checkmate, or its Persian original 'shah mat', means 'the King is dead': whereas King John was alive, undamaged and available for exchange or ransom. We had never held such a bargaining counter and would never hold one such again. The ransom finally fixed was three million crowns; an example of overplaying one's hand, since the total resources of the French Crown were unable to raise this sum, and it was never paid in full. However, what is relevant to our purpose is that the health and well-being, even the self-esteem, of King Jean while in our custody were of the greatest importance, and all the time he was in fact treated as a most honoured guest. As a mark of respect, while being escorted from one privileged prison to another by his captor the Black Prince, he was mounted on a courser, while the prince as a sign of humility rode a hackney. This is the kind of episode that appealed to the Victorian artist: 'every picture tells a story', and it is fittingly commemorated in the Doncaster Cup, which like many racing trophies is not a cup but small monumental group in silver, executed more or less after the manner of Cellini in 1853.

In the course of this book we have occasion to scan three catalogues of horses drawn up for a specific military purpose. Now let us look at a list of horses assembled for a peaceful purpose. It is not an historical one, but a fictitious one, though none the less true to life for all that. Chaucer's *Canterbury Tales* are a group of stories contained within a story, a rambling equestrian outing in springtime, what the poet himself called a chivachee; but this is no longer the *chevalche* in the technical feudal sense, the obligatory mounted escorting of the vavasour by his tenants, but a much freer association in the much looser and more varied society of the later Middle Ages. It is a chance-met cavalcade of English men and women, civilians on their lawful occasions, and overwhelmingly of the middle classes. There are two comfortably rich men, from town and country respectively, in the Merchant and the Franklin, a recently retired cavalry officer who is now a considerable landowner (but not so considerable as the Franklin) in the Knight, while in the Parson and his brother the Plowman we have the humblest grade of ecclesiastic and the highest grade of agricultural worker sprung from the same family: and some two dozen 'average' English people of various stations of life in between these limits.

Chaucer calls them 'wel nine and twenty in a companye', but whichever way one adds them up the total always comes out different and *never* to twenty-nine. My most consistent total is thirty-one. Of these the illustrators of the Ellesmere MS. drew twenty-two. Their horses are not quite such a narrow cross-section, as they range from the worst to almost but not quite the best that was to be had in England. The text actually says that the Nun's Priest rode a jade, the Monk a palfrey, the Cook a capul (which was a mare), the Shipman a rouncy, the Wife of Bath an ambler, the Plowman a mare, the Reeve a stot and the Canon a hackney. Six of these animals figure also in the illustrations, by looking at which we can classify the other sixteen animals pictured by the terms then current among horsemen, and from their tastes and habits and station in life we can suggest, in the same terms, suitable mounts for the other nine (if it is nine) pilgrims of whom there are no pictures.

To begin then with the half-dozen described both in verse and picture. In the words of the Host to the Nun's Priest

> Be blithe though thou ride upon a jade.
> What though thy hors be both foul and lene
> If he wel serve thee, rekke nat a bene,

echoing though unconsciously, the old Norse proverb quoted in an earlier chapter. Foul here means ugly, and the artist has faithfully interpreted this. A jade is simply a bad specimen of any breed, about which no more need be said.

The Monk's palfrey was just one of 'many a deyntee hors' that he kept, partly to go about the country on the business of his house, but far more for his own pleasure, especially hunting. Probably his entire string consisted of palfreys, the traditional mounts for churchmen, since, much as he might have wished to keep a courser, this would be more than his very tolerant superiors would stand. That the palfrey was meant, ideally, to be on the 'thikke' side, with broad chest and well-sprung ribs, is well brought out by John Lydgate in the Prologue to his *Seyge of Thebes*, which is a kind of addendum to the *Canterbury Tales*. Lydgate (who was himself a monk from Bury St Edmunds) determines to join the party:

> The holy seynte pleynly to visyte,
> After sekenesse my vowys to aquyte,
> In a cope of blake and not of grene,
> On a palfry sclendre long and lean,
> With rusty bridle made not for sale,
> My man to-form with a voyed male.

The drab clothes, the shabby saddlery and the empty portmanteau are to be matched with the wrong sort of palfrey, 'sclendre long and lean', whereas it should be short in the back, well covered with flesh and broad behind the saddle; for, as we shall see [1] later, 'sclendre' was a term of disapproval applied to the wrong sort of hindquarters.

The Cook's business did not involve travelling so there was no need for him to keep a horse of his own, and this capul is probably one of the hirelings from the Tabard stables, for Harry Bailey was a jobmaster as well as an innkeeper. One of its stable companions was the rouncy which the Shipman rode 'as he couthe', which means in catch-as-catch-can style. It was a stroke of malicious humour on the jobmaster's part to mount him on a rouncy, which trotted, when the establishment had so many pacers and amblers available. Perhaps none of the latter were up to the burly seaman's considerable weight. But it must have been a long two days out and two days back for the poor fellow. One is reminded of the last coronation procession, when, as the Admiralty staff jogged past, all gold lace and misery, a wag in the crowd bellowed, 'Wot price the crool sea nah, matey?'

As for the Wife of Bath, 'upon an amblere esily she sat', and the

[1] Blundeville.

artist has very properly shown it with its legs in the very act, fore and hind on one side moving forward together. Of the Plowman the verse says 'in a tabard he rade upon a mere'. The tabard was the smock he wore in the fields, and it is just possible that the mare was one of his own plough-team, since he and his brother came from some southern county not very far from London. Perhaps Surrey or Essex, the latter being a shire where the plough-oxen were displaced by horses very early; or rather not by horses but by mares, and this may be the point of the line. There is no picture of him in the manuscript.

Another mare carries the Reeve. It is called by the old word 'stot', which does not at this date seem to have been applied to the female of more expensive breeds: nevertheless it is a 'ful good stot' of its kind, as we should expect since the Reeve is a highly efficient farm manager, who bought only the best, but at the keenest prices, both for his employer and himself. Moreover he came from Norfolk, where a very good sort of rouncy or cob was bred from early times; this one was 'al dappul gray', which the artist has faithfully rendered, 'and highte Scot'. Scot was a favourite farm-hands' name for a horse: it has nothing to do with Scotland but comes from an old English word meaning treasure or taxes or rent (compare 'scot free' and 'to pay scot and lot') and was bestowed on the best horse in the yard, the one that paid the rent.

The Canon rode a hakenay, as befitted a man who did not care about appearances but was totally wrapped up in his hobby, which was alchemy. The fact that these animals bore a French name *haquenai* does not mean that they had aristocratic associations. Among light saddle horses they were the least esteemed. At this time by the test of hard cash they fetched on the average half the price of a palfrey. Fashion comes and goes, and the hackney was to have his turn at the social summit later on. Just now, Chaucer in another poem describes a rich and dashing young man who

> loved wel have hors of price
> He wened have repreved be
> Of theft or mordre if that he
> Had in his stable any hakenay,

which means that he would not be seen dead riding one. It is hard to account for the low rating of the hackney except in relation to its gait. It was a country-bred horse that trotted. We have seen that such horses had their place in the string of every knight who did not compound for scutage, where they fetched a good price, especially the Welsh rouncies. The hackney was cheap and despised because it was a throw-out from some military establishment, being either too lightly built for campaigning or not tall enough to lead a war-horse from in comfort or security. The thriftier sort of landowner was inclined to mount his hunt servants, his riding forester and his yeoman of the mews and his under-falconers on hackneys. He did not use them for travelling (the original function of the 'hack' in the modern sense) because on a bad road surface a palfrey, whether pacing or ambling or racking, is a more comfortable ride than a trotting horse; and medieval road surfaces outside the towns were universally bad. The trotting hackney did not become a 'roadster' in the literal sense until the macadam era dawned. The modern equation: hack = hireling, arose because the hackney when it was cheap naturally gravitated to the hiring trade. For obvious economic reasons hackneys were never imported.

Thus far the combination of verse and picture takes us. From the pictures alone we can see that the Knight and the Squire are riding Destriers, the great war-horses that were almost the symbol of their calling. The Squire's Yeoman, who was a combination of huntsman, gamekeeper and ghillie, may well have ridden a hakenay. The Prioress has a palfrey, probably her own. Her nuns also rode palfreys, whether they belonged to the convent stables or were hired from Master Bailey. This was essential since they rode side-saddle, and side-saddles, only brought into use some twenty years earlier, were still of so clumsy a design that nobody could ride a trotting horse on one with either comfort or elegance. The rider, or rather passenger, sat facing at right angles to the line of advance; there was no stirrup: both feet rested on a sort of dashboard called a planchette. The seat adopted was really identical with the seat when riding pillion behind a man, and as long as this was the only kind of saddle available for women, the demand for palfreys was assured and conversely a limit was set to the number of hackneys bred for the saddle. No wonder that the more practically minded ladies of the older generation stuck to the cross-saddle, as the Wife of Bath did. This situation remained basically unchanged until the reign of Queen Anne.

Friaries did not keep saddle-horses, and the rules of his order commanded the Friar of the pilgrimage to walk about his business as a limitour. In order to ride on the pilgrimage he must have received a special dispensation. His horse must therefore be one of Bailey's job-horses.

The Merchant and the Franklin are the two richest men in this company, and both from the descriptions of their households in the verses and the pictures of their horses in the illuminations we may assume that they kept expensive animals, imported or of imported stock. The Merchant's is probably a palfrey and the Franklin's a courser. Neither the Clerk of Oxenford nor the Man of Law had need of a horse for professional purposes, and they too must have had recourse to the Tabard stables. The same is true of the Carpenter, a character whom Chaucer decided not to develop after all. The other sketchily drawn tradesmen who belonged to the same guild as he, the Webbe (weaver), Dyer, Tapicer and Haberdasher, all belonged to the clothing trade, in which it was customary for masters to provide their own transport for fairly small parcels of goods. They all therefore kept pack-horses (capuls) which they rode on the journey. The Doctour of Physik was not a country practitioner (perhaps he did not practice at all, but lectured in medicine at the university) and therefore also rode a hireling. Of the Parson the text says that his living was so poor that it did not, as most of them did, run to a horse for parochial duties

> to visyte
> The ferreste in his parisshe, muche and lyte,
> Up-on his fete, and in his hand a staffe.

For this reason we do not reproduce his picture here, but instead show a contemporary picture of John Ball, the Kentish parson who was joint leader of the Peasants' Revolt of 1381, riding the sort of horse that the average parish priest might be expected to own (P35). We could put Chaucer's parson down also as a Tabard client, were it not for his poverty. The shilling hire for the stage from London to Rochester, and the further shilling for the stage from Rochester to Canterbury (if one wanted to go on from Canterbury to Dover it would cost another sixpence), was probably more than the poor fellow could lightly afford. The patron of his living may very well have lent him a horse, but apart from that there are his family connections to consider. Perhaps his brother the Plowman lent him another mare from his team, besides the one he rode himself, if it was late in April and the spring ploughing was over. Or, if he was an ox-ploughman, he may have been on good enough terms with his opposite number, the carter of the same estate, to borrow two horses. When the change-over to horse-ploughing was complete the head carter and the head ploughman became one and the same person (head horseman) over large areas of the country, but as long as the transitional stage lasted they existed side by side, equal peers, the twin king-pins of the agricultural structure. In either case the Plowman and the Parson would both ride capuls.

So did the Miller. Besides the deplorable crocks which were kept to turn the mill before the general introduction of windmills in waterless parts of the country, millers were renowned for keeping a very good class of pack-horse or capul, and that shown in the illumination is wearing the typical hempen halter, with a bit attached to it somehow, used in pack-trains.

The Sumnour, the Pardoner and Chaucer himself all seem to be riding Tabard hirelings, but Manciples usually kept their own horses for professional reasons. The Manciple who figures in the Reeve's Tale owned a palfrey, so we may reasonably allow his real-life counterpart one. It is worth noting that the north-country undergraduates in the Reeve's Tale refer to their Manciple's palfrey as a 'capul', showing that in the north this term was applied to a better class of animal than in the south. As the word itself is of Norse-Irish origin there is ground for belief that north-country capuls included palfrey-type imports from Ireland, of the kind later called 'Irish hobbies', shipped by the Scandinavian merchants or Ostmen who still in Chaucer's time had the monopoly of the Irish seaborne trade.

The Canon's Yeoman probably rode a hakenay like his employer. There are in all a dozen hirelings. Jobmasters like Harry Bailey kept a mixed establishment of hackneys, palfreys, capuls and rouncies. It would therefore be reasonable to reckon three of each kind for purposes of this catalogue. Counting individuals who are only mentioned and dismissed in one line or less, there are a maximum of thirty-four pilgrims, with a total of six hakenays (18 per cent), two stedes (6 per cent), one courser (3 per cent), nine palfreys (27 per cent), eleven capuls (33 per cent) and five rouncies (15 per cent). This proportion is probably

20. *Left :* Chaucer's miller mounted on capul, normally used as pack transport for grain, etc. Its chief advantage as a hack was that one could play the bagpipes on its back, and it did not care whether the passenger was drunk or sober. *Right :* Shipman on a rouncy, recognizable anywhere by its prominent buttocks. *Both illuminations from Ellesmere MS.*

valid for the country as a whole, excluding military requirements. If the latter are added in, the proportion of steeds and rouncies will be materially higher, but among this average random sample of fourteenth-century civilians the great majority are riding country-bred animals. Admittedly some palfreys were imported, or of imported stock (let us say one-third, or 9 per cent of the above total). That leaves all the hakenays, all the capuls and rouncies and two-thirds of the palfreys, making 84 per cent or ordinary peace-time requirements supplied from country-bred stock, essentially the same stock as in Roman, and largely the same stock as in pre-Roman times.

On the subject of pilgrimages generally at this period, what Chaucer says about the Wife of Bath points to something of great significance for our purpose. She was greatly addicted to pilgrimages, and embarked on a different one every spring in just the same way as ladies of her age in her situation today are regular patrons of the coach tour and the Madeira cruise. Among those she had sampled was that

in Galice at Saint Jame.

This was the shrine of St James at Santiago de Compostela in Galicia, easily the most popular of continental shrines with English medieval pilgrims, because it was almost directly accessible by sea. It lay, in fact, along the Western Sea Route, which we have mentioned before and shall mention again in this book. But in fact, on landing either at La Coruña or Pontevedra the pilgrim was faced with a further journey up the country of some thirty-five miles to Compostela, which was undertaken in two stages with the aid of contractors who had mules or palfreys for hire. The latter were of course the celebrated ginetes or

21. Spanish jennet at the end of the fifteenth century. *Woodcut dated 1499.*

'Jennets of Spayne', since this part of Spain is the homeland of the tough yet graceful pony called today either *Asturión* or *jaca*, which contributed so much to the breeding of the Irish light horse of medieval times and which had also been used to mount the numerous regiments of Spanish horse that served in the Roman armies in Britain. On this journey English pilgrims might easily acquire a liking for this eminently suitable 'travelling horse', and indeed some would come with the express intention of doing without the contractor but buying an *Asturión* as soon as they landed. Then, if they liked it well enough, they would arrange to ship it home. If not, they could always sell it again down at the port, and still be better off than if they had paid the hire.

We have remarked before on the fragmentation of the Celtic tribes, how different branches of the same people can be found, still bearing the same name, in widely separated areas. Tribes dwelling partly in Britain and partly in Ireland, however, are not very common in the Iron Age. But north of that branch of the Parisii who occupied the plain of the Humber and the Yorkshire Wolds dwelt a numerous and powerful half-tribe called Brigantes; their lands included the whole of the North Riding, County Durham, and marched with the Votadini somewhere in what we now call Northumberland. The other half of the Brigantes lived in County Waterford in Ireland. Not, strictly speaking, the other half, for a smaller fragment of them lived in the extreme south-west corner of the Celtic world. The port of north-west Spain that was known to many generations of British mariners as the Groyne, and is now called La Coruña, was known in Roman times as Brigantium, the Harbour of the Brigantes. The British section of the tribe extended right across the north of the country, and they controlled some of the estuaries on the coast of Lancashire. The Brigantes had not a great reputation as a seafaring people, although there must once have been a time when they could muster enough war-galleys to effect the conquest of County Waterford. But midway between the Irish and Spanish Brigantes lay the peninsula of Armorica.

Armorica we now call Brittany. In the early days of the Roman Empire it was the home of the Veneti—hardy sailors, skilled ship-wrights, keen business men. They seem to have specialized in what is now known as the carrying trade. In the long run it was they who had provoked the Roman invasion of Britain because it was in their ships that British aid was brought to the anti-Roman faction in Gaul that had exhausted Caesar's patience. His information about landing facilities, when he was planning the conquest of the island, was got by interrogating captured Venetic sea-captains.

The Veneti were ideally placed to conduct trade between the Spanish, the Irish and the British sections of the Brigantes. The Brigantes of Yorkshire needed good horses all the time to maintain their security from the Belgic Parisii, pushful newcomers and expert charioteers, probably also breeders of a solid type of war-horse such as is ridden by the giant-slaying equestrian god of Gallia Belgica. The Brigantes of Galicia were able to supply good horses, bought from their near neighbours the Asturienses, horsemen who enlisted in the Roman army in large numbers and who bred the fast, handy, good-looking but rather light *Asturión*. Venetic dealers could ship them either direct to Fleetwood or to some half-way house in Irish Brigantia.

It is a commonplace in the history of fox-hunting to say that it was not an activity that was taken at all seriously before some time in the eighteenth century. But there are exceptions to every generalization of this sort, and in *Sir Gawain and the Green Knight*, a romance written either in Cheshire or south Lancashire some time between 1360 and 1400, we have a description of a fox-hunt which is not, as in the Nun's Priest's Tale of Chanticleer and Pertelote, a mere rabble of villagers in pursuit of vermin, but a regular sport practised by the gentry.

Sir Gawain comes to the castle of the Green Knight, who is a keen hunting man, and is left alone in the castle with Lady Green for three days while her lord is out hunting every day, all day. (The more usual practice was to hunt only after dinner.) The first day is devoted to

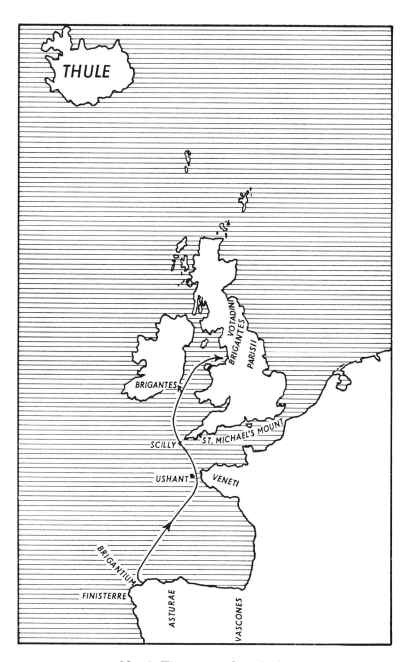

Map 3. The sea way from Spain.

stag-hunting. The second day's quarry is a wild boar. The third day is the day of the fox-hunt, which ends like this:

> And right befor the hors fete they fell on him alle,
> And woried me this wily with a wroth noise.
> The lord lightes bilive and catches him sone,
> Rased him ful radly out of the rach mouthes,
> Hadles high over his hede, halowes faste,
> And ther bayen him many brath houndes,

quite in the modern manner, with the huntsman holding the dead fox above his head, holloaing ('halowes faste') while the hounds bay round him.

We need not be surprised, among the Canterbury horses listed above, to find only one (problemetical) courser. Though this was the hunter proper, it was in fact the very top grade of hunter, corresponding to the modern blood hunter that could have had an alternative career on the racecourse; if we were to translate the medieval prices of good coursers into modern currency (a somewhat futile academic exercise) it would come to thousands of guineas rather than hundreds. Here is Chaucer's own idea of the cream of the hunting field in his day, lightly disguised as the entertainment of Aeneas by Dido:

> An hunting wol this lusty fresshe queene;
> So priketh her this newe joly wo.
> To horse is all her lusty folk y-go;
> Un-to the court the houndes been y-broght,
> And up-on *coursers*, swift as any thought,
> Her younge knightes *hoven* all aboute,   hang
> And of her wommen eke an huge route.
> Upon a thikke palfrey, *paper-whyte*,   cream
> With sadel rede, embrouded with delyt,
> Of gold the barres up-embossed hye
> Sit Dido, all in gold and perre wrye . . .
> Upon a courser, *startlyng as the fir*,   shying like a flame
> *Men mighte turn him with a litel wyr*,   'you could ride him on a string'
> Sit Eneas, lyk Phebus to devise,
> So was he fresshe arayed in his wyse.
> The fomy brydel with the bit of gold,
> *Governeth* he, right as himself had wold.   manages
> And forth this noble quene thus lat I ride
> An hunting with this Troyan by her syde.
> The herd of hertes founden is anoon,
> With 'Hey! go bet! prik thou! lat goon! lat goon!'

The fifteenth-century Scottish poet Gawin Douglas, who was a great admirer of Chaucer, produced a complete translation of the *Aeneid*, from which epic Chaucer's hunting scene is an adapted passage, and in the Douglas version Dido is more ambitiously mounted:

> Hir fers stede stude stamping, redy elles,
> Rungeand the fomy golden bridle jingling.

Of course a real steed would have been a terrific handful for the most dauntless lady, and only really necessary for one of the most ample build. Most ladies did in fact hunt on palfreys. Queen Elizabeth I still did, and these animals again were only a proportion of the native-bred small horses to be seen in the hunting field in all periods of our history. Obviously everyone who kept a horse, no matter what sort of horse, and had inclinations that way, would have hunted on it sooner or later, by hook or by crook.

The feature of the medieval hunting scene that would appear most strange to modern eyes was the large number of steeds or dextrers to be seen out, unless there happened to be a war in progress. Their presence is accounted for by the fact that they had to be exercised somehow, not by their suitability for hunting. In fact they were very unsuitable, and the more so the further one goes back in our history. Medieval England, especially the parts most hunted over, was very heavily wooded, and what Geraldus Cambrensis called the 'majestic proportions' of the destrier made it a liability in woodland country. The rider was in constant danger of doing an Absolom.

All that hunting did for the war-horse, however, was to keep it in hard condition. As schooling for the battlefield hunting was quite useless, the manœuvres required for the two operations being utterly different. Only a dyed-in-the-wool civilian like Mr Jorrocks could say that hunting was 'the image of war without its guilt', and believe that it contained as much as 'five and twenty per cent of the danger'. In war the enemy is not running away all the time, as anyone who had ever heard a shot fired in anger could have told him. And as to guilt, it is to be observed that those who object to hunting on moral grounds are very often pacifists as well.

Medieval hunting countries rode incredibly blind by our standards, and all the blinder because hunting went on through most of the summer, when the leaves were on the trees. There was a 'fence-month' round about June when the does dropped their fawns, and that was about all the close season there was. During Lent inedible game was hunted. Ability to jump was not a factor that worried the medieval hunting man. As long as the open-field system of agriculture lasted (and in many parts of the country that means down to the eighteenth century) there were no fences except about the 'closes', the half-acre plots that ran down behind the houses on both sides of every village street. It would be an exceptional (and unpopular) run that took a line across these. Something tough with a low clearance that was good at scrambling was the *beau ideal* of a medieval utility hunter. Something of the limitations of the destrier as a hunter, as well as of its impressive appearance, can be seen from Paolo Ucello's lovely picture 'The Hunt in The Wood', in the Ashmolean Museum at Oxford.

In the *Histoire du Roy Richard d'Angleterre* by (?) Trevor, Bishop of

St Asaph, there is an illumination showing Arthur McMorogh, King of Leinster, coming to parley with the Earl of Gloucester:

> Un cheval ot sanz sele ne arcon
> Qui lui avait couste, ce disait on,
> Quatrescents vaches, tant il estoit bel et bon . . .

that is: 'He had a horse without saddle or saddle-tree, which was so fine and good, it had cost him, they said, four hundred cows. For there is little money in the country, wherefore their usual traffic is only with cattle. In coming down it galloped so hard that I never saw in all my life hare, deer, sheep or any such animal run with such speed as it did. In his hand he bore a great long dart, which he cast with much skill. Here see the appearance that he made exactly portrayed' (P34).

Elsewhere in the same work the Irish horses are described as running 'up hill and down dale like bounding stags', whereas the English horses 'which often had to stay out in the wet and the wind were all ruined and many of them perished with hunger'. And the poet adds that many knights who had come to Ireland with strings of three and four destriers besides supporting horses had to make their way back to the coast on foot.

A group of wills dating from the middle fifteenth century show just the same classification of horses and 'prestige rating' as in Chaucer's day. Thus in 1451 an esquire of Lincoln, one Robert Sutton, bequeathed 'to my sister Babyngton my yong gray Aumbling stagg at Grysby'. Valuable evidence that there were still a fair number of natural-born amblers about, because 'stagg' is a north-country and north-midland word for a yearling or unbroken two-year-old colt. The next year Baron Willoughby de Eresby left 'to Mawde my wife a yong palfrey, white, and I wol that Maister John Depyng have a bayed palfrey that I bought late and I wol that the two lords mine executers have for their labours for eyther of theme a courser and £10'. Sir Thomas Cumberworth of Somerby by Glandford Brigg in Lincolshire made a will in 1451 leaving to Lord Leo de Welles a horse of the value of £4 and John Standrop a horse of the value of £2 or the cash if they preferred it. Considering the high rank of one of the beneficiaries, the price of horses must have been at the bottom of a slump, seeing that cobs had cost around £6 or £7 a hundred and fifty years earlier. But evidently worse was to come, for if the legatees insisted on a horse each of this value, the executors were to buy them 'if I have none so gode'. Another interesting bequest of Sir Thomas's, out of his stock at Somerby, is 'my best cart and one of my best carthors and my best plogh and one of my best *plogh hors*'. Now a hundred years earlier Sir Geoffrey Luttrell had lived not far from Somerby, but his will does not mention plough-horses and the pictures in his psalter of work on his estate show only oxen working in the plough. This is probably the first reference to the horse-drawn plough that does not specify *mares* as the motive power. This is only part of the evidence, beginning with William Fitzstephen, that the replacement of oxen by horses in the plough began in the flat lands on the eastern side of the country. From first to last the process took six or seven hundred years, but all the time it exerted its influence on 'rough' horse breeding in favour of an animal with a steep shoulder, a rather low centre of gravity and a tireless walk. Since the reserve of breeding stock was in the fens 'where wilde meares renne' (Chaucer's Reeve's Tale) it is easy to see why the lighter, leggier type was eliminated by natural economic demand as much as by unrealistic breeding regulations such as the Tudor monarchs tried to enforce.

CHAPTER SEVEN

Tudor Times

Many horses are requisite for a king.

Hugh Latimer.

TUDOR times are modern times, according to the conventional divisions of the school history book, and while it may be perfectly true so far as politics goes that the medieval order of things came to an end on Bosworth Field with the voice of Richard Plantagenet calling desperately for a horse, 'My kingdom for a horse', yet no great or sudden revolution occurred in the daily life of the people, or of the gentry, or of the nobility or even of the royal family. The change from an English to a Welsh dynasty made less difference than the change from an English to a Norman one had done four hundred years before. In the official eye-witness account of Henry VII's coronation procession (Egerton MS. 985), which was written for the files of the College of Heralds in case this should turn out to be a long reign, too long for the youngest pursuivant then serving to recollect precedent and protocol for the next coronation, exactly the same sort of people are described as riding coursers as appeared similarly mounted in, say, Edward I's coronation progress. Right down the scale, far below Great Horse level, the horses are still of medieval type and function and described in medieval terms.

On the eve of SS Simon and Jude (27th October) 1485 the king returned to the City of London from Lambeth after dining with the Archbishop of Canterbury in his palace, 'riding after the guise of Fraunce, with all other of his nobility upon small hackneys, riding two and two upon an horse'. This was meant as a gesture of humility; the hackney was a mount unworthy of a knight, let alone a peer, and their lordships doubled up so as to occupy less of the already grossly overcrowded South Bank alleyways. Yet the very fact that the 'small' hackney of the late fifteenth century could carry double seems to indicate that it was at least a somewhat larger animal than the hackney of Chaucer's day. It was perhaps more like a rouncy, partly of original English stock but also—for we are speaking here of those who followed the grandson of Owen Tudor—descended from the serviceable 'Powys horses'. Whereas in Chaucer's time the hakenay was a down-graded rouncy.

On 17th January 1506 occurred the meeting of Henry VII and Philip, King of Castile, near Windsor, during the time when the latter was detained in England in the beginning of that year. It is well known how, after setting out from the Low Countries to take possession of his kingdom of Castile, Philip met with a storm, was driven to land on our coast, and how, on hearing of it, Henry invited him to visit him at his court, where he stayed for some time while the damage done to his fleet was being repaired. The Paston Letters refer to the event thus:

William Makefyrr and Darcy and Alyngton.

Ryght worschypfull masters, I recomend me unto you, certyfying you the Kynges Grace and the Kyng of Castyll mett this day at thre of the cloke, apon Cleworth Greyn, ij mylle owt of Wyndesower, and ther the Kyng reseyvyed hym in the goodlyest maner that ever I sawe, and ech of them embracyd oder in armys.

To shew you the Kynges aparell of Yngland, thus it was: hys hors of bay, trappyd with nedyll werke; a gown of pupuyr velvyt, whych he put not of at the mettyng of the seyd Kyng of Castylle; hys hatt and his bonett he avalyd, and the Kyng of Castylle in cas lyke. And the Kyng of Castylle rod upon (a) sorellyd hoby, whych the Kyng gave unto hym; hys apparell was all blak, a gown of blak velvytt, a blak hovd, a blak hatt, and hys hors harness of blake velvytt.

To shew you of the Kynges Company, my Lord Harry of Stafforth rod in a gown of cloth of Tuyssew, tykkyd, furryd with sabilles, a hatt of goldsmyth worke, and full of stones, dyamondes and rubys, rydyng upon a sorellyd curser bardyd with a bayrd of goldsmythes wark, with rosys and draguns red.

And my Lord Markas rydyng apon a bald sorelyd [1] hors, with a deep trapper full of long tassels of gold of Venys and apon the crowper of hys hors a whytt fedyr, with a cott apon his bak, the body goldsmyths wark, the slevys of cremysyne velvyt, with letters of gold.

My Lord of Kent apon a sorelyd hors, balde,[1] the harnes of Venys gold, with deyp frynges of half zerd of lengh—my Lord of Kent cott was one barr of cloth of gold, an oder of cremysyn velvyt, pyreyd with a demy manche cut off by the elbowe, thyes be the lords that bare the bruyt.

[1] Chestnut-and-white.

Sir Hew Waghan apon a bay hors trapped with cremysyn velvyt full of gylt bells, a gown of blak velvyt, and a cheyn of gold, bawdryk wys, worth v. hundreth pownd.

Thys be the sperys, Maxter Sant John apon a blak hors, with arnes of cloth of gold with tasseles of plunkytt and whytt, a cott of plunkytt and whytt, the body of gold smyths werk, the slevys full of spanguls.

John Carr and William Parr cotts lyke, the horsys gray, of Parr trappyd with cremysyn velvyt with tasselles of gold, and bels gylt. Carr hors bay with an almayn harnes of sylver, an ynch brod of betyn sylver, both the cottes of goldsmythes work the bodys, the slevys on stryp of syllver, the order gylt— Edward Nevell apon a gray hors, etc.

Henry VII had a name for being careful with his money, but never spared expense when he saw a chance of getting some return for the outlay, and he had reason to wish to stand well with the house of Castile. This was the family into which his eldest surviving son married. Therefore the 'sorellyd hoby' (chestnut pony) which he gave King Philip must have been a good one, and the Castilian retinue were well accustomed to judge the worth of such animals, since theirs was the homeland of the much-esteemed jennet (ginete). Size and age of the rider was not a factor: Philip at this time was a well-grown man of twenty-eight.

We may assume that the son and grandson of Welsh squires knew where to lay his hands on a good pony when he wished to do honour to distinguished (if involuntary) visitors. How different was the attitude of his successor we shall presently see.

The bard Gwito'r Glyn, who was a contemporary of Edmund Tudor, could recite the pedigrees of living stallions that went back to the days of King Arthur, and there is no reason to believe that such pedigrees were any less authentic than the genealogy of the Tudors themselves. The deficiency in records under which the present authors labour is that there is now no bard living, either English or Welsh, who can recite the pedigrees of Welsh cobs that go back from the days of Lloyd George to those of Gwito'r Glyn.

There is a document among the Chapter House Books of Jervaulx Abbey, now in the Public Record Office. It is a remount officer's return —a list of over 250 horses requisitioned from tenants of Jervaulx estates 'for the duration of the emergency', in modern official parlance, and 'brought away by the inhabitants of Cumberland and Northumberland from Branxton field' (What a long time it takes for a battle to settle to its official name!) on 9th September 1513.

Two demobilization centres were set up, at Morpeth in Northumberland and 'Giltemyn' in Cumberland. I cannot identify the second: was it some forgotten mine by the River Gelt? Here the owners had to attend and 'challenge', i.e. claim their own animals. If these were not forthcoming, they were given a captured Scotch horse instead.

The descriptions in this catalogue, though short, can tell us a good deal about the type of horse in common use in the northern dales, and hence about the probable early history of the Fell and Dale breeds, because a uniform vocabulary is employed throughout, with minor inconsistencies.

Practically all the tenants came from Wensleydale, Swaledale, Teesdale and adjacent parts of Lancashire and Westmorland. There was one only from the East Riding (Risby, near Beverley) and one from Wolsingham, in Durham. Animals were identified by colour, gait (i.e. what they did when they came out of a walk), sex and distinguishing marks, or a combination of some of these four.

Colour is most consistently mentioned, in all cases except in very few where the more substantial owners are given anything up to six horses with no particulars. Of 252 described by colour, no less than ninety-five are grey—seventy-seven plain grey—other variants being dark grey (only one), white, grey, grizzled, dapple grey, one dun grey, one sandy grey.

There are fifty-five black and forty-six bay, including two 'bay blak' presumably what would now be called brown, with forty-three white. After that a steep drop in numbers. Eight dun and only three chestnut, described as soreld or red soreld. One 'bazand' to which we will refer presently, and one 'dosk'.

One hundred and fifty-nine of the horses are identified by sex. There are forty-nine stallions, called in the catalogue either stoned hors or hors. Of mares and geldings there are fifty-five each. Thus more than 20 per cent of the horses are geldings, a figure in marked contrast to the rest of the country where, to judge from the stringent laws enacted a little later by Henry VIII, scrub stallions abounded. (Mare is spelt meare, mere or meer, by turns!)

This may be the reason why the north country as a whole was excepted from the statutes which tried without much effect to impose selective breeding on the country at large. The rest of the horses are described as nags, which at that time meant a horse of either sex for riding, other than the large, specially bred and trained war-horse.

Only 163 animals are designated according to gait. By far the majority are trotting horses—129. Of the rest, eighteen are amblers and sixteen 'rakking hors', etc. Amblers or pacers are still seen today on some northern and midland race-tracks, where the declining sport of sulky-racing just manages to hold its own. In the Arab lands it is much commoner, and in the United States there is no lack of ambling horses either in harness or under the saddle.

But the rakker is totally extinct in England and on the Continent. Only in America, and more especially in the South, is this gait still practised by devotees of the Five-gaited Saddle Horse.

The rack was a medium-slow four-time gait in which the feet hit the ground in clockwise order—off-fore-hind-near-hind-fore, etc. Whereas the amble or pace was useful (at least half, and the more valuable half at that, of the horses on Chaucer's Canterbury pilgrimage ambled), the rack was spectacular to watch in its way, comfortable to sit on, but a very inefficient way of covering the ground and of no conceivable utility to farmer or shepherd.

It is highly unlikely that the dalesmen bred and trained rakkers for their own use, but for sale to the gentry, to better-off townsmen and to the more worldly sort of ecclesiastic.

Taken in conjunction with the coat colours, this factor of pace shows that the horses in question, or the greater part of them, were in fact Fell or Dale ponies (no one can say whether these two breeds were separate in the sixteenth century) or, as they are now widely called, gallowas.

The Fell, and more especially the Dales, has in later times had a tremendous reputation as a trotter, and whereas in Chaucer's day the trotting 'hakenay' was of no esteem compared with the ambling palfrey, so much so that the average prices from 1379 to 1391 were 61s. for palfreys against 24s. for hakenays, in the next century and a half the trotting horse gained enormously in prestige.

The palfrey became more and more a lady's hack, because it was almost impossible to sit the trot gracefully on the side-saddle which had become *de rigueur* for horse-women of all classes by the middle fifteenth century; but even without a stirrup (and there were no stirrups on side-saddles until after Queen Elizabeth's time) it was possible to ride side-saddle at the amble with comfort and elegance.

Some years after Flodden, Henry VIII passed a great deal of busy-body legislation which attempted to teach horse-breeders their business, laying down specifications for stud-horses and brood-mares which certain classes of subject were obliged to keep; and in these Acts he stipulated throughout that the stallions had to be trotting horses.

In this instance we see that 'what Wensleydale thinks today, Hampton Court thinks tomorrow', since the dalesmen were already keeping four trotting nags to one palfrey, either rakking or pacing.

As to colour, we may discount, strange as it may seem, the enormous factor of 40 per cent greys, since greyness is a colour which comes and goes genetically in all breeds. It was once common in the English thoroughbred racehorse, but its incidence has been steadily on the decline since the eighteenth century.

Its genetic significance, and the cycles in which it occurs, are still not fully understood; but it is a negative factor, an absence of pigment that has been designated by a leading authority as 'a sickness', and it is quite distinct from the true white.

White in 1513 was the fourth commonest colour—forty-three among those 252 horses from the Dales—where today it is absent or rare. It is a form of albinism which goes with pink skin, but it also goes with white hoofs, which are markedly softer and less durable than black hoofs. It is no matter for wonder that the white strain has been bred out in four centuries of work in a stony landscape.

The real significance is the predominance of black and bay (together nearly half the total) over the primitive dun (about 3 per cent) and over chestnut (less than one per cent, and of these one at least, 'a red sorel stone hors' from Westmorland, may have been an expensive import, since it belonged to Sir John Conyers, Knt). Black and bay are the commonest colours, together with brown, which is half way between the two, in the Dale and Fell breeds, where chestnut is almost unknown now.

Brown in 1513 was evidently not recognized as a separate colour since the only two animals of this tincture are described as 'blak bay'. Dun is an atavism that may occur in any breed but is rare in the Fell and Dale of today. One horse defied description and the remount clerk wrote it down as 'dosk', meaning dark coloured. The word is very northerly, specifically Lowland Scots. Gawin Douglas has a line:

> The ground stud barrant, widderit dosk or grey
> The ground stood barren, withered, dusky or grey.

There were no piebald or skewbald horses. Nor are there any among pure-bred gallowas today. But very frequent among the darker coats is the mention of 'bausonn'd' blak, bay 'bawsont', etc. This word, which ranges in spelling from baucyn to balsont in a score of different Middle English spellings, all northern or Scots, is obsolete in England now. It is glossed in Latin in this wise: 'Bausatura—macula alba in fronte equina.'

Balzano in modern Italian means 'with white legs'. It meant in English 'having white marks, not on the body'. Again, Gawin Douglas has 'Cam riding on ane bausent sorel stud'. There was however one 'bazand trotting hors', no other colour mentioned. This *may* have meant a piebald, or the body colour may simply have been forgotten.

Before passing to the distinguishing marks, which are described in terms full of regional flavour, we should take note that in no case is size or age mentioned. They were not relevant, since the horses were not required to carry armoured lancers, whose chargers had to be of a certain minimum height and must be in the prime of life (say between six and twelve), since otherwise their joints would not stand up to the weight of the armour.

The only people who had to provide this class of horse were those mustered in the feudal levy as men-at-arms, liable by the terms of their lease 'to take the king's wage with hors and harneys' as the phrase went. 'Harneys' in this context means armour.

Typical of such horsemen was the Leicestershire farmer, Hugh Latimer, father of the Protestant martyr. We do not know the acreage of his holding, but Latimer junior once said in a sermon that he ran a hundred sheep and had thirty cows in milk, employing six men, besides women and boys.

There were few such yeomen (substantial tenants) or franklins (freeholders) in the Wensleydale of 1513. This type of holding was worth about £4 a year rent at the latter end of Henry VII's reign, and many gentlemen in the northern dales, automatically assessed as horse-men on account of their birth, cannot have owned much more than this in stock or cash. They must have had a hard struggle to maintain a sixteen-hand war-horse, which was quite useless for agricultural purposes if only because the shafts of carts and the tackle used for harrows, etc., would not fit it. Besides this, it takes an equestrian genius to train one and the same horse to harrow and plough and carry out the manœuvres required in an armoured mellay.

These horses of the dales were requisitioned for traction—for the artillery teams and to draw the pontoon wagons of the bridging train—but most of all as pack horses (which was their natural bent, and in which they were unsurpassed) to carry the sacks of oatmeal and bundles of arrows and the ankers of coarse-grain black powder for the 'grete gonnes'.

That was why their owners did not go with them, but either stayed at home or served as archers and billmen, to meet old Skot or old Badger again at Giltemyn or Morpeth, if both survived the campaign.

A high proportion of both did survive, since the campaign was won rather quickly and cheaply compared with most major episodes in the perennial Border war. Though the economic foundations had been shot from under it the military side of the feudal system still functioned very well north of the Trent.

When the commissioners of array mustered the militia of midland counties they would be confronted by an unmilitary shower of chicken-stealers, bribed or blackmailed substitutes, the human flotsam of a hundred parishes officered by dithering country justices like Shallow and Silence, or the wrong type of old sweat like Ensign Pistol and Corporal Bardolph.

Things were very different when the Earl of Surrey summoned the power of Richmondshire. Billmen and pikemen and archers mustered by companies and bands under Lord Scrope of Bolton and Lord Dacre, for 'The Erle forgat not to send to all lords spiritual and temporal' (the Abbot of Jervaulx being a lord spiritual for this purpose) 'to certify what number of able men they were able to make within a hour's warning . . . then he wrote to all the gentlemen of the shires aforesayd to be with him at Newcastle the first day of September with all their retinew according to the certificate' (*Hall's Chronicle*), and away they went over the Tees and into the bishopric, across the Wear and the Derwent, the Tyne and the Wandsbeck, the Coquet and the Alne, till they came to the Water of Till below Cheviot and face to face with the power of Scotland, grossly overestimated by Hall at a hundred thousand horse and foot.

The requisitioned horses were delivered to the headquarters of the Master of the Ordnance, Sir Nicholas Appleyard, at Durham, already loaded with contributions in kind, such as oatmeal loose and in bannocks, sheaves of arrows and panniers of gun stones.

Meanwhile the Scots had begun hostilities a month before by a deep raid over the western marches designed to seize horses and supplies for the mounting of the main operation. This was frustrated by Sir William Bulmer who, with two hundred professional mounted archers and eight hundred other archers raised by gentlemen of the Borders, caught the raiders on the way home at Millfield. 'The archers shot so wholly together that they made ye Scottes give place and five or six hundred slayn and four hundred and more taken prisoner and the prey reskued, beside a great number of geldings that were taken in the country' (Hall).

When dawn broke on the 9th of September the English forded the Till and both armies pivoted on their east flank for many hours until the Scots were facing north below the Hill of Flodden, with the English astride the road to Scotland, and still no shot fired. The order of battle, so far as the dalesmen were concerned, was the Lord Dacre on the right wing and the Lord Scrope's contingent in the rereward as a tactical reserve under the Earl of Surrey himself, with the Dales horses in the transport columns of these two formations.

When finally the battle joined, it was with an artillery duel that was quickly won by superior counter-battery work: 'Then out brast the ordinaunce on both sydes with fyre flamme and hideous noyse, and the Master Gonner of the Englishe parte slow [slew] the Master Gonner of Scotlande and beat his men from their ordinaunce, so that the Scottishe ordinaunce did no harm to the Englishe men.'

This did not happen till four o'clock in the afternoon, and by the time the sun set at half past six it was all over. The King of Scots had been killed in action leading a desperate counter-attack on foot, and his army had lost twelve thousand dead for a total English casualty figure of fifteen hundred dead and prisoners.

As for the dalesmen under the Lord Dacre, his right wing in the main battle 'stoode still all day unfoughten with all'. The rereward played a decisive part but was not committed until late in the day, when the Scots had shot away all their arrows, so that Richmondshire men under the Lord Scrope cannot have suffered very heavy losses out of the fifteen hundred. Nor can their horses, since they were not in the fighting echelon at all and would only come under Scottish artillery fire, which was ineffective after the first few salvoes.

It is more than likely that a few Dales horses were taken to remount Bulmer's mounted archers, who had been in contact with the enemy for nearly six weeks. But this unit had only been two hundred strong on 1st August, and however many horses it had lost there would, by 9th September, be a good many archers who would never need another horse. Moreover they did not actually shoot from the saddle, so their equine casualties would not be as heavy as among men-at-arms who had to ride at the enemy and close with him.

In fact, more horses were lost on the night after the battle when 'many men lost there horses and such stuffe as they left in there tents by the robbars of Tyndale and Tyuidale'.

To return to the distinguishing marks, which are in great variety, both natural and artificial or accidental. Of the first we have mele mouthed; kloudy faced; thyn mayne; two wall eene; sterne in the forehede; freyned (with marks on head or face looking like a bridle). Of the second, topping (forelock) kutt; shorn mayne; cut tailed (docked?);[1] a few 'brynt' with brands which are called simply 'burns' (Thomas Gardiner of Furness had a white trotting mare brynt on the nere buttok); only one brand is described—a blawing horn on nere buttok.

There is a great variety of ear-marks. Ears are shorn (right off: accident?); cropt (lopped half way up); stowed (tip cut straight across); forkstowed (nick in centre of tip); ritt or ritted (slit); bitted and undirbitted (triangular cuts out of edge) on far or nere ere, or both.

Ritt and stowed are Northumbrian usage today, according to Mr Henry Tegner, of Morpeth (Morpeth!).

Bitted, forked and ritted were ear-marks for sheep described in the Shepherd's Book that circulated in Westmorland, Cumberland and Lonsdale in the last century for the identification of strays.

A few accidental blemishes are new, perhaps the result of the battle. Gaull'd, from ill-fitting government saddlery, nere ere cut of (not cropt or shorn), with oon eye (about ten of these) and Grete burns (probably gun-blast). Older blemishes are whyte sadill blaynes (old galls) and oon syde of the nose tyned whyte. White hairs grow out of scar tissue, and this was a punctured wound.

Teine was Chaucer's word for a sliver of metal and is Lowland Scots for the prong of a pitchfork. But in the *Yorkshire Dialogue* of the late seventeenth century we have 'he's tenged, he'll dee', where the patient has been gored by a bull-seg. Miss Frankland, of Ravenstonedale, says that 'teng'd' in Westmorland now means stung by wasp, bee, cleg, etc. Some 'freyned' faces were no doubt due to badly fitting bridles in the past. One mark which may be a brand is 'rovel on nere buttok'.

A 'rowell' might be a brand in the shape of a spur, or rather of its business end, but the word 'burn' is not used here and it could be a laceration from the heel of a rider who had come off backwards.

The right side of an animal throughout is the 'far' side, never 'off'. This logical opposite of 'nere', used throughout for the left, is modern usage in Northumberland (here I am indebted to Mr Tegner).

Again, according to Miss Frankland, of Ravenstonedale, all these terms are still applied to the ear-markings of Westmorland sheep, and she adds that in those parts it is nowadays correct to refer to the *far* side of a sheep, cow or pig, but not of a horse.

When I first saw this document I had hopes that the remount officer's clerk would prove to be a North Riding man, since he spelled phonetically names like Rauf Paycock (for Ralph Peacock) of Grynton in

---

[1] More likely with some hair cut out on one side, as New Forest agisters do today, for identification.

Swaledale, where my grandfather's grandfather farmed. But his idiom turns out to be more northerly than that.

It is distinctly Border, though whether he was a Northumbrian or a Berwickshire prisoner of war picked out of the cage as a 'scholar', or an independent citizen of neutral Redesdale, we shall never know.

On second thoughts, he could not have been a genuine Redesdaler; the 'robbars' didn't care how long the war on the Border went on, so long as they could stay in the robbing business and make a decent profit out of both sides. But one and all their youth was spent too busily in learning how to help themselves to other people's live-stock for them to have any time left for the practice of penmanship.

After all, the most significant item in this useful and salty vocabulary of Tudor horsemen is an omission. If the word galloway were already current in 1513 for a fast, tough little horse, surely it would have found employment here? Yet by 1598, if that was the year when *2 Henry IV* was written, it was used by Shakespeare on distant London's Bankside.

In their time, Wensleydale breeders had produced ambling palfreys that were second to none. The market charter of Askrigg in Wensleydale was granted in 1202 by King John in consideration of a gift of one palfrey for the king to hunt on. The kind of palfrey that could be used as a hunter, especially with the royal staghounds, was the very best. Such charters were often granted for a financial consideration, and we have seen that in the reign of King John north-country rents were often offered and asked in terms of palfreys, the equivalent of a more or less standard sum in marks: and when the quarter day came round the tenant paid either cash or kind, whichever was convenient. Can this be a foreshadowing of the modern racecourse slang 'pony', meaning twenty-five pounds?

Such then were the horses of small and middling tenants under Henry VIII. William Youatt quotes an equally revealing though less comprehensive document about the stable of a great north-country landowner in the year before Flodden.

This is the ordre of the chequir roul of the nombre of all the horsys of my lordis and my ladys that are apoynted to be in the charge of the hous yerely, as to say, gentil hors, palfreys, hobys, naggis, cloth-sek hors, male-hors. First, gentil-hors, to stand in my lordis stable, six. *Item.* Palfreys of my lady's, to wit, one for my lady, and two for her gentil-women, and oone for her chamberer, four hobys and naggis for my lordis oone saddill, *viz.*, oone for my lorde to ride, oone to lede for my lorde, and oone to stay at home for my lorde there. *Item.* Chariot hors to stond in my lorde's stable yerely. Seven great trottynge hors to draw in the chariott, and a nagg for the chariott-man to ride; eight. Again, hors for lorde Percy, his lordship's son and heir. A grete doble trottynge horse, for my lorde Percy to travel on in winter. *Item.* A grete doble trottynge hors, called a curtal, for his lordship to ride on out of townes. Another trottynge gambaldynge hors, for his lordship to ride upon when he comes into townes. An ambling hors for his lordship to journey on

138

dayly. A proper amblyng little nagg for his lordship when he goeth on hunting or hawking. A great amblynge gelding or trottynge gelding to carry his male.

Twenty-seven in all, and a fair cross-section of the equine population. The six 'gentil hors' are coursers, imported or of imported stock, probably Italian, at any rate still called by the Italian word which more or less corresponds to the term 'thoroughbred', as in

Dimmi, caval' gentil', ch'é di Rinaldo?

The four palfreys are of the kind we have met throughout the Middle Ages, predominantly of selected native pony stock. Four hobbies and nags for my lord and one for the chariot man: undisguised ponies. Seven trotting chariot horses: down-graded war-horses, not handy enough for the tourney, or the battlefield itself. Three 'great' war-horses for the young lord, one docked. Two amblers, one for travelling and one for hunting, of the same type as the palfreys of the countess. Another down-graded war-horse to carry the heavy cloak-bag. In all, eleven Great horses, six imported coursers and ten native-bred pacers or amblers. More than a third of all the horses attached to a great household were still country-bred. The tallest one of all was 'to travel on in winter'—to keep his lordship as high out of the mud as possible.

King Henry VIII has come in for a lot of abuse as the Destroyer of Ponies, all because of his very copious laws about horse-breeding, which occupy ten densely printed pages of black-letter type in Rastell's *Statutes*. Indeed on the strength of this printed evidence it has been argued that there can be no continuity between the British pony breeds

22. Facsimile of a statute of Henry VIII concerning horse-breeding.

before and after about 1540, because this king decreed the wholesale slaughter of everything under fourteen hands. However, before we lightly dismiss him as the Knacker's Friend, let us consider what can have made him so set against ponies. Firstly, they were useless for military operations, or for his idea of military operations, which was great big men like himself equitating around on chargers whose efficiency had really begun to decline, in the balance against archers and hand-gun men, long before his father won the battle on Bosworth Field. Henry was a keen but very amateurish soldier; not all the years of bitter experience were to teach him that war was something more than an armoured fashion parade for Top People. He could not see that the future of mounted warfare belonged to the hobilar. Secondly, in peace or war, ponies are an indifferent plinth for the *persona* of what Dr Johnson was later to call sadly 'a bulky man'. And what Henry cared deeply about was the *bella figura*. Thirdly, he was unsure of himself genealogically. He wanted to be *legitimate*. It had been enough for his father, the Lucky Harry of his day, to be King of England by the right of his arms and to continue so by the use of his wits and never mind the *Almanach de Gotha*. But Henry VIII badly wanted to be descended from the Lancastrians, the Plantagenets, the Angevins, the Normans, Aeneas, Hercules, the Trojans and Brut of Albion. He did not much want to be descended from Edmund Tudor, son of Owen Tudor, the Welsh squire who had the luck and good sense to marry Henry V's widow. So that every time he saw an undersized horse he thought of the little Welsh stallions running on the mountains, and it cut him to the quick.

That all his efforts did *not* result in a wholesale putting-down of horses is clear from contemporary, and immediately subsequent, accounts—not literary accounts, but the pedestrian record of market prices. Since half the horse stock of the country was sub-standard by his specifications, the survivors of his massacre of the innocents, if it had come off, would automatically have doubled in price, the demand being constant. But this did not happen, any more than the disastrous fall in the price of leather, due to a glut of hides, which would have been another inevitable result, is to be traced in the middle sixteenth century. Moreover the laws as he laid them down could not possibly be adminis-tered, as the necessary disinterested agents were lacking. The country was not swarming with Gentlemen from the Ministry asking to inspect stallions and fill in buff forms. Let us see what the laws actually demanded of breeders (23 Henry VIII (1532)):

(1) *Export*

It was a felony to 'carry or send out of this realm beyond sea any horse or gelding with entent to sell the same' or any mare above the value of 6s. 8d. for any purpose whatsoever. It was permissible to take one's own horses for the purpose of travelling abroad but licences had to be obtained. Such officers as the Governor of Calais and the Wardens of the Scottish Marches were empowered to grant licences.

It was likewise a felony to 'sell, exchange, give, convey or deliver into the Realme of Scotland . . . or sell, exchange, convey or deliver unto any Scottish man within this realm of England or Wales the town of Berwick or the Marches of the same with intent to be conveyed into Scotland any horse gelding or mare'. The penalty was a fine of £40 (more than twice what the living of most parishes was worth in those days, for instance), and an Act of Queen Elizabeth's in 1559 added a year's imprisonment. 'And it shall be lawful for any persons as well spiritual as temporal being the King's subjects inhabiting the aforesaid Marches to arrest any Scottish man leading such horse into the realm of Scotland.' The horse to be forfeit and half its price due to the Crown and the other half to the person making the arrest.

(2) *The Keeping of Brood Mares*

There are no penalties quite on the scale of the above in the other statutes such as those concerning the keeping of brood mares:

'Every person which shall have any ground enclosed with a hedge ditch wall or pale within which any deere shall be kept, containing the quantity of one myle in compass, shall keep two mares being not spaied, able and apt to bear foles, each of them 13 handfulls at the least from the lowest part of the houfe of the foot unto the highest part of the shoulder, every handfull to contain 4 inches of the standerd, upon paid of forfeiture of 40s. for every moneth lacking the said mares contrary to this Act.'

The owner or farmer of such a park compassing four miles and above was to keep four mares of the same specification, or 'scantling' as it was called, as the foregoing.

Casualties were to be replaced within three months 'and the lord, etc. of the ground shall not *willingly* after the first day May 1537 suffer any of the said mares to be covered and lept with any stoned horse under the stature of 14 handfulls'. Penalty 40s. There was a proviso that this act, 27 Henry VIII (1536) 'shall not extend to Westmerland, Cumberland, Northumberland and the Bishopricke of Durham. Nor also shall extend to the finding of any mares (in parks, etc.) the herbage of which is common to the tenants of the townships next adjoining the same'. Such parks were less rare than one might think, where the lord of the manor empaled all or part of the common grazing to keep his deer in and the tenants and some freeholders retained their right to graze stock within the pale. It was after all in miniature the same basic situation as in the New Forest, where the Crown alone had the right to keep deer but without prejudice to the grazing rights of a large body of commoners. But it was of course the thin end of a wedge which by the late eighteenth century led to the total enclosure of most English commons. For the moment it provided a handy excuse for those landlords who did not want the bother of keeping brood mares and borrowing fourteen-hand stallions.

(3) *Keeping Stallions*

Every Archbishop and Duke of this Realm beginning the Feast of the Archangel Michael the year of Our Lord 1544 shall have, find, keep, maintain and sustain seven stoned trotting horses for the saddle . . . three years and upwards, in height 14 handfulls from the nether part of the heare of the houfe unto the upper part of the widderson, that is to say the upper part of the shoulders.

The forfeit was £20 for each month of default.

'Every Marquis, Earl, and Bishop whose diocese is worth £1,000 a year' was to keep five stallions as above.

'Every Viscount, Baron, and Bishop whose diocese is worth 1,000 marks [£666] a year' was to keep three stallions as above.

'Every spiritual person worth 500 marks and every temporal person worth 600 marks [£400]' was to keep two stallions as above.

'Every spiritual person worth between £100 and 500 marks [£333 13s. 4d.] and every temporal person whose wife shal weare anie goune of silke or anie frenche hoode or bonet of ueluet with anie habilement, paste or edge of gold etc.' was to keep one stallion as above with effect from Michael-mass 1545. The penalty was £10 for every three months of default. These stallions were subject to military requisitioning, for it was provided that if lost in the service of the king's wars two years were allowed to effect a replacement, thus allowing the owner to replace with one of his own colt foals without paying out money. Replacement with cart or pack-horse stallions was expressly forbidden. Only 'stoned trotting horses' would do. How times had changed since Richard II's days![1] The above clauses are taken from 38 Henry VIII, which was repealed by Philip and Mary, perhaps because it bore too hardly on the clergy.

(4) *Depasturing Stallions on Commons*

'Forasmuch as the breed of good and strong horses is a great help and defence to the realm and a great comoditie to the inhabitants thereof, which is now much decayed by reason that little stoned horses and Nags be suffered to pasture in forests etc. and to cover mares feeding there, *Therefore for the encrease of stronger horses hereafter be it enacted* that no commoner or commoners within any forest, chase, moore, marish, heth, common or wast grounde at any time after the 31st March 1543 shall have or put forth to pasture in any such ground etc. any stoned horse or horses being above the age of two yeare and not being of the altitude and height of 15 handfulls.'

[1] A fairly clear demonstration of the feeling against trotting horses for *civilian* saddle use is given in the course of the play *Friar Bacon and Friar Bungay*, 1594, by Robert Greene, where the Devil offers to carry the poor scholar Miles to Hell on his back, who accepts, but . . .

'I pray you, goodman friend, let me move a question to you.'
Devil: 'What's that?'
Miles: 'I pray you, whether is your pace a trot or an amble?'
Devil: 'An amble.'
Miles: ''Tis well. But take heed it be not a trot: but 'tis no matter, I'll prevent it.'
(*Puts on Spurs.*)

Devil: 'What dost?'
Miles: 'Marry, friend, I put on my spurs; for if I find your pace a trot or else uneasy, I'll put you to a false gallop: I'll make you feel the benefit of my spur.'

From which we learn that the Elizabethan phrase for canter was 'false gallop'.

This Act, 32 Henry VIII (1541), was not applicable to Cumberland, Westmorland, Northumberland, the Bishopric of Durham, Rutland, the Soke of Peterborough, Hertfordshire, Middlesex, Surrey, Sussex, Derby, Nottinghamshire, Monmouthshire, Dorset, Devon or Cornwall. It was further restricted by 8 Elizabeth (1566) which says:

'Forasmuch as the moores, marishes and fenne groundes of the shires hereafter mentioned by reason of their rottenness and waterish-ness are not able to breed beare and bring forth such great breeds of stoned horses as by the statute of 32 Henry VIII is expressed, without peril of miring and perishing of them, and other horses dare not be put forth for fear of Promoters [i.e. informers who could claim half the fine] whereby the breed of horses decayeth in those places . . . the marishes and seggy fenne grounds within the shires of Cambridge, Huntingdon, Northampton, Lincoln, Norfolk and Suffolk shall be of none effect in the lawe. Nevertheless be it ordained that no person shall put into any marish to pasture anie stoned horses being above the age of two yeare old and not being of the height of 13 handfulls.'

The Act was not to apply to ineligible horses which had escaped from enclosed land, but only one escape per horse per year was allowed after 1st March. Owners were given four days to remove them, if known. If unknown, four days after the impounding had been announced in church the following Sunday.

This Act, 32 Henry VIII, also contains the clause that has been cited as implying the destruction of all pony stock. Here is the gist of it. There were to be annual drifts, as they say in the New Forest and on Exmoor, of all moors, wastes, chases, parks, marshes, etc., to be completed within fifteen days, on payment of 40s. fine for default by those respon-sible be they private landlords, keepers of royal parks and chases or headboroughs, etc., of townships adjoining wastes and moors. In the course of these: 'If there shall be found any mare filly fole or gelding that then shall be thought not to be able or like to be able to beare foles of reasonable stature, or not able or like to grow to be profitable labours, by the discretion of the drivers aforesaid, or of the more number of them' (this is where several free-holders or tenants with common pasture rights were responsible for the drift) 'then the same drivers shal cause the same unprofitable beastes every one of them to be killed.' Note that no height specification as in the case of selected brood mares or stallions is laid down. Only 'of reasonable stature . . . by the discretion of the drivers aforesaid'. One can imagine the sort of dialogue that would go on to determine the discretion of the more number of them, when George has condemned a filly belonging to William's cousin's son-in-law, George and William being themselves two of the drivers aforesaid, and both owners of stock themselves! Obviously only the hopelessly undersized runts or hideous unsound barren mares would be put down. (No compensation.)

When old Harry had been dead eighteen years and the disastrous reigns of his first two successors were fading from the memory of their outraged subjects, Thomas Blundeville published his *Fowre Cheifest Ofyces Belonging to an Horseman*. The three last 'offices', equitation, stable management and feeding, were translations, indeed the first was simply the unsold sheets of F. Grisone's *Riding and Breaking Great Horses*, in English, bound up with the new material. But the section on breeding was original, Blundeville's 'Owne smal knowledge', not classical and continental texts 'applyed to the use of this our countrey.' The endearing thing about Blundeville is that through the stately phrases every now and then we can hear his very Norfolk voice twanging away thus: 'they fare to be curste and frowarde' or 'I hard oure souldiers say'.

Blundeville's Epistle Dedicatory was to Lord Robert Dudley, Erle of Leycester, Master of the Quene's Maiestie's Horses, etc. In it he expressed the concern that 'the Quene's highness may not onely cause such statutes as were made in her noble father and deare brother's tyme (both of good Memory) touching the bredyng of horses upon Commons, to be put into execution; but also that all such parkes within this realm, as be in her highness hands, and mete for that purpose might not wholly be imployed for the kepyng of Deere (which is altogether a pleasure without profit) but partly to the necessarie bredyng of horses for service, whereof this realm of all others at this instant hath gretest nede.'

That was in 1565. Nothing happened until 28th April 1580, when there appeared *A Proclamation for Horsemen and Breed of Horses for Service: by the Queen*. It is in effect a rocket, of Churchillian virulence, aimed at lords lieutenant and sheriffs. Based on recent muster reports which had condemned the unmilitary showing of militia units in general but in which the horsed sections had figured, not for the first time, as an even greater waste of public money, it says flatly that the queen, 'being given to understand that the most necessary and profitable laws provided for the breed and encrease of horses are either not at all put in execution, or very negligently', was about to appoint an extraordinary commission and to 'make choice of certain Noble men of this realm and others of her Privy Council' to see that existing laws were carried out. No new sanctions were contemplated but loyal subjects were given fair warning that in future the existing penalties of fine and confiscation would actually be imposed.

One can almost see the Director of Remounts (Yeomanry) going out to be measured for a bowler hat! But probably even this high-level pep-group did not have the effect they were intended to produce, and down to the Civil War of the mid seventeenth century the average size of horses, other than those specially bred in enclosures from selected and largely imported stock, would appear, from what documentary evidence we have, to have remained that of the 'old-fashioned' New Forest type, round about 13 hands.

Let no one imagine, however, that we can disregard Tudor legislation on such matters with impunity. In 1959 a New Forest commoner brought an action in the county court for recovery of a pony which had strayed off the Forest on to a private freehold, been impounded and, not being claimed after a certain interval, been sold in Ringwood market. The plaintiff lost the action through inability to identify the pony certainly enough, but the defendant also came in for a wigging from the bench for not complying scrupulously enough with the terms of the Sale of Horses Act, 1555, whose workings are thus described in Samuel Butler's *Hudibras*:

> Buyers you know are bid beware
> And worse than theives receivers are.
> How shall I answer hue and cry,
> For a roan gelding, twelve hands high,
> All spurr'd and switch'd, a lock on's hoof,
> A sorrel mane? Can I bring proof,
> Where, when, by whom, and what ye were sold for,
> And in the open market toll'd for?
> Or, should I take you for a stray,
> You must be kept a year and day
> (Ere I can own you) here in' th' pound,
> Where, if y'are sought, you may be found:
> And in the meantime I must pay for all your provender
> and hay.

This statute, 2 & 3 Philip and Mary, c. 7, commanded the 'chief keeper of every faire and market overt' to 'yearly appoint and limit out one certain and special open place . . . and shall write or cause to be written in a book the colour with one speciall mark at the least of every such horse' as should be sold in the aforesaid place. After sale the horse was to remain in the open market 'openly ridden, ledde, walked, driven or kept standing, by the space of one hour together at the leaste'. The object was to make the sale of stolen horses more difficult, but it does not seem to have been achieved, to judge by the preamble to 31 Elizabeth, c. 12, which states: 'Whereas through most counties of this realme horse stealing is growen so common as neither in pasture nor in close, nor hardly in stables, the same are to be in safety from stealing, which ensueth by the ready buying of the same by horse-coursers and others in some open faires or markets farre distant from the owner . . . ' The Elizabethan statute added to the compulsory recording of sales and the prohibition of immediate removal the requirement that vendors must be personally known to the toll-keeper of the market or vouched for by some regular trader there. It adds that accessories to a horse-theft (which would include Butler's 'receivers') were to be denied benefit of clergy. You have been warned!

It is in the reign of Queen Mary that the word cob, in the form 'cobbe', first becomes common. It does not yet mean a horse, but we can see the kind of horse it is going to mean soon. In the political satire *Respublica*, a 'merye enterlude' for the stage written in 1553, perhaps by

Nicolas Udall, there is a character called People, a west-country peasant ruined by the encroachments of the local 'cobbes' who have taken his grazing rights from him:

> Vive or zix yeare agone chad vour kine to my pail
> And at this present howre cham scarce worth a good cow tail.

Cobs in People's parlance are the hard-faced men who had done well out of the Reformation. Their sheep are eating smaller men's cattle off the common grazing, and in any case they press hard for the enclosure of commons because their share will bring them scores of acres of workable land, whereas the small commoner's share, that was worth having if it meant only half a dozen goose-gaits, will be useless when converted into a freehold strip that will only give room to grow a couple of rows of cabbage. Cobbes have permanently a prosperous and well-nourished air. It takes two yards of leather to make them a belt, and three yards to make their horses a girth. They have rather large feet and they trot steadily on their way regardless of other people's toes. For some reason they and their sons never get pressed for the king's wars in Ireland or elsewhere, but when they have passed military age they sit on tribunals to try conscientious objectors. Of course they have had no military experience but they have been on the roster of special constables for years. Why, they even have a medal and a diploma in a glass case on the parlour wall at home. The etymology of the word cob is obscure, but all are agreed that it means something rotund and uppish.

'That time ch'ad a widge and hir vole and ten sheep,' says People. This is the first we have heard of the Anglo-Saxon *wicg* since about 1200, when it appears in a south-country homily for Palm Sunday.

That time, when People counted himself a man, is symbolized by his ownership of a horse (or pony). The ten sheep represented subsistence level, the 'widge and hir vole' something more, the 'vour kine' prosperity. Vocabulary and spelling of his lines do not exactly reflect the dialect of north Devon or west Somerset in Mary's time—they are the standard synthetic 'Mummerzet' of the Elizabethan stage, the way Londoners thought western yokels talked. But they do show that the west was thought of as a country where small husbandmen went in for horse breeding as a matter of course. When People complains to Oppression, the official, and is told 'Ye must tarry time ere we can your purpose serve', the retort that comes naturally to his lips is 'Yea, and then while grass shall grow the horse shall sterve'. People speaks for all the 'zelie poor volk' of churlish but not servile status (in medieval terms), whether he actually came from Exmoor or not. So long as he had one 'widge' and her 'vole' running on the common he was a man: below that level, something less. We might do worse than listen to him.

The Calendar of State Papers contains two Scottish applications to buy English horses. One is by Sir Adam Otterburn, King's Advocate and Recorder of Edinburgh, to Chancellor Cromwell, dated 1535, on behalf of King James V.

'Quarfore I wryte at this tyme to remember yow of ane restreyne yat was made in tymespast yat na horse suld be sold be Inglysemen to Scotismen whylke suld now cese in tyme of lufe and kyndnesse. It may be ane singular signe of lufe that my Soverane's servandis may buy horse in Ingland to [for] His Grace, whylk is gevin to dalie rydin and to take plesour apon gude horsis, and sykelyke privilege to Inglisemen to sell ye said horsis to His Grace's servandis.'

The other, dated 1539, is a personal application from James V to Henry VIII:

'We presentlie desyres of yow yat ye would gif your licence to selle to oure servandis horses to ye noumer of 24; and of yeme 16 swift trottand geldingis and ye residue well goyng hacknayis.'

Evidently by stipulating for a majority of geldings King James thought his chance of a licence would be improved, since the question of exporting breeding stock would not arise, and at that time only entire stallions were used as war-horses.

These requests are of course the direct result of the English law of 1532. James V had become an orphan at the age of one, when his father was killed by the English at Flodden, but Henry's policy towards the Scots was alternate doses of terrorism and conciliation, the carrot and the stick. It all depended on the current state of Anglo-French relations. This was the carrot phase, and James got the horses.

In 1540 one spectacular result of the alternative 'big stick' policy became apparent. The Scots had developed such a feeling of military inferiority towards the English, at least so far as cavalry went, that they passed an Act of Parliament in that year forbidding anyone under the rank of general to appear mounted on the battlefield; because they remembered their resounding victories over Edward I which had been won by the courage and skill at arms of their infantry alone.

Yet this feeling was confined to the Scottish government and regular army, open to Highland influence. The perpetual war along the Border, which had been going on at least since the time of Aulus Plautius and perhaps began before that in the form of a feud between the Brigantes and the Otadini, was and remained until its end in 1603 essentially a war between guerrilla bands of light cavalry, in which the Scottish raiders were no less well mounted than the English. How could they be so, since the same horses were continually changing hands by capture and ransom? Indeed, in many ways the horses of south-west Scotland, the Carlisle sector of the front, were much esteemed in Northumbria, and by the beginning of the seventeenth century the fame of the Galloway horses had spread as far as the south of England.

Two years after the death of Henry VIII, quite early in the reign of his daughter's rival, Mary of Scotland, a survey of the Hebrides was undertaken by Donald Monro, High Dean of the Isles, an official on the staff of the Bishop of Sodor and Man. Of the Isle of Duray (Jura) he remarked that it was 'full of nobell coelts' and that 'be foure myle of sea toward the Southeist fra Ronin [South Rona, next to Raasay] layes ane litle ile half ane mile lang callit by the Erish Allan nan Eache, that is in English the Horse Ile, gude for horse and uther store, pertaining to the Bishop of the Iles'. And that is pretty well all the High Dean has to say about horses, except that a great many small islands of about the size of Eileen nan Eachen, if they have water and good grazing on them, are described by him as 'guid for store', though often uninhabited. By this phrase he means the sort of island where people would put store cattle or sheep or goats ashore in the spring and take them off fat in the autumn. They might equally well have put young colts and fillies ashore for the same purpose, as people are known to have done on the numerous islands of the North Atlantic which bear the Norse name Hrossey or Horsay and other variants.

We have an anonymous description of the Western Isles of Scotland, written some time between 1577 and 1595. It is an official document, no doubt written at the command of James VI, as part of his scheme for increasing the revenue to be got from the Isles (which never came to anything). It is not very detailed in the matter of live-stock; it seems to be more interested in the resources of corn, salmon and fighting men to be drawn on by the central government, and mentions the hunting facilities at some length, no doubt in view of the king's well-known passion for the deer-hunt, but all it says about horses is this:

'There is na horse ner meires in [St Kilda] . . . Raarsa [Raasay] is ane Ile of 5 mile lang and 3 mile braid, their is na woods but great heich craigs in this Ile. It is commodious for corn and all kinds of bestial and cheifly horses. Romb [Rhum] is ane Ile of small profit. Lismoir is commodious for nowt [cattle] and horses. Great Hwnay is gude for corn, nowt and horses.'

Of course St Kilda was so small that there was little employment for a horse or even for working oxen. There, as in the poorer parts of the Shetlands, people tilled the fields with the breast-plough or even with a spade. But the laconic entry about Rhum is disappointing in that it fails to confirm the tradition about the antiquity of the herd of ponies still to be found there.

Let us here say a word about the notorious Armada stallions. In various districts along the west coast of Great Britain, and in Ireland, it is claimed that the local breed of horses obtained a vigorous injection of fresh blood from some marvellous sire that had swum ashore, or come ashore in some way, from one of the ships of the Spanish fleet making their way home after their defeat in August 1588. It is quite true that something between seventeen and twenty-four badly damaged Armada ships put in, or were driven in, to various bays on the west coast of Ireland, one on the Fair Isle, and several on Mull. Only one came ashore on the coast of Devon, the *San Pedro el Mayor* at Bolt Point. But the

San Pedro was not a galleon but a hulk, one of the two hospital ships, and as such can hardly have carried any horses. The losses of the Armada are pretty well accounted for in documents of English and also of Spanish origin. But as early as 14th August, when what remained of the Spanish fleet was still under unified command and was still far to the south of the Shetlands, which they had to clear before entering on the long leg down the Atlantic seaboard for home, the Duke of Medina Sidonia ordered all horses and mules to be thrown overboard because the crews were already on a water ration of one pint per day per man, and there was no water left for live-stock to drink. Discipline in the Spanish fleet was good; but even if some captain had managed to disobey the order, then it is impossible that any horse should have survived the battering that these ships were still to receive from the weather. Moreover a neutral captain interrogated by the English reported seeing on that date hundreds of horses and mules, some swimming, some floating dead in the North Sea, far out from land *off the east Coast.*

Nor is it necessary, to account for an accession of Spanish blood, to have recourse to this unlikely story. The seaway from Spain to Ireland and western Britain was not long nor difficult even for primitive ships. The Phoenicians had followed it, at the right time of the year. We have seen that Robert de Belesme imported Andalusian steeds, either through the Mersey or the Channel ports in the eleventh century. If the horse for which Art McMorrogh paid 400 cows was imported, it could as well have come from Spain as anywhere. Down to Elizabethan times there was a thriving trade between Spain and Irish ports like Galway and Limerick. Jennets of Spain must have come direct into England (and also to Ireland, where their progeny out of Irish hobby mares grew up and in turn were exported to England) for many centuries in the seaworthy and roomy Basque ships. From Santander to Wexford is only 700 miles in a straight line, passing Ushant and Land's End, due north: turn right for Bristol and Fishguard, keep straight on for Wicklow, Dublin, Dundalk, Belfast and the Clyde. No longer than the distance from Aberdeen to Ireland or to Dover from Bergen or Oslo or Gothenburg. (See Map 3, page 123.)

The bell tolled at Sheen on the Thames on 25th March 1603. Some time in the dark hours before sunrise a light went out in an upper chamber of Henry Tudor's old palace, and by that men knew that the indomitable old woman who would not take to her bed despite all the urging of the 'little man' had died sitting upright in her chair. In the courtyard below, Sir Robert Carey, late Warden of the Middle March, saw the light go out and knew it for the signal he had been waiting on for weeks. The first of many horses that had been standing saddled ready for this hour was led out, and he mounted and took the road for London and the north. By evening of the same day he was at Doncaster, and by evening of the 26th at his own house, Widdrington in Northumberland. The next morning at Norham Castle on the road to Edinburgh he sustained a bad fall, with injuries to the head and a broken thumb. Yet though the king had gone to bed, it was not yet midnight of the 27th when Sir Robert dismounted stiffly in the courtyard of Holyrood House, muttered in a dazed voice the password to the archer of the guard, and reeled upstairs nursing his injured hand to rouse James Stuart from the first of his sleep and hail him King of England.

Just under four hundred miles in about sixty-six hours was something of a record, perhaps unbeaten since the days of the Roman *cursus publicus*. In Henry VIII's time men had marvelled that a message could be carried from Greenwich to Stirling (408 miles) in six days and six nights.

CHAPTER EIGHT

Stuart Times

> 'I give unto Alexander Smith my second sonne one
> gray mare called Long-legs and the filly which was
> bred under her and one bay mare which is called
> Thickeknee and the stoned horse coming 3 yeares old
> and the one half of the mare under which he was bred.'
> Will of Barnard Smith, Camshouse, Wensleydale,
>   1672.

IN 1603 the crown of England became united with that of Scotland.
No one lamented the old queen's death more keenly than a certain
community composed partly of her subjects and partly of those of the
neighbouring realm. There had always been people who could not make
a living without the Border. Indeed, there had always been people who
could not even stay alive without it, ever since the times when the
losing side in the perpetual faction fight between the rival dynasties of
Northumbria had made a habit of taking refuge at the Scottish court, and
claimants for the Crown of Scone down on their luck, like Malcolm, sat
it out among the Sassenachs waiting for better times. By now this sort
of thing had descended in the social scale. But when the bell tolled in
1603, Eliots and Armstrongs, Nicholsons and Heslops, even some of the
less prosperous scions of the name of Percy and Douglas, looked at each
other with the unspoken question: what should they do now, without
the Border?

They were soon to find out. King James had not been on the throne two
years before publishing a proclamation *in both realms*, enjoining all the
dwellers in the Middle March, the Debatable Land between Cheviot
and Irthing, in Tevidale, Redesdale, Bewcastledale, Wilgavey, Gilsland,
Esk, Tynedale, Ewsdale and Annandale, to put aside their bills and
bows, their hagbuts and dags, their sallets and jacks; worse than that,
they were forbidden to own a horse, mare or gelding above the value of
50*s.* sterling or £30 Scots. We have seen and shall see later in this
chapter what sort of a horse one could buy for 50*s.* at that time, and of
course no true Redesdaler ever actually *paid* that much for a horse. Yet
they had a knack of acquiring horses which they sold for much more than
that. The king argued logically if uncharitably that no one in those parts

with a fifty-shilling mare could have come by her honestly. But more than that, he knew as well as anybody that without horses of a certain quality the Border way of life, as it had been for countless generations, could not be carried on. This was the beginning of the end: not all at once, but slowly and surely, the Borderers were reduced to shepherding for a living. Only the recurrent wars of Commonwealth and Covenant allowed, for a time, a Borderer who was at odds with his neighbour to 'make his cows to walk' as the saying went. The rank-riders and the moss-troopers, in their inimitable way, had contributed much to light-horse breeding in both realms, providing a valuable exchange of blood on either side of the Border. And now this work was to be carried on, on a smaller and meaner, but still not negligible scale, by the tinklers and the drovers.

At the furthest end of King James's jurisdiction lay the islands of Shetland, where public business had only just ceased to be transacted in Norwegian, and where customary law was still partly after the use of Edinburgh and partly after that of Bergen. In the Court Book of Scalloway the proceedings for the year 1604 are among the earliest to be engrossed in English (of a sort). One action, for the unlawful seizure, or 'wrongeous gripster' of a plaintiff's goods and stock, concerns twenty-one horses and mares. These words, when used unqualified in Scalloway courts, mean Shetland ponies: if some other kind of horse is meant, then the kind of foreign horse is specified.[1] The valuation in this case is in Dutch gulden, because the only currency that circulated in the islands was that brought in by the Dutch fishermen and herring-brokers. It works out, per head, at 288s. Scots or 24s. sterling. Of course this is not the market price but a claim for restitution, and the plaintiff's lawyer pitched it as high as he reasonably could. The 'foud' or agent of Earl Patrick Stewart the landlord, who tried the case, let the valuation stand because in addition to the civil damages there was a criminal fine involved, proportionate to the value of the stock wrongeously griped; and Earl Patrick was determined to wring the uttermost farthing from his earldom, which was more or less a private estate. Still, the valuation must bear some not too distant relationship to the market price.

A closer valuation of hill-bred stock, taken from an inventory of goods (1622) in the estate of Adam Midleham of Gill, near Aysgarth in Wensleydale, concerns 'Two bay and 11 gray mares, and one bay nag and one gray mare, one sanded [bay-dun] mare, one gray nagge, one young gray mare and one gray cold stag [yearling colt]'. The first lot are valued at £40 for the thirteen, or about £3 1s. 7d. each, and the second at £8 6s. 8d. for the six, or £1 13s. 4d. a head. There was no estate duty then, so there is no 'writing-down' to be discounted.

The stag which is not a deer we have met before, in Lincolnshire nearly a hundred years before. The colours, predominantly bay and

[1] Such as 'ane donewe kurseour naig, gangand in the Yle of Foulay' mentioned in the court proceedings of 5th July the same year.

grey, accord well with the pattern of the Flodden inventory of Dales horses. So do the two nags. 'Nag' now becomes much commoner in English usage. It first occurs in English in 1400, according to the dictionaries. The word was unknown to Chaucer. It means a riding horse, but not a 'great horse'. In other words, it can be either a palfrey or a rouncy, according to the old terminology. Farm workers, until the tractor age, preserved this distinction with admirable clarity in most parts of England, as they would talk of the plough-horse or cart-horse stables, on one side of the yard, and the 'nag-stables', where the saddle-horses were kept, on the other. It is a modern urban vulgarism born of ignorance to refer to a Shire horse as a nag. The word is actually a childish diminutive of Nicholas, though it has long gone out of use in this sense.

Which brings us to the hobby. 'Hobby' first occurs in Scotland and was written and pronounced hobyn, in 1375. John Barbour uses it to describe the Irish horses at the battle of Carrickfergus, but this battle occurred nearly seventy-five years before the time when he wrote. Hobyn and Robin are both Scottish diminutives of Robert. The English pet-name for Robert at the same period was Dobbin, Dobyn. It is now a child's name for a cart-horse or a farm-horse, and the image conjured up by it is that of a Clydesdale or a Shire. But it is well known that the language of children is intensely conservative and often reflects the colloquial English of the Middle Ages. Hobby and dobbin are the same thing because the farm-horse or cart-horse and the pony were once the same thing.

During the sixteenth and seventeenth centuries it became customary for the English to refer to the Shetland as the 'Scotch hobby' and the Connemara pony as the 'Irish hobby'. The military term in the late Middle Ages for light horseman was 'hobilars', i.e. soldiers mounted on hobbies, who did not wear armour but either buff leather or quilted jackets; Barbour uses the term to mean mounted archers in particular, but the moss-troopers of the intermittent Border war were also typical hobilars. Richard Head, Anglo-Irishman and *very* minor Restoration playwright, describes his return from England to Ireland in 1660 thus: Having landed from the Dublin packet he was invited to board the 'Ringsend coach, as he called it, it was wheelbarrow fashion only it had two wheels not much bigger than a large Cheshire cheese'—almost the exact words of Birt describing, with illustrations, an Inverness country cart a hundred years later, and quoted below. 'The horse that drew this princely pygmy chariot I at first mistook for an overgrown mastiff, but viewing him narrowly found him the extract [by his shape] of a Scotch hobby. Well, up I mounted . . .'

There is a splendidly horsy picture in Ben Jonson's *Bartholomew Fair*, 1614, of low life at the autumn horse fair of West Smithfield. At this time, in addition to the weekly Friday horse-fair, there was a fort-night of solid horse-coping which did not move its venue to Barnet, just clear of the north London suburbs, until 1853. Jonson's character

Knockem, described as a 'horse-courser', is not really a dealer on his own account but a dealer's groom or 'runner-up', the lowest kind of nagsman who, when sober, would sometimes also ride out the horse for sale in front of the buyer. He was also a highly self-satisfied amateur vet. Here are some samples of his talk which illustrate the Jacobean use of the words 'hobby' and 'nag':

Waspe : You are in Smithfield, you may fit yourself with a fine easy-going street nag, for your saddle, again Michaelmas term, do: has he ne'er a little odd cart for you to make a caroch on, in the country, with four pied hobby-horses?

Dan Jordan Knockem (a Smithfield horse-dealer) : Body o' me! She has the mallenders, the scratches, the crown scab, and the quitter bone in t'other leg.

Ursula (the roast-pig woman, who has scalded her leg) : Oh, the pox! Why do you put me in mind of my leg thus, to make it prick and shoot? Would you have me in the hospital afore my time?

Knockem : Patience, Urse, take a good heart, tis but a blister as big as a wind-gall. I'll take it away with the white of an egg, a little honey and hog's grease and have thy pasterns well rol'd,[1] *and thou shalt pace again by tomorrow.*

Northern (a clothier, from the north country) : I'll nae mair, I'll nae mair, the ale's too mighty!

Knockem (about as drunk as Northern) : How now, my galloway nag! The staggers, ha? Give him a slit in the forehead. Chear up, man. A needle and thread to stitch his ears. I'd cure him now, an I had it, with a little butter and garlic, long pepper and grains. Where's my horn? I'll give him a mash presently shall take away his dizziness.

Here enters the galloway. It is worth a round of applause. Jonson, as we see here, thought of it as something characteristic of the north country. As a matter of fact this is not its *première* on the English stage. It figures in Shakespeare's *2 Henry IV*, Act II, where again, as 'galloway nag', it is used mockingly of a little man. So it is small, and comes from the north country. What else? There are two lines in Michael Drayton's *Polyolbion*:

> As much upon his match the Western horseman lays
> As the rank-riding Scots upon their galloways.

I do not think this means that the Scots raced and betted heavily on galloways. More likely it is a pun, rank-riding Scots being moss-troopers and their ponies heavily laden, on the outward journey with rations and ammunition, and on the return with loot. Fynes Moryson in 1617, talking of Oldenburg in Germany, says that the wagons travelling over Lüneburg Heath were drawn by 'very little horses, like to the galloway nags of Scotland'. This might seem conclusive evidence that the galloway, as its name implies, is of Scottish origin. But there is a shade of doubt, because not for another hundred years, until 1706, does any Scottish author refer to a galloway *horse*. In earlier Scottish authors, where Galloway does not actually mean the province of that name, it

---

[1] Bandaged.

means the men from that province. The shade of doubt is slightly deepened by the fact that English people seem to have been quite unable to distinguish, around 1600, between the two Gaelic words now Anglicized as Galloway and Galway. The map of Ireland in Norden's atlas of 1607 spells both the bay and the town of Galway as 'Galloway', and Fynes Moryson spells both indifferently 'Galway' and 'Galloway' on the same page of his *Itinerary*. There was moreover a stretch of road in north Lancashire, long since disused, which appears in old documents as 'Galwathgait', though plainly it is the road to Galloway, not to Galway. We cannot disregard the possibility that the galloway, in the mouths of some Englishmen at least, was the Galway pony and not the local breed of south-west Scotland.

Another Gaelic word, also signifying, in practice if not in actual meaning, a pony, now became current in English. In 1598, the year when *2 Henry IV* was first staged, Edmund Spenser wrote *A View of the Present State of Ireland*. Deploring the fact that the regulations about sale in market overt, which we have noted were brought into force here by Queen Mary, did not apply in Ireland, he says that 'if any one of them have stollen a cowe or a garron' they can dispose of it easily, the more so as stock on commons were not branded as they were in England. In the same work, incidentally, is a most interesting passage on Irish horsemanship—'Never sawe a more comely horseman than the Irish man, nor that cometh on more bravely in his charge'—and mentioning Irish accoutrements, strange to him but familiar to us both from modern experience and from what we have read above about Irish saddlery in Giraldus and in the biography of Richard II: some innovations (from Spain?) and some relics of the late Bronze and early Iron Ages: ' . . . his stronge brasse bit, his sliding reins, his shaunkpillion without stirrops . . .' The brass bit was the pre-Norman (indeed pre-Roman) snaffle. The sliding reins might be a running martingale but more probably they were double reins, not sewn to the snaffle-rings but passing through them in one piece so that when used together they allowed considerable play; but if the rider let go the upper loop and took up the slack of the lower rein, the upper one slid up the neck till it came to rest behind the ears, resulting in a strong gag action. The shaunk-pillion is a pilch.

The word garron is not now current in Ireland, only in Scottish Gaelic. It means a gelding (*gearran*).

How familiar were these five authors with the meanings of the above words in the countries where they, and the animals they stood for, originated? Drayton and Shakespeare had never been out of England, the latter probably never north of the Trent. Jonson had been to Scotland—once—never to Ireland; Spenser to Ireland but not to Scotland. Moryson had been everywhere. This is what he has to say about the Irish hobbies, which according to him consumed the whole of what little hay the Irish made. 'Their horses called hobbies are much commended for their ambling pace and beauty: but Ireland yields but few horses for service in war and the said hobbies are much inferior to our geldings in strength to endure long journeys being bred in the soft fenny ground of Ireland are soon lamed when they are brought into England.' Elizabethan travellers had not been of this opinion. Holinshed's *Chronicles*, 1577 edition, contains this passage about Irish horses: 'The nag or hacknie is very good for travelling, albeit others report the contrary, and if he be broken accordingly, you shall have a little tit that will travel all day without bait.' Why does Holinshed say hackney, whereas all others classify the Irish light horse as an ambling palfrey type? Either the term was losing its strict meaning in terms of gait (unlikely, to judge by other authors of the same period) or else the clue lies in the words 'broken accordingly'. Presumably it could be trained to trot by the use of diagonal hobbles, as pacers are artificially produced now from trotting stock by training in parallel hobbles. When Moryson mentions service in war he means trotting horses, since this was the requirement laid down in the laws of Henry VIII and Elizabeth concerning the breeding of remounts.

What did Holinshed mean by a tit? He meant what north Yorkshiremen mean now. Before the modern pattern of horse breeding became set, some time in the eighteenth century, North Riding people distinguished broadly between two kinds of small horse: the chapman horse, a short-legged animal with a long, strong body, probably the best packhorse ever seen in Britain, and the galloway, a 'nag' or saddle-horse of local origin that would also go in harness. The chapman horse as such has gone, or rather it has grown up into the Cleveland Bay. But country people of the older generation in Cleveland call anything about fifteen hands a galloway, from the undersized thoroughbred, for whose benefit special 'galloway races' were organized at York and Thirsk from the reign of George I onwards, to the western cow-ponies and juvenile jumpers they see on television. To them a light, fast galloway is a tit, as it was in the eighteenth century and probably much earlier. It must have a turn of speed and a dash of breeding, what old Blundeville called a 'pretty fine horse'. We have met this word before. It is the old Norse adjective *teitr*, meaning, when applied to horses, fresh and gay. Meaning, when applied to men, 'market-fresh'.

The conception of a *small* trotting horse does not seem to have entered much into the Jacobean, and still less into the Elizabethan, scheme of things. To illustrate this it is best to go back to 1565, when Blundeville brought out his book *The Fowre Cheifest Ofyces Belonging to an Horseman*. Only the section on breeding need concern us here, because nothing comparable to it was written in the following century. Blundeville's book is not only concerned with the 'breed of horses for service in war' which so occupied the minds of Tudor governments (he gives a recipe for this, by putting the tallest native mares to Neapolitan stallions, which is no doubt what Henry VIII was after), but also deals with racehorses, hunters and 'fine ambling horses to travaile by the way'. Here is what he has to say about the last-named:

How to Breed Amblers. 'If any man seke to have a race of fine ambling horses to travaile by the way, then I would wish his stallion to be either a fayre Jennet of Spayne or at the least a bastard Jennet, or else a fayre Irish ambling hobby, and the mare to be also either a bastard Jennet bred here in this realm, having an ambling pace, or else some other of our ambling mares so that she be fayre and well proporcioned.'

The Irish Hobby, 'The Iryshe Hobby is a pretty fine hors, haveing a good Head, and a body indifferently well proporcioned, saving that

23. Irish chief, his pony and horseboy, from Derricke's *Image of Ireland*, 1581.

many of them be slender and thin buttocked, they be tender mouthed, nimble, light, pleasant and apt to be taught and for the most part they be amblers and therefore very meet for the saddle and to travel by the way, yea and the Iryshe men both with darts and light spears do use to skirmish with them in the field. And many of them do prove to that use very well, by means they be so light and swift; notwithstanding I take them to be very neashe and tender to keep, and also to be somewhat skittish and fearfull, partlye perhaps by nature and partly for lack of good breaking at firste.'

The Jennet of Spayne. As there has been from time to time some considerable linguistic confusion about this animal it will be as well, early on, to define the origin and meaning of the term. It was in the beginning the Greek word γυμνήτης, meaning a light-armed soldier. In the army of the Byzantine Empire, which owned the provinces of Africa that later became the Barbary States facing Spain, some of these auxiliary troops were Berbers, and from *gymnetes* a Berber word *zenetes* was derived. The Moslem conquest of Spain was the work of Arab generals and Berber other ranks, chiefly mounted archers, and the Christian Spaniards adopted the word *jineta*, meaning horsemanship of the flashy North African kind as displayed in the *razzia*, and *jinete* for a light horseman and hence for the sort of horse he rode—in English parlance a hobilar and a hobby. The latter meaning, however, is not the more usual one and did not for long prevail. The fact, however, that a Spanish verb *jinetear* means 'to parade on horseback, to practise *haute école*', etc., must signify that the *jinete* was held in some esteem. In parts of Spanish America *jinetear* means 'to break horses'.

The modern Spanish term for a pony is *jaca*, which is none other than the medieval English hakenay, curtailed (*j* in Spanish is pronounced approximately like English *h*). The native Spanish breeds of pony all come from the north-western provinces of Galicia and Navarre, and another Spanish word for pony is *Asturión*, from the province of Asturias also in the same northern region. Now remember that on Hadrian's Wall there were two regiments of Iberian cavalry from Asturias. But throughout history the regions of Galicia, Navarre and Asturias have been those most accessible by sea from Britain and Ireland and *vice versa*. One of the earliest human migration routes by sea (that of the Bronze-Age Beaker People who built Stonehenge) leads from the Biscay coast to the west coast of the British Isles. (Map 3.)

Why the same word was adapted in English as *jennet* and *hinny* (fairly close approximation to the first two syllables of *jinete*, phonetically) to mean the offspring of a stallion and she-donkey will perhaps never be known. But it may be a joke, like the old slang phrase for a donkey 'Jerusalem pony'; or it may be a trade term invented specially for the purpose of blinding the customer with science, much as the modern fishmonger in defiance of ichthyology labels his skinned conger eel 'rock salmon' to make it more acceptable to the suburban housewife. 'Why this ain't no common mule, lady. It's a genuine jennet like what they 'ave in Spain. Hinny the Dons call 'em.'

Blundeville described the Jennet of Spayne thus: 'Finely made, both head, body and legges, and very seemely to the eye, saving that his buttockes bee somewhat slender, and for his fine making, lightness and swiftness withal he is very much esteemed, and especially of noble men, as Camerarius sayeth which Oppian also affirmeth, saying that the Jennet in swiftness passeth the Parthians and all other horses whatsoever they be, even so far as the Egle excedeth all other birds in the aire but therewith he saith that they be but smal of stature, of small strength and of smal corage, all which things seem to agree very well with those Jennets that be brought hither into England unless it be the last poynt. For I have haerd some of the Spaniards set such praise on their Jennets corage, as they have not letted to report that they have carried their riders out of the fields, I cannot tell how many miles after that the Jennets themselves have been shotte clene through the bodies with harquebushes. Which report I have hard to be true by divers of our owne souldiers, whyche if it be trueth indede, it doeth the better counter-availe their smal stature and little strength, which is manifest to all mens eyes that do behold them . . . and as from their foleage unto their full age they be very obedient and tractable, so from thenceforth they fare to be curste and frowarde. . . . The pace of the Jennet is neyther trotte nor amble, but a comelye kinde of goynge like the Turke.' By Turke he means Arab, of whose 'travelynge pace' he says it 'is neither Amble, Racke, not Trotte, but a certaine kind of easy trayne'. There is only one possibility left: the 'easy trayne' of the Jennet and the Turke must be a tripple.

It is pretty clear, from the general tenor of Blundeville's work, that he regarded the Irish hobby as the poor man's *ginete*. The order of

24. English palfreys of Blundeville's time (1558).

preference, for a potential dam of palfreys, is a jennet of Spayne, a half-bred mare by a jennet of Spayne, an Irish hobby mare (not easily to be met with in England then) or one of the majority of English country-bred mares which paced. Throughout his work on breeding Blundeville refers to a mysterious body known as 'our mares'. For instance, in the military remount passage he recommends first Flanders mares, because they trot, second those of 'our mares' which are of high stature, and trot 'as *some* of our mares do'. Again, on the breeding of 'swift runners' he recommends a Barb or 'Turk' stallion, or a stallion partly of this stock, and one of 'our mares'. But the latter is to be chosen 'so high as may be' implying that the mares he had in mind were for the most part smaller than the fourteen- or fifteen-hand oriental stallions. The overwhelming impression left by Blundeville is that the great majority of English country-bred horses in his time were under fourteen hands and natural pacers or amblers. This was still true, but decreasingly so, in the age of James I.

In the household account books of that monarch, which are now at Dun Mhuire, Killiney, Co. Dublin, is a catalogue of a present from James I to Philip III of Spain, consisting entirely of clothes, livestock and sporting guns; it includes ten horses, 'of which fowre amling, and fowre amling mares'. The spelling is faintly suggestive of some Scottish official. From what we have seen, sending ambling horses to Spain was coals to Newcastle. Of the numerous Spanish breeds at that time, only the famous Andalusian, ancestor of such diverse breeds as the Lipizzaner and the Welsh Cob today, was a natural trotter. This present was loaded in the ship *Peregrine*, of Ipswich, in 1614.

Commissioned portraits of individual horses, sometimes in hand but more commonly ridden by the owner, become more numerous as the seventeenth century advances. They are of little interest for our purpose, since in the nature of things they portray the owner's most expensive equine possession, either of Great Horse or of 'gentil', which means in practice oriental, stock. Country-bred horses appear only incidentally in the background, either working in the fields or travelling the road, of landscapes. Since 'blasted heaths' were not popular as a landscape subject, ponies grazing on commons—'marginal land' in the modern phrase—only turn up as a lucky accident.

Utility horses only figure in utility pictures, such as illuminated estate maps, which still had to make sense to people who could not read. One such shows ponies and other animals grazing in a little wood called 'Stocks Close, parcel of Pickwood Farm', near Shaftesbury in Wiltshire. This farm and the adjacent lands of Aldbourne Chase and Lye Plain once belonged to the Duchy of Lancaster, and in 1607 the duchy went to law with two farmers, the brothers Waldron, on some question of grazing rights arising out of the partial enclosure of the Chase and Plain.

Attached to the papers was a beautiful large-scale coloured 'Plotte' or map, done by the duchy surveyor who, in addition to marking every separate enclosure and almost every tree, and attaching little labels with such legends as 'this coppice is called Hart Hooke & the tenants have ye grazing but ye Duchy hath ye conies therein', drew in little figures of domestic animals. The style is primitive but quite realistic, and there is no doubt at all that this is just what the stock of small farmers in the reign of James I looked like (P41).

The ponies that we now call New Forest, because they are confined to that forest, were once spread over the whole of central southern England in a continuous belt of common and waste land from the south coast to the Thames valley. It was not until this process of enclosure began to accelerate, in the reign of James I, that the shrinkage of rough grazing really began. The picture which we see in Stocks Close is not a flattering one, but, on the other hand, it is not an unhandsome one. Taking them all in all, these are a set of ancestors of which no one need be ashamed.

It does seem probable that when an exceptional case arises, and the owner has some reason to commission a picture of a horse that owes its origin entirely to 'our mares', more or less subtle measures are taken to suggest that it is really something much more stately and distinguished. It would have been unthinkable for Van Dyke to paint Charles I as

Munnings painted George V on his favourite shooting pony Jock, rendering with the same affectionate realism the old gentleman and the old garron.

Such a subtle transformation has taken place in at least one equestrian portrait of Queen Elizabeth I. We remember her best, and shall remember her for ever, just as we shall remember Winston Churchill, in the act of telling us what to do in a crisis which in the event never happened at all. 'I think foul scorn that any Prince of Christendom should dare to invade the borders of my realm; to which, rather than any dishonour shall grow by me, I myself will be your general. But I do assure you I do not desire to live to distrust my faithful and loving people. Let tyrants fear. I have always so behaved myself that under God I have placed the chiefest strength and safeguard in the loyal hearts and goodwill of my subjects, and therefore am I come amongst you as you see . . . ' As they saw: scrawny, painted, bewigged, the wrong side of fifty, yet emitting that mysterious electric charm which if present in sovereigns and platoon commanders will draw men after them into battle, but without which they will not be followed into a cocktail party; riding side-saddle on a comfortable white palfrey, a steady animal lent by the Cecils and deliberately chosen because it would stand when asked and because it was of a convenient height if the queen wished to converse a little with some captain of a foot company as he stood sword in hand at the head of his pikemen or arquebusiers.[1] From such a rostrum was the famous Tilbury oration delivered, but the official artists must have a horse of a stature to fit the heroic words. All of the engravings derived from the official picture show the queen on a white war-horse or a white courser of state. Only in the picture of her in Gaywood church at King's Lynn, stiff and primitive but true to life in its unsophisticated way, can we see her mount for what it really was, a palfrey like the palfreys ridden by her small staff, which consisted only of the portly, ageing Captain General, Robert Dudley, and the handsome young Master of the Horse, Robert Devereaux, Earl of Essex. The horse was known to its owners as 'Tilbury' for ever after, and when they came to have its portrait painted (it can still be seen at Hatfield House) attendants were very carefully excluded from the foreground, nor is there any measurable object in the foreground from which its size could be deduced.

Thirty years before, when Robert Dudley was himself a handsome young man of twenty-six, he had been Master of the Horse, and at the accession progress of the queen through London had followed her coach leading her 'Palfrey of State'. This was a concession to femininity;

[1] We think also that she must have borne in mind the conduct of her ancestor Edward III before Cressy, reported thus by Froissart: 'The king was mounted on a small palfrey, having a white wand in his hand, and attended by his two marshals. In this manner he rode at a foot's pace through all the ranks, encouraging his army and entreating that they would guard his honour and defend his right; so sweetly and with such a cheerful countenance did he speak that all who had before been dispirited were directly comforted by hearing him.'

25. James I, hawking.

kings on such occasions had a 'Courser of State', but it was difficult to
find coursers that would carry a side-saddle.

James I was almost certainly the last British monarch to ride a palfrey
in public on state occasions. After him, Charles I and every subsequent
king down to William III rode Neapolitan chargers. This breed was
available in James I's time, but its associations were strictly military.
James was a pacifist, not on moral grounds but for the excellent practical
reason that the sight of a drawn sword made him feel queer. He was not
in the habit of reviewing troops either, since this was almost certain to
occasion the distressing sight. But he was very fond of hunting (another
blow to the Jorrocks dictum) and had to progress about the realm quite
as often as those who preceded him on the throne. The best-known
picture of him hunting (in the second edition of Turberville's *Noble*

Art) shows him on a palfrey that looks as if it was out of one of 'our mares'.

Sometimes the law is very helpful in providing us with a written picture of stockbreeding affairs at a given place and time, if only because it compels people who are normally strangers, if not enemies, to pen and ink, to set down certain details in a certain set form. We have already seen some of the effects of 2 & 3 Philip and Mary, c. 7, and 31 Elizabeth, c. 12, as they affected sixteenth-century breeders and as they affect people today. In the little west Yorkshire village of Adwalton, a fair, unlicensed and unsupervised, had been held time out of mind for the

26. Subjects of James I, hunting.

sale of horses. It became, over the years, a notable resort of horse-thieves and their fences, so much so that in 1577 Queen Elizabeth granted a charter to one John Brooke, his heirs and assigns for ever, to hold the said fair, take tolls therefrom, and render to the Exchequer an annual consideration of twenty-six shillings and eightpence. It would thus be in someone's interest to control the proceedings and record all transactions at Adwalton, and cost the Crown nothing in official salaries.

Normally the register of transactions would have been preserved for only about a year after each fair, but by great good fortune two leaves for the Whitsun fair of 1631 were preserved in Viscount Allendale's muniment room at Bretton Park, near Wakefield. In 1927 this document was printed by Mr Wilfrid Robertshaw in the *Bradford Antiquary*; it is long since out of print and it is by the kindness of Mr Robertshaw himself that we are able to summarize the information from his personal copy of the paper, which was very appropriately illustrated by a repro-duction of Rowlandson's water-colour 'The Horse Fair', at that time in the possession of the novelist and connoisseur, the late Desmond Coke. This was painted at Southampton about 1777, but it shows the pro-cedure of toll-taking and registration taking place properly as laid down by the Acts of 1555 and 1589. Southampton fair, by the way, must have been a great outlet for New Forest breeders, but so far we have failed to turn up any old documents relating thereto. As the Acts required the address and calling of the vendor to be stated, it would be easy to pick out the New Forest commoners from any Southampton toll record, and we take the opportunity to request any reader who may know of any document relating to this fair to communicate with us.

The record of one hundred separate transactions begins as follows:

THE FOURTH FFAIRE OR MARKETT HOLDEN ATT ADWALTON THE SECOND DAYE OF JUNE 1631

1 William Wager of Badsworth in co. York Husbandman sold one blacke fillie slitt in both eares trots unto John Birrie of Bingley parishe co. aforesaid husbandman price xlij*s* Edward Tongkinson of Pontefract avowcher

2 John Lewis of Barmbrough in co. York chapman sold one sandye fillie with a white starre trots unto Robert Barrett of Kildwick parishe in co. York price 1*s* vi*d*
John Abson of the same avowcher

3 John Lewis aforesaid sould one browne fillie with a white starre trots unto John Preston within the parische of Longpreston co. York price iij*li* iiij*s*
John Abson aforesaid avowcher

4 Richard Oxley of Harlington in co. York chapman sold one gray fillie with a white starre trots unto Wm. Dearnillye in co. Derbye price iiij*li* iiij*s*
John Abson aforesaid avowcher

5 Richard Oxley aforesaid sould one bay fillie with a starre and a snip trots unto John Whitticars of Rosendale co. Lancaster price iij*li* xix*s*
John Abson aforesaid avowcher

6 Richard Oxley aforesaid sould one browne bay fillie with a white starre trots unto Samuell Atkinson parishe of Skipton in co. York price iij*li* iiij*s*
John Abson aforesaid avowcher

7 Richard Oxley aforesaid sould one sad bay maire trots unto John Atkinson of Kildwicke parische in co. York price iij*li* xviij*s*
John Abson aforesaid avowcher

8 John Lewis aforesaid sould one bay fillie trots unto Wm. Kinge of Thorpe in Craven in co. York price iij*li* iij*s*
Edward Tyas aforesaid avowcher

9 John Bladworth of Thorne in co. York chapman sold one blacke fillie trots unto Wm. Smyth of Steeton in co. aforesaid price iij*li* iij*s* iiij*d*
Jervice Thornborough of Snayth avowcher

It will be seen that the descriptions combine the details given in the Flodden requisition and the Falkirk *Rotulus Equorum*, but unlike them this is a commercial record and therefore the prices are true market prices and not artificial legal assessments.

The resemblance in terminology to the Flodden roll is striking, when we consider that more than a century had passed. But the area where the horses were bred lay not very far to the south of Wensleydale where the bulk of the Jervaulx tenants lived, and the two documents agree in not particularizing the size of animals, not even in the rough sorting into *dextrarii* and *runcini* to be found in the Falkirk roll. The reason in each case is the same: all the animals sold were the common horses of the countryside and they varied but little in height; in fact, they were all Dales galloways.

In all on this day 101 animals were sold, but only 91 for cash. The remaining five deals were swaps, mostly level swaps. Very little was given 'to boot'; in one case only sixpence, a mere luck-penny, but no doubt enough to make both parties to the deal comfortably drunk in those happy days.

Farmers comprise the biggest single group in the fifty-three vendors. Ten husbandmen, that is small and middling farmers, more like the Jervaulx tenants, some of whom were their ancestors, and five yeomen or more substantial farmers, often freeholders like Chaucer's Franklin. Next come ten chapmen or travelling merchants. No one is described in the register as a professional horse-dealer, but it is clear that the chapmen acted in this capacity. It was a chapman's horse, sold by Richard Rudde of Milnrowe in Lancashire, which made the top price of £7 3s. 3d. on this day (an iron-grey gelding that racked and trotted), and between them the ten chapmen sold more than half the animals on offer. John Lewis of Barmbrough alone sold fifteen, and Richard Oxley of Harlington sold fourteen. There were nine clothiers (this was and is a wool-manufacturing district) and five vendors in the trades ancillary to clothmaking: a shereman, a dyer, a mercer, a cardmaker and a taylor. Also three carpenters, three tanners, two ropers, and one each of the following: blacksmith, shoemaker, butcher, roughmason, ironfounder and skinner. It is impossible to classify these last trades, except the ironfounder, as either urban or rural, since they can be either; but it will be seen that all of them, under seventeenth-century conditions, required pack-horses to carry on their business. Therefore when a horse is not specifically called a 'nag' (saddle-horse) it is likely to be a pack-horse.

It was too early in the year to sell weaned foals, so the colts and fillies sold at the lowest prices are probably yearlings. Two fillies went for 6s. 8d. each. The preponderance of mares and fillies over geldings, and still more so over colts and stallions, is marked. The total cash turnover was nearly £280, an average price of £3 1s. 4d. We may suppose that these represented fair prices for a good class of utility horse, because when twenty years later the Commonwealth commissioners valued the royal Thoroughbred stud at Tutbury the average price of bloodstock there was only twice the top price at Adwalton—£14 3s. against £7 3s. The royal mares and youngsters were assessed at anything from £10 to £35.

In the matter of coat-colours, the general similarity to the Flodden imprest roll is most striking. There are thirty-seven grey, iron grey or dapple grey; twenty-three bay or yellow bay or sad bay, six brown or bay-brown, fifteen black and five each of sorrel, dun or mouse-colour or dun-bay or sandy, and 'grissel' (a new term for roan, replacing the earlier 'liart'); three white and two skewbald called 'baybald'. The medieval term sorrel is in the process of being replaced by the modern term chestnut, as illustrated by the transitional form used in one case— 'chestnut sorrel'. We have the same low incidence of chestnut, dun and 'fancy' colours and the same combined predominance of black-brown-bay, modified by an epidemic of greyness which has not yet burnt itself out. The pattern is moving visibly towards the present-day standards of colour in the Dales pony, and also towards the uniform bay of the Cleveland, which was originally called 'the chapman horse'.

Among nags, the palfrey is on its way out, but not without a struggle. Eighty-nine per cent of these horses trotted, but twenty-five of them also racked. The ambler as such has gone from the scene, and there are twice as many dual-purpose palfrey-hackneys as there are specialized racking palfreys (twelve).

'Far' is still used for the off side. Brands where they occur are some-times so called, sometimes called 'burns' as in the Flodden roll; and nearly uniformly on the near shoulder—only one on the buttock. They consist, where described, of a single initial letter. There is a marked decline in ear-marking, but these marks are described in the same terms as in the Flodden roll. This probably indicates, taken in conjunction with the relative scarcity of brands, a decline in breeding on commons. But there had always been more enclosed land in the West Riding proper than in Wensleydale and Wharfedale.

Right from the beginning of coaching in England, in the fourteenth century, there had been isolated cases of the very largest animals put to the shafts and the traces. Side by side with the wagon teams in the Luttrell Psalter there is a magnificent illumination, a two-page spread, showing a coach and six. It antedates by some forty years the first *written* mention of the 'whirlicote', but it is a whirlicote, and a king-sized one. Space forbids our doing justice to the picture and therefore we do not reproduce it. The vehicle is what the travelling people of today call an 'open lot'; that is, it has a tunnel-shaped tilt, semi-rigid, on hoops. But it is of enormous length, in plan more like a timber-tug than a carriage, and the interesting thing from our point of view is the team. Instead of the miniature Punches which are drawing Sir Geoffrey's wagons on other pages, this team consists of large horses whose height can be judged by that of the outrider; they are of the stature, the con-formation and even of the colour of Sir Geoffrey's charger, which, fully barded and armed at all points, graces the frontispiece of the psalter. This was not a picture of the Luttrell family equipage. No such vehicle is mentioned in the knight's will, where it would certainly have been mentioned if that had been the case. There was perhaps not another like it in the country. Almost certainly it belonged to the king; to have devoted six expensive destriers to this purpose would have taxed even the considerable resources of Sir Geoffrey beyond their capacity. His principal esquire (a white-collar job—he had his own groom) would have maintained that this harness work would spoil them for the field or the tilt-yard. Again, in the 1512 inventory of the Northumberland establishment we have seen a team of seven great trotting horses (one spare and six-in-hand?) for the chariot.

But these were exceptional, and were to remain so until late in the seventeenth century. We show here (27) the funeral equipage of the second

The hearse of the righthonorable ROBERT: DEVOVREVX Earle of Essex

27. Funeral of the Earl of Essex.

Earl of Essex, who died in 1646 after commanding the parliamentary forces in the Civil War. Little of the conformation of the horses is visible under the trappings, but it is plain they are no bigger than the harvest team of the Luttrell estate three hundred years earlier. And this was no mean funeral. It was an old tradition, ending only with some conservative East End undertakers in the 1950's, to bring out the tallest (black if possible) horses for hearse work, and to equip them with plumes to make them look taller. This latter embellishment is of ancient Assyrian origin, and the horses which were actually buried with Scythian kings in the Iron Age wore just such plumes at the time of immolation. The Essex funeral, plumes and all, indicates the early Stuart standard of height for carriage horses.

There now occurred a second major revolution in the equestrian life of this country, on a scale to balance the revolution of 1066. Once again it concerned primarily the Great Horse, and once again it had secondary effects which reacted profoundly on the life of the Little Horse. The Civil War of the mid seventeenth century was the last war in which the cavalry arm of English forces was mounted on Great Horses, or the closest approximation to them that could be produced; throughout the conflict cavalrymen on both sides wore a considerable amount of armour of a type that had been discarded by European forces as the Thirty Years War in central Europe, which began in 1618, progressed. At the beginning, as the forces of king and parliament were both built up from scratch, there was a great shortage of suitable cavalry remounts, and there are horrible stories of landowners and tenants who put down all their foals and turned over their brood mares to the remount officers of one side or the other out of patriotism. As soon as it became clear that this war was not going to be 'over by Christmas', it also became clear that such measures would not do, and both sides began breeding and importing heavy horses. One of the reasons why the Parliament won was that its greatest strength lay in the region where heavy horses were produced: in Northampton, Bedford, Huntingdonshire (Cromwell's home county), Cambridgeshire, East Anglia. At least half the land-owners of Lincolnshire and east and north Yorkshire were for the Parliament also. Royalist strength was in the far north, Lancashire, the West Midlands, Wales and the west country, not areas which produced heavy horses in any number. Moreover the parliamentary forces con-trolled east coast ports where heavy horses could most conveniently be shipped in from the Low Countries. When the Civil War came to an end therefore there were large numbers of heavy horses to be absorbed somehow into the peaceful life of the country: and it was then very difficult to get Englishmen not actually on the point of starvation to eat horse.

Many historians of our larger breeds have noticed this fact; the latest of them, G. E. Evans, in his splendid saga of Suffolk horses and Suffolk ploughmen, *The Horse in the Furrow*, says that Suffolk was perhaps the first county to begin using heavy horses in the plough—perhaps as far back as Queen Elizabeth's time—but that the change-over from oxen was enormously speeded-up in the seventeenth century because 'the Great or military horse was being released [by the abandonment of armour] for what the farmers considered his proper use'.

As soon as the Civil Wars ended in 1651 the market was flooded with big horses, which began to replace the ox-team in front of the plough. But ploughing does not go on all the year round. Once having scrapped his ox-yokes every farmer who could afford it faced the heavy cost of re-tooling and adapted his wagons also for traction by heavy horses. The 1650's must have been a booming time for country harness-makers and for wainwrights.

Though the old order of things lingered on, in the north and the west, far into the eighteenth century (later than that on Exmoor), this second revolution was completed in less than thirty years. The Great Horse displaced not only the ox from the plough but the Little Horse from the wagon. How impossible it was to put the clock back is demonstrated by an episode from Monmouth's rebellion in 1685. During these last thirty years a new kind of stockbreeding had sprung up in the low-lying parts of Somerset, where colts of war-horse stock were bred on cheap marsh grazing; the farmers, perceiving that these big animals could be worked in draught very young, broke them to the traces at two and sold them 'up the country' at three and four. The six regiments of farm labourers and miners who constituted Monmouth's infantry did very well, under indifferent higher leadership, against the professionals of James II. They almost pulled off, at Sedgemoor, that most difficult of operations, a night attack in formation where every man was not familiar with his position and duties by long habit and arduous training. But Monmouth's cavalry, apart from his bodyguard of forty young gentlemen mounted on hunters, never looked like doing any good. Somebody in Monmouth's army had remembered that the colts on the marshes represented the third and fourth generation descendants of the Civil War chargers. They forgot that such chargers demanded a long course of training beginning at about five. The thousand cavalry horses of Monmouth's army would not stand fire at three years old: at worst, they panicked utterly at the flash of a pistol: at best, they could not be induced to close with the enemy, and Monmouth's mounted swordsmen could not get within striking distance. One of the volunteers in this engagement was a young man named Daniel Defoe. We shall hear what he has to say later on.

The most striking evidence of this revolution, pictorially, is to be found in a book published in the middle of Charles II's reign, 1674. The title is nothing to do with horses: it is Loggan's *Cantabrigia Illustrata*, primarily concerned with the architecture of the colleges. But the foregrounds of all the plates are full of little figures of people and horses. For instance, there are loose horses wandering about the front court of King's College, grazing in front of the famous chapel, presumably hacks belonging to the master and fellows. But the two general views of the town, panoramas of the east and west aspects, are the most striking. At one blow, it seems, the ordinary horses of the eastern counties have assumed modern stature and proportions. There are hare hunters returning home on hunters that would not be quite out of place in Cambridgeshire today. There are three formidable ladies side-saddling down the road on animals that might have come out of a mid-twentieth-century hiring stable. It is early in harvest time but the hay has been late, and in the middle distance is a cart full of loose hay, with the carter walking beside his team. From the height of his head in relation to the croups of the horses we can see that these are the size of modern cart-horses. In the foreground labourers are loading stooks of corn on to another wagon, but this is drawn by horses of the old capul stature. The figure of the labourer pitching sheaves into this wagon bears the same proportion to the team as the labourers in Geoffrey Luttrell's psalter. The only other horses of 'medieval' size are those, in some of the other plates, bearing panniers and ridden by female figures who are either market women or possibly bedmakers returning home with academic shirts to be laundered. There is also a country carrier's cart or diligence, with a tubular canvas tilt, being driven in the same way as Algernon Percy's chariot in 1512; that is, not from the box. The driver is just visible on the far side of the team, mounted on a thirteen-hand nag. The smaller horses have not yet quite disappeared, but the scene is utterly transformed from what it was in James I's time.

John Spreull, alias Bass John, an old Covenanter who had been present at the battles of Drumclog and Bothwell Brigg, lived from 1646 to 1722. He was much opposed to the Union of Scotland and England, and in 1706 published a book, now somewhat rare, entitled *The Accompt Current between England and Scotland Balanced.* He is the first Scottish author to mention galloways *as such.* 'Fine Scots galloway horses,' he says, 'many of which they covet and carry away into the borders of England.'

He had both ridden and dealt with them in his time. 'Search the custom books at Port Glasgow where I myself entered and payed [export] dutie for 50 or 52 mostlie all ston'd horses and maers which I shipped in a great ship of 400 Tunn for Surinam an Dutch Plantation [in the West Indies] for a brood of horses, and they were almost all Highland Galloways excepting some few. All which arrived safe with the other goods at the port, and an great price by sugars got from them which I forbear to mention, for such who ridicule one thing may ridicule all.

'And for certaintie the borderers on both Scots and English side came oft to Dunbarton fair and bought small droves of them when they carried up their cattle. And what gentleman did ever ride post in any or all of the roads of England and never met with a Scots galloway, if they have not, I am sure I have, and I have frequented the roads there both in Journeying and in posting, more than many, and still when I had some Scots galloway it was coveted and often bought from me. And I can aver as a truth that an Scots galloway of 40 or 50 shils ster. per piece will ride farder and kill and beat and founder an English Geldin of 20, 30, 40 or 50 £ ster. price. If they continue long I know them ride 40 or 50 miles a day; and then they are kept easilie and can feed upon the Orts of others. It's true English Geldins 30, 40, or 50 £ ster. price may run, and course, and do wonders, yet I shall kill them with a Scots Galloway of 40, 50 shil or 3 or 5 £ ster. price, through long fatigue and time, scarcity and wants incident.'

Notice he says run when he means gallop, as modern Americans do. Notice also that, like the Scots applicants for English import licences under Henry VIII, his standard of comparison for Scots horses is with English geldings. It would be interesting to know if the horse population of Surinam (Dutch Guiana) today shows any trace of the Highland galloway strain.

Daniel Defoe said in his *Tour Through Scotland*, Letter XXI: 'Besides the great number of sheep and runts [black cattle] which they breed here [in Galloway] they have the best breed of strong low horses in Britain, if not in Europe, which we call pads, and from whence we call *all* truss-strong small riding-horses Galloways; these horses are remarkable for being good pacers, strong, easy goers, hardy, gentle, well broke, and above all, that they never tire, and are very much bought up in England on that account.'

An interesting Scottish lease granted the year after William III died by the Earl of Breadalbane to one John MacNab comprises not only hill pasture but stock also, to be returned, or the value made up, to the landlord on expiry of lease, but the increase of the stud to belong to the lessee. The date was 11 June, and the stock comprised thirty mares either with foal at foot or in foal. There should have been a stallion but the landlord had none suitable and handed MacNab 100 merks Scots to buy a suitable one on his behalf. The value of the stock, in Scots merks, Scots pounds and English pounds, appear in the following table.

	M. Sc.	£ Sc.	£ Ster.
Stallion	100	66 13s. 4d.	5 11s. 1d.
Mares each	30	20	1 13s 4d.
Foals each	15	10	0 16s. 8d.

The same article, of average quality, would be worth today about the same sum in sterling as it was worth in the Scots currency of 1702, actually on the hill or at the nearest market. The price would rise steeply nowadays as soon as one had moved it by road or rail. The prices make sense in comparison with Bass John Spreull's rather combative statistics flung in the teeth of the English, and the only noticeable difference from present-day prices, *mutatis mutandis*, is that if one had a stallion today worth only £66 13s. 4d. one would not keep it entire.

CHAPTER NINE

Hanoverian Times

Then Peers took pride, in horsemanship to excell:
Newmarket's glory rose, as England's fell.

Alexander Pope.

DANIEL DEFOE's *Tour Through England and Wales,* mostly relating to
the year 1722, contains a great deal of information about English farming
and stockbreeding early in George I's reign, and much valuable matter
about horse-breeding in particular, but its evidence concerning pony-
breeding is completely negative by contrast to what he says about
Galloway. He calls Exmoor 'a filthy, barren ground. It gives indeed,
but a melancholy view, being a vast tract of barren and desolate lands'.
Somerset, he says, exports 'Colts, bred in great numbers in the moors,
and sold into the northern counties, where the horse copers, as they are
called, in Staffordshire and Leicestershire, buy them again, and sell
them for London for cart-horses and coach-horses, the breed being
very large.' By the last four words we see that the old order of things,
whereby draught-horses were invariably smaller than saddle-horses, had
gone for ever—it had gone within the last sixty or seventy years. But
how do we account for the large colts 'bred in the moors'? The fact is
that to Defoe and contemporary Londoners 'moor' meant marsh or fen,
not a heath. They thought of the swamp outside the old Moorgate.
He speaks indeed of the 'moors or marsh grounds which extend themselves up the rivers Perrot and Ivill into the heart of the country'. As
for London, we learn from him that West Smithfield horse market was
still, after more than six hundred years, being held every Friday as in
Fitzstephen's time; the number of animals turned over was very great
but the class of horse more restricted, only the more expensive sorts
being found there; Smithfield was no longer the place to go for a pack-
horse, a plough-mare or a hackney.

He has a revealing remark about the standards of height prevalent in
his day, when in the course of a report on the cloth towns of west
Yorkshire he describes the horse he rode there as 'not a very small pad;
of fourteen hands and a half high'. The pad is what the palfrey of earlier
ages had now generally come to be called; it was the traveller's horse

par excellence; as likely as not, it still paced where others trotted, since if often had to carry a side-saddle or a pillion for female passengers; it was still predominantly of native stock; and the 'very small' ones would be around thirteen hands. We also see by his account of the West Riding that at that place and time the demand for pack-horses was greater than it had ever been or was ever to be again in England. The textile trade had expanded enormously in the last generation but it was in the hands of a multitude of small masters whose stock was not counted by the complete wagon-load. Moreover it was carded and spun and woven and waulked and bleached in different establishments: some of the processes were put out as piece-work in the worker's own homes distributed in small parcels, and collected again, by pack-horses, a vast number of which threaded their way along the narrow tracks over the increasingly grimy moorlands and splashed across the increasingly polluted becks that ran into the Nidd and the Aire, the Wharfe and the Don. Of the descendants of Chaucer's Webber, Tapicer and Dyer Defore says 'every clothier must keep a horse, perhaps two, to fetch and carry for the use of his manufacture'. There was still no local network of carriage roads to carry this great traffic of raw materials, part-finished cloth and piece-goods, and perforce it went by pack. Even if some wholesalers sent it to London or to the ports by wagon, many of them supplied pedlars whose stock was retailed from panniers carried on a pony. The same was true of the Sheffield cutlers not far away.

This is not the place to retail Defoe's illuminating remarks about the increasing trade in large coach-horses, or in 'galloping horses' in the midlands and in north Yorkshire, except to note that in his time the majority of breeders did not record pedigrees 'for a succession of ages, as they say they do in Arabia and in Barbary . . . yet they will advance the price of a horse according to the reputation of the horse he came of'. That is to say, the price of young stock depended chiefly on the sire's performance (individual performance, not the known quality of his other progeny) and hardly at all on the dam or on the ancestry of the sire. It seems that the passion of the Celts and of the early English for genealogy had quite died out. No longer could a minstrel sit on the ale-bench interminably grinding out heroic pedigrees, while his spellbound audience was willing to stand him another horn of mead as often as he chose to pause and take breath between the stanzas in which Sceaf begat Scyld and Scyld begat Seaxnot who begat Hengest who begat Oisc *da capo*; all of which Defoe would find just as boring as you and I would. And so it was in the horse world also, except in a very narrow circle centring on Newmarket Heath.

The landowning class of the eighteenth century, that age of agricultural improvement, lost all interest in the breeding of native ponies because they were bewitched by that most marvellous of all inventions before the railway—the wonderful galloping machine which we call the Thoroughbred. Who can blame them? What we find less easy to forgive is the itch of these people and their dependants to improve the past as well as the present. For more than two thousand years there had been a class of monument, peculiar, so far as is known, to the lowland zone of Britain, in honour of the equestrian gods and heroes of past ages; these were the White Horses carved on the chalk hills such as Uffington in Berkshire, originally part of the cults of Epona, Rudiobus, Magog, etc. Landlords had regarded it as a pious duty to pay for and otherwise encourage the cleaning and repair of these, our oldest equine pictures, as the old Berkshire ballad says:

> The owld White Horse wants zettin to rights
> And the Squire hev promised good cheer.
> Zo we'll gee'un a scrape to kip 'un in zhape,
> And a'll last for many a year.

Perhaps the finest of these monuments was that at Westbury in Wiltshire, which up to 1778 seems to have preserved the lineaments of an Iron Age horse as seen by an Iron Age artist. But in that year Lord Abingdon's steward, charged with the duty of repair, found that it resembled a cart-horse; as well it might, for the Wiltshire cart-horse of the 1770's probably did resemble pretty closely a warrior's horse of two thousand years ago. So he had the outline filled in and a new image cut, facing the other way, with a profile along the approved Newmarket lines of his own day. Eighty years later the memory of the original monument was still strong enough for the white horse to be remodelled again, this time facing the right way, but no one could remember what the outlines of the original had been, so that the work of that conscientious meddlesome Philistine Mr Gee could not be quite undone, and is with us yet.

In speaking of various imported sires and their performance in competition with 'the gallopers of this country'—meaning Yorkshire—Defoe reveals two things. Firstly, like many people today, he believed in a 'native' English strain in the Thoroughbred, but, like the same people today, failed to realize that while this element undoubtedly existed in a sense, it owed its genetic, but not its environmental qualities, to a long series of imports stretching back with some interruptions to Roman times and perhaps earlier—all imports from the Near and Middle East, a very few direct but the most part via Italy and Spain. If we take his knowledge of horses to be that of the average well-informed Englishman of his day—and it was probably well above that average—we find that the distinction between the Spanish jennet proper, which was a pony from north-western Spain, and the Barb and the larger Andaluz, had vanished from the English memory. Defoe runs them all together as the 'Barb or Spanish jennet *from Cordova*'—which is in the south.

The Welsh part of Defoe's *Tour* is nothing like so comprehensive as the English. Yet he does say, of Montgomeryshire, that 'This county is noted for an excellent breed of Welsh horses, which, though not very

large, are exceeding valuable, and much esteem'd all over England.' As
to his standards of 'exceeding value', we can only say that the biggest
price he mentions as asked *and given* for a horse is 150 guineas (at
Penkridge fair in Staffordshire, which he reckons the greatest horse mart,
for quantity as for quality, in England). Farther north, in Teesdale, he
notices that the exigencies of Queen Anne's wars had led to a demand
for more substantial horses for senior officers' chargers at the expense
of speed and 'fineness'. This does nothing to temper his admiration for
the studs of north Yorkshire in general, but if the tendency he remarks
was at all general it cannot but have had its effect on the type of Dales
horses proper as well as on the 'gallopers' of Bedale and Northallerton.

We shall consider, as under the Hanoverian dynasty, two accounts of
life in the Northern and Western Isles of Scotland, by Martin Martin
and Alexander Buchan, because though their original narratives date
from the time of William III and Queen Anne, yet they were re-edited
in later years and one of them was not printed until the 1770's. First as
to the North Isles: Martin Martin (1703) on Shetland:

It produces little Horses commonly called Shelties and they are very
sprightly tho' the least of their kind to be seen anywhere: they are lower in
stature than those of Orkney and it is common for a man of ordinary strength
to lift a Sheltie from the ground, yet this little creature is able to carry double.
The Black are esteem'd to be the most hardy, but the Pied ones seldom prove
to be so good; they live many times till 30 years old, and are fit for service all
the while. These horses are never brought into a house, but exposed to the
rigour of the weather all the Year round, and when they have no grass, feed
upon the sea-ware, which is only to be had at the Tide of Ebb.

The same on Orkney. 'These horses are of very small size, but hardy,
and exposed to the Rigour of the Season during the Winter and Spring.'
It should be explained that in the North Isles generally though the
autumn ('da hairst') is a comparatively mild season, yet the spring ('da
voar') is a savage and dreaded season of cruel, killing weather.

To Martin we owe the theory, not well substantiated historically,
that there was a special St Kilda breed of pony. He simply says: 'St
Kilda horses are of a lower size than in the adjacent isles.' But what
isles can properly be described as 'adjacent' to remote St Kilda, called
in Gaelic Hirta, which means 'Death'? Moreover we have seen that in
Dean Monro's time there were no horses at all in Hirta. They can only
therefore have been introduced at the earliest during the second half of
the sixteenth century. Buchan, as we shall see, does not perceive any
indication of a separate St Kilda breed. Proceeding, as Monro did, island
by island, Martin has these notes about horses.

Borera. 'I saw a mare which I was told brought forth a fole in her
second year.' (This calamity, and it is always a calamity, sometimes
happens today on Dartmoor and Exmoor. But in the Hebrides and
farther North, it would be much more unusual, since both the Sheltie

and the Highland pony are thought to mature much later, at least in their natural environment, than southern breeds.)

Rhum. Again, as in the sixteenth-century accounts, Rhum is not mentioned as producing horses.

Arran. 'The cattle are horses and cows of a middle size.'

Lewis. 'The horses are considerably less here than in the opposite continent [i.e. the mainland of Ross] yet they plow and harrow as well as bigger horses, though in the spring time they have nothing to feed upon but sea-ware.'

North Uist. (Four-horse and two-horse ploughs are mentioned, sometimes preceded by a one-horse ripping-plough which simply spitlocked the turf to mark out the lines of the furrow. Presumably evidence that horses were numerous but small.)

In isolated and today uninhabited *North Rona*, as far to the north of the Butt of Lewis as St Kilda is to the west of Harris, there were no horses at all. A Rona boy came to Lewis, and a foal ran up to him in a field, so scaring the boy that he jumped into a bed of nettles. 'They are mightily pleased at the sight of horses, and one of them observing a Horse to neigh, asked if that Horse laughed at him.'

Eriskay. (Here Martin met sixty South Uist men riding along the strand, on their way to gather cockles.)

Barra. (Here the tenants paid the landlord a heriot of their best horse, as the Anglo-Saxons, and presumably the Northmen did, but the custom had a Gaelic name, *Each-fuin* = horse-fine.)

Skye. (Martin observed the horses ran out summer and winter and the only hand-feeding was with straw—if it *was* hand-feeding: he may have meant grazing on the stubble.)

Lingay. 'The horses are very strong and fit for the Pad [riding saddle, pilch] tho' exposed all winter and spring in the open fields' (at least they were fields, not as in some islands, just 'the hill', or the foreshore).

'The natives are much addicted to riding, the plainness [flatness] of the country much disposing both men and horses to it. They observe an anniversary cavalcade on Michaelmas Day, and then all ranks of both sexes appear on horseback. The place for this Rendezvous is a large piece of firm sandy ground on the seashore, and there they have horse-racing for small prizes, for which they contend eagerly. There is an ancient custom by which it is lawful for any of the inhabitants to steal his neighbour's horse the night before the race and ride him all next day provided he deliver him safe and sound to the owner after the Race; the manner of running is, by a few young men who use neither saddle nor bridles except two small ropes made of bents instead of a bridle nor any sort of spurs but their bare heels, and when they begin to race they throw these ropes on their horses necks and drive them on vigorously with two pieces of long dried sea-ware . . the men [spectators] have their sweethearts behind them on horseback.'

The Michaelmas cavalcade was recorded by Martin also on Coll,

Lewis and Barra, by Buchan also in a rudimentary form on St Kilda. This ancient custom appears to have been a Viking and not a Gaelic heritage, because Michaelmas belongs to the Germanic cycle of quarterly feasts, based on a corn husbandry, together with New Year, Lady Day and Midsummer, while the Celtic cycle of feasts, based on stock-rearing, was marked by Beltainn in mid May, Lugnasad, Samhain, and Imbolc, the English Candlemas or feast of the returning sun (2nd February). But the Vikings had saddles, bridles and spurs before they came 'west over sea'.

There had been some decadence since the Gaelic minstrel sang of the mounted heroes in 'bright Arran of the fresh grass'. Probably due in the long run to the shipbuilding, timber-housed Viking with his fatal broad axe, which deforested the Islands and deprived all domestic stock and large game of grazing and shelter from the Atlantic gales, reacting also on the human economy. On Barra the cavalcade was called 'feast of St Barr'—a saint otherwise unknown to the calendar. Races on the strand still take place in Ireland in our day.

Of the second sight, 'in Irish called Taish', Martin says that not only people, including children, but also cows and horses had it: no other animals. But horses had been known to tear up their tethers, or if travelling the road 'sweat violently and start suddenly [shy] at the same time as their riders, or even as men at a distance from them, had seen the wraiths of dead or absent persons'.

We last heard mention of St Kilda towards the end of the sixteenth century, when the surveyor remarked that it contained no horses at all. But by the end of the seventeenth century it had acquired some. In the posthumous papers of the Rev. Alexander Buchan, who had been the first resident minister there from 1705 to 1730, we learn that 'Their horses exceed not the number of twenty, all of red colour, very low and smooth skinned: and are employed only in carrying their turf and corn and at their anniversary cavalcade, when for divertisement the inhabitants ride their horses at Michaelmas. This they never fail to observe. They begin at the shore and then ride as far as the houses; they use no saddle of any kind, nor bridle, but a rope of straw, which manages the horse's head. And when they have all taken the horses by turn, the show is over for that time.'

Buchan adds that 'the richest man in St Kilda has not above eight cows, two or three horses and eighty sheep'. Before that the level of poverty both in goods and live-stock had been even lower. During Buchan's incumbency the population rose to thirty or thirty-three families, almost two hundred souls, perhaps the greatest density it ever reached. During the incumbency of Buchan's predecessor, Martin Martin, who did not reside full time, there had been only twenty-seven families with eighteen horses among them.

St Kilda lay sixty miles west of the Long Island and belonged to The MacLeod of Harris. This worthy proprietor, mindful of the welfare of his tenants, as Highland landlords traditionally are, sent a boat annually in May to the island containing a chaplain to baptize any children who might have been born since last May—and a steward to collect the rent. The latter was usually an illegitimate half-brother or son of The MacLeod. It is true the crofters had no money, but The MacLeod's steward condescended to take meal or fleeces or dried mutton in lieu. Such an expedition was accompanied by Martin Martin in the spring of 1697. To the St Kildans, poor devils, The MacLeod was the mightiest monarch on the face of the earth. Did his income not amount, to their certain knowledge, to twenty-seven sheepskins full of meal and hundreds of gross of gannets' eggs annually from St Kilda alone? Martin says: 'They account riding one of the greatest of earthly grandeurs, and told me, with a strange admiration, that MacLeod travelled not on foot as they supposed all other men did, and that they had *seen several* horses which were kept on purpose for him to ride on.' Perhaps the purposeless riding rite at Michaelmas was a memory of a Michaelmas horse fair seen somewhere on the mainland, or at least on the Long Island, by some travelled St Kildan, or perhaps it had been added on to the traditional ceremony of the oat-harvest, when everyone felt so rich that they exclaimed, and acted: 'Look, I am the richest man in the world, like The MacLeod who rides on horses.' Buchan's description of the score of horses sounds very much like Shetlands except for the curious term 'smooth-skinned'. Probably they were shelties, not straight from Shetland but from somewhere in the Outer Hebrides. There were no horses on St Kilda when it was finally evacuated in 1928.

Some much more literary tourists travelled the same ground in the reign of George III. Samuel Johnson's favourite pastime was to drive at speed in a post-chaise, but in the Isles he was forced to walk, go by boat or by even more lowly means. Boswell says of their holidays on Coll, 1773, '[the laird of] Col and Joseph [their servant] and some others, ran up to some little horses, called there *Shelties*, that were running wild on a heath, and catched one of them. We had a saddle with us, which was clapped upon it, and a straw-halter was put on its head. Dr Johnson was then mounted, and Joseph very slowly and gravely led the horse. I said to Dr Johnson, "I wish, Sir, *the club* saw you in this attitude".'

This was in fact only four days after Michaelmas. Was Col meaning some obscure joke in this connection? If so, it was completely lost on Boswell and on Johnson, though the latter was interested in old Highland customs. By this time the Michaelmas cavalcade had entirely died out in the Inner Isles, but as Johnson himself remarks, if he had visited the Outer Isles and indeed some of the inner ones, such as Eigg and Canna, where the population was still Catholic, he might have been able to see many such ancient usages. He noticed that the Presbyterian clergy were very hard on any kind of ceremony, however secular, if it were even remotely connected with a saint's day.

Of this particular occasion Johnson says: 'Here I first mounted a little Highland steed, and if there had been many spectators should have been somewhat ashamed of my figure in the march. The horses of these islands, as of other barren countries, are very low. They are indeed musculous and strong, beyond what gives their size reason for expecting: but a bulky man upon one of their backs makes a very disproportionate appearance . . . ' Elsewhere in the *Journey to the Western Isles*, he says, of the Inner Hebrides in general: 'Their horses are like their cows, of a moderate size. I had no difficulty to mount myself commodiously by favour of the gentlemen. I heard of very little cows in Barra, and of very little horses in Rum'—here follows a truly Johnsonian passage—'where perhaps no care is taken to prevent the diminution of size, which must always happen, where the greater and the less copulate promiscuously, and the young animal is restrained from growth by penury of sustenance. I have seen the chief man of a very wide district riding with a halter for a bridle and governing his hobby with a wooden curb.'

He agrees with the sixteenth-century surveyor that 'the rent of Rum is not great'. But he goes on to record, and his is the first evidence we have, that 'The horses are very small but of a breed eminent for beauty. Col, not long ago, bought one of them from a tenant (the laird of Coll then owned most of Rhum) who told him that as he was of a shape uncommonly elegant, he could not sell him but at a high price; and that whoever had him should pay a guinea and a half. There are said to be in Barra a race of horses yet smaller, of which the height is not above thirty-six inches.'

Of their mode of travelling in Skye Johnson says: 'We were furnished therefore with horses and a guide. In the islands there are no roads nor any marks by which a stranger may find his way. The horseman has always at his side a native of the place who by pursuing game or tending cattle or being often employed in messages or conduct has learnt where the ridge of a hill has breadth sufficient to allow a horse and his rider passage, and where the moss or bog is hard enough to bear them. The bogs are avoided as toilsome at least, if not unsafe, and therefore . . . the journey is made from precipice to precipice . . . which however . . . causes more alarm than danger. The Highlander walks carefully before, and the horse, accustomed to the ground, follows him, with little deviation. Sometimes the hill is too steep for the horseman to keep his seat, and sometimes the moss is too tremulous to bear the double weight of horse and man. The rider dismounts and all shift as they can.'

He said that Hebridean hay 'by most English farmers would be thrown away' and that there was only one mile of carriage road in Coll. 'Wheel carriages they have none, but make a frame of timber which is drawn by one horse with the two points behind pressing on the ground.' This is evidently not a sled but what is called in North America a travois, such as the Indians used. 'On this they sometimes drag home their sheaves, but often convey them in a kind of open pannier, or frame of sticks, upon one horse's back.' The open pannier would be the equivalent of the old Shetland *keishie*, woven out of flags, because there were no sticks in Shetland. Boswell, watching a funeral in the churchyard of Durinish in Skye, reflected that in all their travels since they left the mainland they had seen, not only no hearses, but no wheeled vehicles at all, only sleds and pack-saddles.

It is curious that of these two synoptic witnesses Boswell should have so much the less to impart about horses—Boswell, who fancied himself as the heir to a landed estate, and who so enjoyed being addressed as Affleck after the family property. But it is the middle-class provincial urban scholar, Johnson the Fleet Street hack, who notices the wooden bit. We should notice it too, because it points backwards in time. We can only date the domestication of the horse, and the sheltie in particular, by the presence of metal bits. What if, before that, there were bits of more perishable fabric? It is Johnson alone who notes the absence of selective breeding (though Boswell in his way was something of an expert on promiscuous copulation) and the stunting of the breed by early weaning and poor doing of young stock. Johnson alone assesses the quality of the forage, notices the 'musculous' thighs of the Coll pony, gives concrete details of price and measurement, Johnson alone reports the special strains of Barra and Rhum. Another English traveller in the very same year (1772) assures us that 'everyone' in the Isle of Arran has a horse, to the number of 1,058, and that consequently the island is overgrazed and fodder has to be imported.

Birt's *Letters from the North of Scotland* give a detailed if somewhat depressing picture of Highland ponies kept at Inverness in the years between 1715 and 1745. He says: 'You see a Man dragging along a half-starved Horse little bigger than an Ass, in a Cart, about the Size of a Wheel-Barrow. One Part of his Plaid is wrapt round his Body, and the Rest is thrown over his left Shoulder; and every now and then he turns about, either to adjust his Mantle, when blown off by the Wind or fallen by his stooping, or to thump the poor little Horse with a great Stick. The Load in this Cart, if compact, might be carried under his Arm; but he must not bear any Burden himself, though his Wife has, perhaps, at the same Time, a greater Load on her Loins than he had in his Cart:—I say on her Loins, for the Women carry Fish, and other heavy Burdens, in the same Manner as the Scots Pedlars carry their Packs in England.

'The poor Men are seldom barefoot in the Town but wear *Brogues*, a Sort of Pumps without heels, which keep them little more from the Wet and Dirt than if they had none, but they serve to defend their Feet from the Gravel and Stones.

'They have three several Sorts of Carts, according to the enclosed Sketches, of which that Species wherein they Carry their Peats (being a light Kind of Loading) is the largest; but as they too are very small, their Numbers are sometimes so great, that they fill up one of the Streets (which is the Market for that Fuel) in such manner, it is impossible to pass by them on Horseback, and difficult on Foot.

'It is really provoking to see the Idleness and Inhumanity of some of the Leaders of this Sort of Carts; for, as they are something higher than the Horse's Tail, in the motion they keep rubbing against it till the Hair is worn off and the Dock quite raw, without any Care being taken to prevent it, or to ease the Hurt when discovered.

'Some of these Carts are led by Women, who are generally bare-foot, with a Blanket for the covering of their Bodies, and in cold or wet

28. Slide-car at Inverness, about 1730, called in Gaelic *car-slaoid*.

29. Inverness, 2-wheel cart, about 1730, of a pattern called in Welsh *car-meidre*.

Weather they bring it quite over them. At other times they wear a Piece of Linen upon their Heads, made up like a Napkin-Cap in an inn, only not tied at top, but hanging down behind.

'Instead of Ropes for Halters and Harness, they generally make use of Sticks of Birch twisted and knotted together; these are called *Woodies*; but some few have Ropes made of the Manes and Tails of their horses, which are shorn in the Spring for that Purpose.

'The Horse-Collar and Crupper are made of Straw-bands; and, to save the Horse's Back, they put under the Cart-saddle, a Parcel of old Rags.

'Their Horses are never dressed or shod, and appear, as we say, as ragged as Colts. In short, if you were to see the whole Equipage, you would not think it possible for any Droll-Painter to invent so perfect a Picture of Misery.

'If the Horse carries any Burden upon his Back, a Stick of a Yard long goes across, under his Tail, for a crupper; but this I have seen in Prints of the loaded Mules in Italy.

'When the Carter has had Occasion to turn about one Sort of these Carts in a narrow Place, I have seen him take up the Cart, Wheels and all, and walk round with it, while the poor little Horse has been struggling to keep himself from being thrown.

'The Wheels, when new, are about a Foot and half high, but are soon worn very small: they are made of three pieces of Plank, pinned together at the Edges like the Head of a Butter-Firkin, and the Axletree goes round with the Wheel; which having some Part of the Circumference with the Grain and other Parts not, it wears unequally, and in a little Time is rather angular than round, which causes a disagreeable Noise as it moves upon the Stones.

'I have mentioned these Carts, Horses, and Drivers, or rather Draggers of them, not as immediately relating to the Town, but as they increase, in great Measure, the wretched Appearance in the Streets; for these Carters, for the most Part, live in Huts dispersed in the adjacent Country. There is little Need of Carts for the Business of the Town; and when a Hogshead of Wine has been to be carried to any Part not very far distant, it has been placed upon a kind of Frame among four Horses, two on a Side,[1] following each other; for not far off, except along the Sea-Coast and some New Road, the Ways are so rough and rocky that no Wheel ever turned upon them since the Formation of this Globe; and, therefore, if the Townsmen were furnished with sufficient Wheel-Carriages for Goods of great Weight, they would be seldom useful.

'The Description of these puny Vehicles brings to my Memory how I was entertained with the Surprise and Amusement of the common People in this Town, when, in the Year 1725, a Chariot with six monstrous great Horses arrived here, by way of the Sea-Coast. An Elephant, publicly exposed in one of the Streets of London, could not have excited greater Admiration. One asked what the Chariot was: another, who had seen the Gentleman alight, told the first, with a Sneer at his Ignorance, it was a great Cart to carry People in, and such like. But since the making of some of the Roads, I have passed through them with a Friend, and was greatly delighted to see the Highlanders run from their Huts close to the Chariot, and, looking up, bow with their Bonnets to the Coachman, little regarding us that were within.

'It is not unlikely they looked upon him as a kind of Prime-Minister, that guided so important a Machine; and perhaps they might think that we were his Masters, but had delivered the Reins into his Hands, and, at that time, had little or no Will of our own, but suffered ourselves to be conducted by him as he thought fit; and therefore their Addresses were directed to the Minister, at least in the first Place; for motions would not allow us to see a second Bow, if they were inclined to make it.

'It is a common Thing for the poorest Sort hereabouts to lead their Horses out in Summer, when they have done their Work, and attend them while they graze by the Sides of the Roads and Edges of the

---

[1] i.e. a litter.

Corn-Fields, where there is any little Grass to be had without a Trespass; and generally they hold them all the while by the halter, for they
are certainly punished if it be known they encroached ever so little upon
a Field, of which none are enclosed. In like Manner, you may see a Man
tending a single Cow for the greatest Part of the Day. In Winter the
Horse is allowed no more Provender than will barely keep him alive, and
sometimes not even that; for I have known almost two Hundred of them,
near the Town, to die of mere Want, within a small Compass of Time.
You will find in another Letter how I came to know their Numbers.

'Certainly nothing can be more disagreeable than to see them pass the
Streets before this Mortality, hanging down their Heads, reeling with
Weakness; and having Spots of their Skins, of a Foot diameter, appear-
ing without Hair, the Effect of their exceeding Poverty: but the Mares
in particular, are yet a more unseemly Sight.

'When the Grass in the Season is pretty well grown, the Country
People cut it, and bring it green to the Town for Sale, to feed the
Horses that are kept in it; as others likewise do to Edinburgh, where
there is a spacious Street known by the Name of the Grass-Market;
and this is customary in all the Parts of the Low Country where I have
been, at the Time of the Year for that kind of Marketing.

'Hay is here a rare Commodity indeed; sometimes there is none at
all; and I have had it brought me forty Miles by sea, at the rate of
Half-a-Crown or Three Shillings a Truss. I have given Twenty-pence
for a Bundle of Straw not more than one of our Trusses, and Oats have
cost me at the Rate of four Shillings a Bushel, otherwise I must have
seen, as we say, my Horses' Skins stripped over their Ears. But this is
not always the Case; for sometimes, after the Harvest, Oats and Straw
have been pretty reasonable.

'A certain Officer, soon after his Arrival at this Town, observing in
what a miserable State the Horses were, and finding his own would cost
him more in keeping than was well consistent with his Pay, shot them.
And being asked why he did not rather choose to sell them, though but
for a small Matter, his Answer was, they were old Servants and his
Compassion for them would not suffer him to let them fall into the
Hands of such Keepers. And indeed the Town Horses are but sparingly
fed, as you may believe, especially when their Provender is at such an
extravagant Price.'

We should perhaps qualify these remarks by observing that they refer
only to suburban horses. It may well be that the condition of garrons in
the countryside proper was slightly better than this, since they had a
wider range of grazing, and since the Gaelic genius for organization is
never seen at its best in an urban setting.

The antiquary Charles Cordiner, in 1780, described the transport
amenities of the Mackay country, the north coast of Sutherland, thus:

'All they who wish to penetrate into the remote and desert district of
Strathnaver, must be furnished with the hardy ponies of the country; a

[continued on page 187

44

46

42

45

43

47

48

49

50

51

52

53

54

55

56

57

58

59

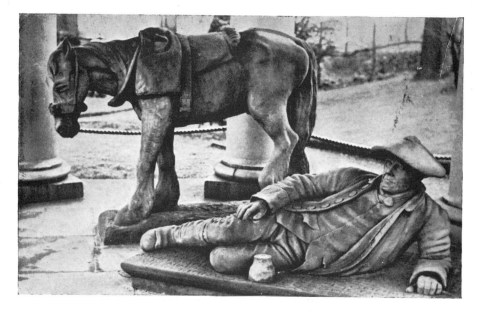

60

61

62

63

64

65

THE CELEBRATED TROTTING PONY, "STRAWBERRY GIRL,"
13 HANDS 2 INCHES,

The Property of MR. JOHN WILSON, Liverpool.

(RIDDEN BY CHARLES BASNETT)

Winner of many Handicaps, including the Borough Stakes of £60 at Blackpool, on Tuesday, July 17th, 1882, beating Eighteen others; also the North Lancashire Handicap of £140 at Blackpool, Tuesday, July 17th, 1882, beating Sixteen others, in the First Final-Heat, none of them being within the distance, were all disqualified. Won the First Prize at Farnworth Show in both Saddle and Harness, in September 1881; also the First Prize at Altrincham Show in both Saddle and Harness, on September 28th, 1881. Won the Silver Cup, value 10 guineas, at Bootle Show, for the Best Pony in Harness under 13 hands 2 inches; also the First Prize at Farnworth, in September, 1882, for the Best Pony in Harness, under 13 hands 2 inches.

68

69

70

71

72

74

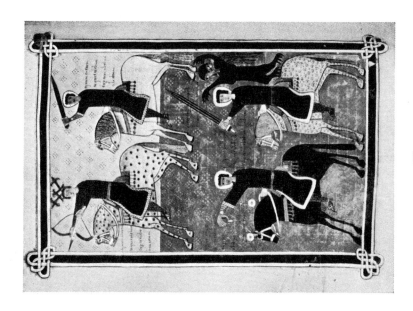

73

jumano pptrf figuo qd mnuit: abnuit.
it: q nug Rennit q: quonenf ahquib;
panem 7 abfceffum indicit. P̄ retta
dil opttu uin inhac gente fedendo . mu
amtef. ab erel ftando. urinaf emittunt
7 prfctib;t C̄am muheref q: oīm maref
iaut. et diuantatif ceurib; ubiifq; u
u coufc a q: protenfifecuitare folent
neceffitare. Be etc hefiefta. t mutct lan

75

76

77

78

NOTES ON THE PLATES

42–6. Details from the engraving 'A Prospect of Cambridge', 1675. Compare the horses here with the text figures of hunters at the beginning of the chapter on Stuart Times, drawn only sixty years earlier. All are docked, which had been unusual in James I's time. 43 and 45 are hunters, the rest utility saddle horses.

47. Gilpin's demonstration picture, about 1785, of the improved and the 'ordinary' New Forest horses.

48. West Yorkshire clothiers carrying undyed cloth on pack-horses, 1814. The white or grey pony was then still common in the Dales. See also P62. *Walker's 'Costume of Yorkshire', 1814.*

49. 'Haymaking at Beddgelert', from a painting by Moses Griffith (1747–1819) now in the possession of his great-nephew of the same name. Cob mare working in the slide-car (compare text figure) that was common to the whole highland zone of Britain and is still to be seen in parts of Ulster today. She has her foal at foot, showing more quality than she does.

50. Detail of Welsh landscape by Rowlandson, 1792, with cart of local pattern, drawn by a cob of similar size to but different conformation from that in P49. Wheels of 'clog' type, variation on the ancient pattern shown in P57, P62 and text figure 51.

51. Welsh cob mare carrying pack saddle, with foal at foot, 1866.

52. Pack-horse Bridge, Dobpark, Washburndale, West Yorkshire. The height of the parapet is the level at which the load hung down from the saddle on either side.

53. Highland Pony of 'Mainland' type, used for deer-stalking, grazing in Strath Conon. *Photo by D. M. G.*

54. Dark Age stag hunter and war-horse from Pictish tombstone. *Photo by D. M. G.*

55. The old type of 'one-stilted' plough in use in Shetland, from a photograph taken in 1861. It cannot be, as so many things in Shetland are, of Scandinavian origin. It was also in use in the Hebrides, and is probably the pre-Belgic type of plough common to the whole Celtic world before the first century A.D. This one was drawn by three ponies and an equally small ox (*left*). Probably all Neolithic draft animals were this size. *Photo from collection of A. J. Cluness, Lerwick.*

56. Crofters loading peat on pack-ponies, Shetland, 1960. *Photo by A. J. Cluness, Lerwick.*

57. Highland girl with pony and cart leading peat and rushes for thatching, 1886. The halter is a 'widdy' made of twisted twigs, the rest of the harness is spun from straw and horsehair. *Painting from Highland Museum, Kingussie.*

58. 'North Atlantic Pony'. The Highland ponies of the Nature Conservancy and Department of Agriculture for Scotland herd on the Isle of Rum. *Photo by courtesy of Mr Peter Wormall, the Warden of Rum.*

59. Highland ponies in Ross-shire belonging to Sir John Stirling. *Photo by D. M. G.*

60. 'Beside him, fed among the graves a pony, the companion of his journey, whose extreme whiteness, as well as its projecting bones and hollow eyes, indicated its antiquity. It was harnessed in the most simple manner, with a pair of branks, a hair tether, or halter, and a sunk, or cushion of straw, instead of bridle and saddle. A canvas pouch hung around the neck of the animal, for the purpose, probably, of containing the rider's tools, and anything else he might have occasion to carry with him.' *'Old Mortality' by Sir Walter Scott, 1821.*

Apart from the obvious symptoms of old age and malnutrition, this specimen of the West Lowland pony shows the coarsening of the whole frame which preceded the 'growing up' of some strains into the great Clydesdale Horse. Geographically the scene is Galloway. But this animal is not a 'galloway' in anybody's sense of the term at any time. *Statue by John Currie, 1840, Balmaclellan Churchyard. Photo by 'The Galloway News'.*

61. Photograph dated about 1868, bearing the inscription 'Racing Galloway', in the family of Mr J. K. Ridler of Porlock. In fact this animal was bred on Perriton Hill near Minehead, out of a locally bred pony mare by a blood horse. It was what some people in West Somerset called a 'galloway' nearly a hundred years ago. But obviously it had little enough to do with Kirkcudbrightshire and all that, nor had its ancestors. The total impression is of a horse, not a pony.

62. Digging peat in Langstrothdale. The cart is of medieval type and the pony of a colour locally regarded as very typical until quite recent years. *Walker's 'Costume of Yorkshire', 1814.*

63. Landscape near Skelwith, above Elterwater in Westmorland. In the foreground the herd, since disbanded, belonging to the National Trust. *Photo by J. Hardman.*

64. The modern Frisian Horse. *Photo by Frisian Horse Society.*

65. The modern Fell Pony. *Photo by D. M. G.*

66. The most celebrated of the Wilson ponies bred up from original Fell stock.

67. Old Grey Shales painted by G. Garrard, A.R.A., about 1824. Shows several pronounced Arabian features.

68. *Ambition*, C. Beart's Roadster Sire. Foaled, 1863, Red Roan, 15.1½ hands.

    Owner and Breeder: C. Beart, Stow Bardolph, Downham Market, Norfolk.

    Sire: Phenomenon (Bultitaft's) 579 by Cambridgeshire Shales 110.

    Dam by Performer (Baxter's) 552 by Prickwillow (Cobbins') 607.

    G. dam: Kitty by Norfolk Cob (Sharpe's) by Marshland Shales 435.

Sire of

Ambassador (Coker's) 25	d. by Great Gun (Sutton's) 323.
Ambition (Hubbard's) 27	d. a Shales Mare.
Ambition (Savage's) 28	d. by Fireaway (Savage's) 242.
Ambition (Turner's) 29	d. by Perfection (Jackson's) 541.
Ambition (Warman's) 30	
Ambition (Hopkin's) 31	d. by Quicksilver (Jackson's), *app.*
Ambition (M. Beart's) 32	d. by Fireaway (Bett's) 239.
Ambition (Saunders') 33	d. by Phenomenon (J. Saunders').
Prince Royal 641	d. by Prickwillow (Cobbins') 607.
Rival 673	d. by Quicksilver (Jackson's), *app.*

    Prizes won: In 1867, 1st Royal Agricultural Show of England, 1st Norfolk Agricultural Show, 1st Cambridge Agricultural Show; in 1868, 1st Royal Agricultural Show of England; in 1869, 1st Islington, 2nd Manchester Royal Agricultural Show, 2nd Yorkshire Agricultural Show; in 1870, 2nd Royal Agricultural Show of England, 2nd Norfolk Agricultural Show; in 1871, 2nd Islington, 1st Long Sutton Agricultural Show; in 1872, 1st Islington, 2nd Beccles; in 1873, 1st Islington, 1st Norfolk Agricultural Show, 1st Long Sutton. Afterwards sold for export to France.

69. Phenomena, the celebrated trotting mare. (Ps 67, 68, and 69 are reproduced by the kindness of Mr Ernest Hutton, one of the most celebrated breeders of modern Hackneys.)

70. The two sons of the master of the Dartmoor Fox Hounds, John and Charles Bulteel of Pamfleet, near Manaton, on Dartmoor in 1835. *Picture in possession of Miss Georgiana Bulteel.*

71. Photograph taken in 1861 of farmer's wife on pony outside the yard of a West Somerset hill farm. *In possession of Mr J. K. Ridler, Porlock.*

72. The September sales at Beaulieu Road. One of the three annual auctions organized by the New Forest Pony Society.

73. Spanish war-horses of the late eleventh century. Illustration from a manuscript of the *Commentary on the Apocalypse* by Beato de Liebana; shows the four horsemen of the Apocalypse: written and illuminated about the year 1100, that is within a year or two of the draft imported from Spain by Robert Bellesme. *British Museum.*

74. Modern Welsh Cob.

75. Marginal drawing of Irishman riding horse, from the *Topography of Ireland* by Gerald de Barry. *National Library of Ireland.*

76. Connemara yearling colt on English showground.

77. Connemara mare on coast of Galway. *Photo by Mrs Brooks, Errislannen, Galway.*

78. The Feast of Bishop Blaise. The annual Guild procession by the Clothiers of Wakefield, masters, journeymen and apprentices riding the horses normally used in their business, under pack-saddles, or to carry the master when buying or selling away from home. The one on the right of the bottom row would be accounted a passable Fell pony today. *Walker's 'Costume of Yorkshire', 1814.*

continued from page 182]

breed, I believe, originating from the Orcades' (and this is about the
only specific mention we have of a native Orkney pony; Cordiner rather
implies that it is no longer found on the islands). 'These being accustomed to climb among rocks; to jump between hillocks among bogs; to
feed on birch-leaves or any green stuff that grows among the hills, are
the only proper horses for the journey. Large horses cannot take that
route, not only on account of the exceeding roughness of the rocky
heaths: but, as it is not practicable to carry hay and corn into the wilds,
the finding of good grass being extremely precarious . . . '

Among Scottish authors, as opposed to English travellers in Scotland,
of this period, there is a most noticeable division between east and west.
While all Scots writers about the Lowlands frequently mention animals
which must from the context be ponies, those from the east side of the

30. Country cart from Upper Clydesdale, eighteenth century,
illustration from *The Gentle Shepherd*, by Allan Ramsay (compare
P32 and P57).

country do not employ the word pony in any form. That is to say, Scott
does not do so when he is writing about the Lothians, or when he is
putting dialogue into the mouths, say, of Berwickshire people. He only
does so when his characters come from the Galloway side or when the
scene of the action is laid there. James Hogg, the Ettrick shepherd, whose
native heath was the eastern Border country, and most of whose rural
poems are about the basin of the upper Tweed, does not use the word.

But in the western Lowlands we have two famous poets of rural life
whose home lay a little to the north of Galloway proper, but still between
it and Dumbarton, where Bass John Spreull used to buy 'Galloway
garrons'. The first in time is Allan Ramsay, an Edinburgh barber and
bookseller, who was born on a farm in Leadhills, near the source of the
Clyde in south-west Lanark. He is best remembered for his dialect

31. Burns ploughing.

pastoral play *The Gentle Shepherd* (30), and in his poems about the scene of his boyhood he mentions 'pownies' often enough. This is also the spelling used by Burns the Ayrshire ploughman. Here (31) is a picture of Burns ploughing, showing what sort of horses he used in the plough. In his letters we have many intimate accounts of his riding pony, named after Jenny Geddes, the Protestant heroine who helped the Reformation along by throwing her stool at the Dean of Edinburgh in the middle of the sermon. This little mare was as ugly as sin and as bad-tempered and pugnacious as her namesake, but remarkably tough and thrifty. The eerie adventure of his best-known hero, Tam o' Shanter, took place on a pony called Meg who rescued Tam from the pursuing witches by crossing running water with him, but at the cost of her own tail:

> the carlin claught her by the rump,
> And left poor Maggie scarce a stump.

It is Burns who sings the astonishing versatility of the West Lowland 'pownie' in 'The Auld Farmer's Salutation to his Auld Mare'. After a very thick New Year's Eve the farmer appears in the stable with a double measure of corn as a 'hansel'—at what hour of the first morning of the year we will not inquire. She is upwards of twenty-nine years old and has borne ten good foals, the least of which he sold for £13 2s. 0d. For English readers this poem is a tougher morsel to chew on, linguistically, than anything Gawin Douglas or John Barbour ever wrote, but it is worth the effort. How we should like to know just what were the

> sma', droop-rumpl't hunter cattle

that the old mare beat so consistently, between bouts of ploughing and

32. Illustration from *St Ronan's Well* by Sir Walter Scott, 1825, showing heroine riding galloway.

bearing foals, in impromptu races at local fairs and weddings! She could jump, too:

> and could hae flown out-owre a stank
> Like ony bird.

Burns in his own person never knew the infirmities and the indignities of old age, but in this simple, deeply felt poem he speaks for every old man that owns an old horse:

> When thou was corn't, and I was mellow
> We took the road aye like a swallow.
>
> .   .   .   .   .
>
> We've worn to crazy years tegither;
> We'll toyte about wi' ane anither;
> Wi' tentie care I'll flit thy tether
>   To some hain'd rig.
> Where ye may nobly rax your leather,
>   Wi' sma' fatigue.

Now to the south again. Here are some extracts from *Remarks on Forest Scenery*, by William Gilpin, M.A., prebendary of Salisbury and vicar of Boldre in the New Forest, near Lymington. London, 1808, is the date of publication, but it was actually written in the late 1780's, just after the American Revolution had ruined the New Forest trade in export mules.

'A diminutive breed of horses runs wild in the New Forest. In general, however, the horse is private property, though sometimes with difficulty ascertained. Numbers of people, who have lands in the neighbourhood of the forest, have a right of commoning in it; and most of the cottagers who border on it assume that right. Many of them have two or three mares; and some, who make it their business to breed colts, have droves.

'The horse is gregarious. Herds of twenty or thirty are often seen feeding together; in summer especially, when they have plenty of pasturage, and can live as they please. In winter they are obliged to separate, and seek their food as they can find it. In general, indeed, they are left, in all seasons, to take their chance in the forest. Where there is no expense, there can be no great loss; and what is saved is so much gained. In marshy parts a severe winter often goes hardly with them. But in dry grounds, where heath and furze abound, they pick up a tolerable winter-subsistence; especially if they have learned the little arts of living, which necessity teaches. Of these arts, one of the most useful is to bruise and pound with their fore-feet the prickly tops of furze. This operation, which I have often seen performed, prepares the rigid diet of a furze bush in some degree for mastication; and renders it rather less offensive to the palate. From observing perhaps this instinct in a horse, furze is sometimes pounded in a mill, where fodder is scarce, and affords a wholesome nutriment for horses.

'When such colts as have long run wild are to be caught for sale, their ideas of liberty are so unconfined, from pasturing in so wild a range, that it is matter of no little difficulty to take them. Sometimes they are caught by slight of hand, with a rope and a noose. But if this method fails, they are commonly hunted down by horsemen who relieve each other. Colt-hunting is a common practice in the forest. The colts which feed on Obergreen are sometimes taken by the following stratagem. In this part runs a long bog, described under the name of Longslade Bottom, which is crossed by a mole thrown over it. With this passage the colt is well acquainted, and on being pursued is easily driven towards it. When he is about the middle of the mole, two or three men start up in front, and oblige him to leap into the bog, where he is entangled and seized.

'At all their neighbouring fairs, these horses are a principal commodity, and are bought up for every purpose to which a horse can be applied. Diminutive as they are, you may often see half a dozen of them straining in a waggon; and as it is fashionable to drive them in light carriages, their price has been enhanced. It is a little fortune to the poor cottager, if he happens to possess three or four colts that are tolerably handsome and match well. He can probably sell them for ten or twelve pounds a piece.

'In point of value the New Forest horse would rise higher if the same care was taken in breeding him as was formerly taken; and which is still in some degree taken in the neighbouring forest of Bere; where, I have heard, the keepers are ordered to destroy all horses which at three years of age are under thirteen hands; and all mares under twelve.

'There is another evil likewise which tends to injure the forest-colt; and that is, putting him to business at too early an age. Tho a small horse attains maturity earlier than a large one yet these horses, bred chiefly by indigent people, and generally of little value, are introduced proportionately sooner to labour, than abler and better horses commonly are.

'The fame and exploits are still remembered of a little beautiful grey horse which had been suffered to run wild in the forest till he was eight years old, when he had attained his full strength. His first sensations on the loss of liberty were like those of a wild beast. He flew at his keeper

33. 'Spangle, a favourite poney of H.R.H. the late Princess Charlotte,' who died in 1817. (Compare P47.)

with open mouth; or, rearing on his hind legs, darted his forefeet at him with the most malicious fury. He fell however into hands that tamed him. He became by degrees patient of the bit, and at length suffered a rider. He was well known on every road in the county, the favourite of every groom, and the constant theme of every ostler. But in the chase his prowess was most shown. There he carried his master with so much swiftness, ease and firmness that he always attracted the eyes of the company, more than the game they pursued.

'I have also heard of a grey mare belonging to Mr Powney, Member for Windsor, which does equal credit to the horses of this country. She was purchased at the age of six years in the neighbourhood of Broken-hurst, wild from the forest. While she was breaking, she fell lame, which disqualified her for use. She run wild, therefore, two years longer; when she was perfectly sound. From this time she became the favourite of her master. She was rather more than thirteen hands high; was finely made; had a round body; beautiful head and neck; and limbs like those of a deer. But her motions were still more admirable. Her paces and mouth were uncommonly pleasant; and her power of action was surprising. Nothing but a bred horse could lead her in the chase; and with a weight proportioned to her strength, neither hedge nor ditch could oppose her. The beauty of her form, and the perfection of her motions were such that no judge of a horse, who had once seen her, ever forgot her. Mr Powney rode her till she was twenty-three or twenty-four years of age.

'The New Forest horse is often supposed to be of Spanish extraction, from ancestors imagined to have been shipwrecked upon the coast of Hampshire, in the time of the Armada. But I look on this as a species of the ancient vaunt, *genus a lode summo*, and to deserve as little attention. Some of them have a form which would not disgrace so noble a lineage. The grey horse represented in the annexed plate (P47) is among the most beautiful. But in general the croup of the forest-horse is low, and his head ill-set-on, having what the jockies call a *stiff jaw*. Of this defect a resemblance is given in the horse on the left, whose head is set on as those of the New Forest horses commonly are. Their claim therefore, to high lineage, must in general rest more on their good qualities than on their beauty—on the hardiness of their nature—on their uncommon strength—on their agility and sureness of foot, which they probably acquire by constantly lifting their legs among the furze.

'But tho the form of the New Forest horse is seldom beautiful, yet as the ornament of the forest-scene, he is very picturesque. The horse in his natural state, rough with all his mane about him, and his tail waving in the wind as he feeds, is always beautiful, but particularly in so wild a scene as this, which he graces exceedingly.'

The illustration is a lithograph by the author's brother, Sawrey Gilpin. It will be seen that the Rev. William does not use the word 'pony' throughout, and that he too does not believe the Armada story. The surname Powney which just happens to figure in this anecdote is interesting. This is the way 'pony' is spelt when it first occurs in Scotland.

The scheme for this first half of our book provides for the tracing of the history of the Little Horse in Britain down to the year 1800, then for an assessment of the position at that date on a local instead of a chronological basis, to show how the pony status in each region differed from the status in the same region today. But arbitrary datelines are deceptive things, and in order to round off the picture it seems necessary to trespass a short way over the boundary, in order to profit by the evidence of William Cobbett, that notable horseman, in his *Rural Rides*. It will be remembered how frequent are the references to ponies in Ramsay's *Gentle Shepherd*, written at the end of the first quarter of the eighteenth century. The date of the best edition of this play is 1808; it is finely printed, with charming aquatint plates (none of them, alas, shows a horse of any kind), and a glossary of Scots words, which are translated for the benefit of standard English speakers, that is educated people with the speech habits of southern England. For them, the glossary renders the word 'pownie', which any suburban Londoner would recognize and interpret correctly today at sight, as 'A galloway, a small nag'. (Most modern Englishmen have some idea what is meant by a small nag, but few outside the north country will be much enlightened by talk of a galloway; at best, they will probably conjure up a mental image of black oxen.) Yet only twenty-four years later, Cobbett, in 1832, talks of people 'as ragged as forest ponies in the month of March'. Now Cobbett was emphatically a south-country man—the son of a farm labourer near Farnham, and an educated (superbly self-educated) man. Widely travelled, he had hardly ever been in Scotland, he hated all Scots with a bitter hatred, and his clumsy attempts to imitate their pronunciation in

34. Mineral train, from industrial light railway prospectus, 1824.

writing are among his less felicitous efforts at satire. Yet something had happened between 1808 and 1832 to make the Scots word 'pony' come spontaneously to the lips of such an Englishman.

One other passage in the *Rural Rides*, dealing with the country of the Fell ponies, marks the end of an era and the beginning of a new one for our purpose. Writing from North Shields, also in 1832, Cobbett says: 'They have begun to make a railway from Carlisle to Newcastle and I saw them at work on it as I came along. There are great lead mines not far from Hexham and I saw a great number of little one-horse carts bringing down the pigs of lead to the point where the Tine becomes navigable to Newcastle; and sometimes I saw loads of these pigs lying by the roadside as you see parcels of timber lying in Kent and Sussex and other timber countries: no fear of it being stolen: their weight is their security. . . .' Now the lead-mines of the north country had been worked steadily since Roman times; but only in the last few years before Cobbett wrote had there been any subsidiary roads in Tynedale passable for 'little wheeled carts'; the lead had all gone by pack-train, and the standard lead-pig, heavier than a man could carry, was cast to weigh half a pack-horse load, so that one went on each side of the pack-saddle. Now the little wheeled carts were to put the pack-horse as such out of business, and the railways were almost as soon to put the draught-horse out of business as a long-range carrier. The native ponies and cobs and the few remaining pack-horses bred from the same stock were hence-forward to work on the farms, or no farther away from them than the nearest market-town, except for the pit-ponies which were to stay in the industry for another hundred years.

John Byng, later Viscount Torrington, as a tourist and diarist between the years 1781 and 1794, was almost as indefatigable as Cobbett. An old soldier like Cobbett (not an ex-sergeant-major, however, but an ex-lieutenant-colonel of Foot Guards), the son of a landowner and not of a farm labourer, he had opinions and a mentality remarkably similar to Cobbett's. On most of his journeys he rode a pony which rejoiced in the name of Po. One of his diary notes reads: 'T. Bush is gone forward 3 days in advance, upon a black Galloway, leading my grey poney.' So he distinguished between the Galloway and the pony, with or without an *e*. It may be relevant that he was a south-country man. Passing through Swaledale in 1792 he saw the pack trains coming down from the lead-mines but does not describe them as made up of ponies: evidently the Dales looked to him like a full-sized horse. The most interesting item in his diaries from our point of view is the last item on the card at Faver-sham races, in Kent, for 19th October 1790. A race was to be run for:

THREE WHIPS
Value a Guinea and a Half

By Ponies not exceeding thirteen hands high. To run one two-mile heat. The first best Poney, a Whip value 14*s*. The second best, ditto, value 10*s*. The third best, ditto, value 7*s*. 6*d*.

Mr Thos. West's Rosebud, and Spider, are not to run for any of these prizes.

CHAPTER TEN

Geographical Interlude

BRITISH NATIVE BREEDS

THERE is a sense in which all British ponies are 'Celtic ponies'. This is best illustrated by reference to the map prepared by Professor Kenneth Jackson of Edinburgh for his *Language and History in Early Britain*. It shows the successive stages of the conquest of Britain by the Anglekin and the imposition of their language as evidenced by place names, in four zones.

Area I: East of a line from the Yorkshire Wolds to Salisbury Plain and Southampton Water. Here only the names of larger rivers are Celtic, notably those rivers which drain into the Wash. The only towns with Celtic names are those which were considerable Roman habitations at the time of the English invasion.

Area II: East of a line down the watershed of the Pennines and along the Ribble, interrupted by Merseyside and the Wirral, continuing up the Dee and down the Severn, then roughly along the eastern boundaries of Somerset and Dorset. Here the names of small rivers and hills are frequently Celtic, also those of forests, even where these now contain no standing timber.

Area III: Bounded on the west by the coasts of Cumberland and Lancashire, the present Welsh border, the south coast of the Bristol Channel, and the Tamar. Throughout the area, names even of inhabited places are often Celtic, and most hill, river and forest names.

Area IV: Cornwall, Wales, Scotland and Ireland as a whole are excluded from this pattern, since the same gradation of Celtic elements from south-east to north-west is not observable in either country.

In the far north of Scotland, Shetland and Orkney have been saturated with Norse place names, but there is a stratum of recognizable Celtic place names underneath the surface; the coast of Sutherland and Caithness is peppered with Norse names but the hinterland is not. On the West Highland coast in the Hebrides and in Galloway Norse names are numerous, but have often been Celticized by reconquest from the Scandinavians.

Area I represents the zone of English conquest down to about 550, Area II to 600 in the south and 650 in the north; Area III to about 700

196

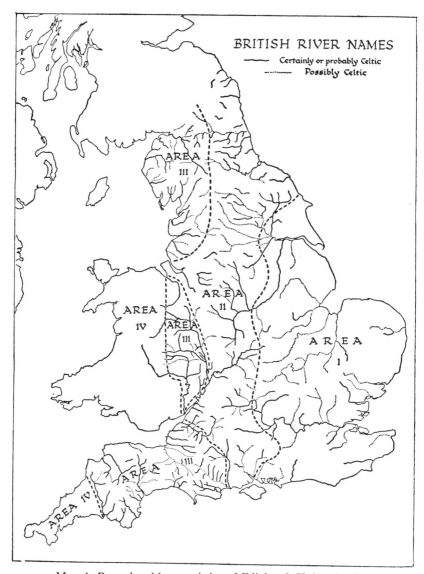

Map 4. *Reproduced by permission of Edinburgh University Press.*

in the north, to about 650 in the centre and to about 730 in the south-west. This applies to England only. English and Norman place names in Wales and Cornwall are so scarce as not to count for this purpose. The political conquest made no impression on the solid mass of Celtic place names. Now superimpose on this map the pattern of British pony breeds as they are today, or were recently, (illustrated in Map, page 197). From north to south the following lie wholly in Area IV, or outside this pattern: Shetland, Highland, Connemara, Welsh. In Area III lie the Fells, Exmoor, Dartmoor. Close to the border of III with II lie the Dales

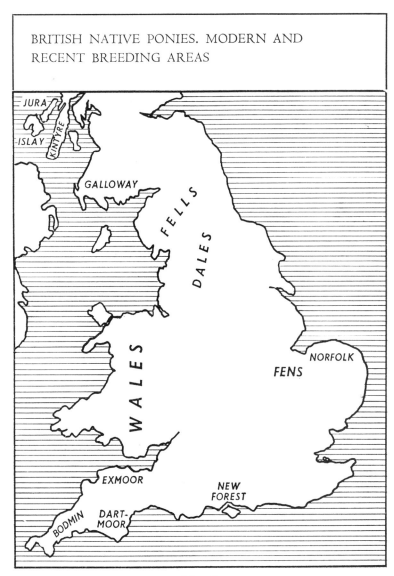

BRITISH NATIVE PONIES. MODERN AND
RECENT BREEDING AREAS

JURA

ISLAY

KINTYRE

GALLOWAY

FELLS

DALES

WALES

NORFOLK

FENS

EXMOOR

NEW
FOREST

BODMIN

DART-
MOOR

Map 5.

of Yorkshire and Durham, and the New Forest. Moreover in the mid
Yorkshire sector of Area II, only a little to the south of the homeland of
the Dales pony, lies Airedale, once the British kingdom of Elmet, not
conquered by the Northumbrians until 620, and still containing a wealth
of Celtic place names, including Leeds, which was not even a Roman
town, though Ilkley (Olicana) was.

In Area I no trace of a characteristic native breed of pony remains,
only the vague memory of one which lies far back behind the ancestry
of the Norfolk roadster. But precisely here, in the fen country sweeping

round from south Lincolnshire to Norfolk, and fanning out from the shores of the Wash, is the only thing that could be called a concentration of Celtic river names in the whole area. Chaucer spoke of Trumpington Fen, 'where wilde meares renne', and we have seen the concern of Tudor governments with the undersized horses bred on the marshes of this region.

Again, in Area IV, there were distinctive types of Cornish pony that have only passed into oblivion within living memory. It is the merest historical accident that we do not today recognize a separate Bodmin Moor or Goonhilly 'breed', descendants of the twenty palfreys with which the Cornishmen bought themselves free of King John's forest laws.

Now let us see, region by region, how the local breeds of pony have fared since the beginning of the nineteenth century, the point at which we ceased to consider their history in the country as a whole.

CHAPTER ELEVEN

The Far North, the Highlands and Islands

Wi da ebb dey goed doon in da geo
Ta nibble da bleeds o waar:
Da sea hit cam in an it laid dem i soe
An carried dem God kens whaar.

J. S. Angus, *Echoes from Klingrahool.*

THE greater their kinship the more they vary, yet every breed bears a resemblance to another. This rash statement having been made, it may not be long before members of the various pony societies and the breeders themselves, jealous of their ponies' pedigrees, fall upon us and smite us; we fear they will come, from Shetland and from Exmoor, to bury not to praise!

This is only an attempt to apply normal critical standards and normal historical method in a field where neither seem to have been much in use hitherto. It may well fail just because it is a first attempt: but the attempt will have been worth making if it only provokes some other interested persons to probe for evidence that no doubt exists but has eluded us. It will be of some use, for instance, if we make the point that the early history of this subject cannot be studied in a vacuum, because the breeding and use of horses were so closely integrated into the life of the country, in all parts and at all social levels. By contrast, the history of the Thoroughbred, for instance, *can* be studied almost in a vacuum because the people who made its history were a small minority; in many ways they were untypical of Englishmen of their day, and the common-places of English life (much less of Irish or Welsh life) as most people lived it did not apply to them. It is not simply the fact that Thoroughbred ancestry alone is well documented before the middle of the nineteenth century; the fact that the vast majority of racehorse owners never had to worry about where the next meal, or even the next quarter's rent, was to come from, makes the writing of their history and that of their animals a very different proposition from ours.

199

At the risk of labouring it, we must point out another consequence of the familiarity, in former days, of very wide social circles with the horse in common use. We should point out that down to the 1840's inability to ride a horse was not simply the equivalent, in modern terms, of inability to drive a car: it was more like not being able to ride a bicycle. Virtually it confined one to the limits of the parish, and prevented the performance of any but the most modest business operations, at some time, at some stage. Therefore every man of the slightest ability or enterprise could cope, competently if not artistically, with horses in some measure. One does not think of Dr Johnson as primarily a man of affairs or an equestrian sportsman; yet we have seen above that even he knew more about horses than the average Fleet Street resident of today—and he never repeated his monumental howler about the function of the pastern.

In the age of the classic British historians—let us say from Gibbon to Macaulay—most people knew the elementary facts about horses, whether they were townsmen or countrymen, whether they were gentle or simple. And they took such knowledge for granted in their readers. Since history as studied in those days was almost entirely political and constitutional, such knowledge again formed but a small part of the required background. But just at the point in time where social history, economic history, the specialized history of arts and agriculture, industry and warfare, began to come into its own, it could no longer be assumed that a knowledge of equestrian ABC's was part of the historian's equipment or could be assumed on the part of his readers. For example, the classic French work of Gautier on *Chivalry* (1881) was written by a man who plainly could barely distinguish a rouncy from a destrier (as our readers can by now); and the great modern work of Marc Bloch on *Feudal Society* (1940) contained but the slightest references to horses (though these are sound where they occur). For the study of a machine-less society, and its equestrian mainspring, which only moved at all in so far as it moved on horseback, this is *Hamlet* without the Prince of Denmark, or, if you like, *la Chevalerie* without *le Cheval*. If by this book we can bring about, on the part of persons better qualified than ourselves, a marriage of these two skills, history and horsemanship, then something will have been achieved. ANIMAL MANAGEMENT should be required reading for students of the Middle Ages: ENGLISH SOCIAL HISTORY the same for all who aspire to speak with authority of the past of the British native breeds. Only thus can they learn to distinguish the possible from the impossible.

Professor James Ritchie tells us the 'Shelties' or 'Shulties' are the smallest breed of horses in existence: the smallest recorded specimen measured 26 inches; they are representatives of that small race which inhabited Scotland (and not only Scotland) in prehistoric days. Ponies of their type can be recognized in cave paintings of the Old Stone Age, especially in the caverns of the Dordogne and Altamira, where they appear side by side with the quite different 'Mongolian' type of stiff-maned horse. *Piebalds*, 'proto-Shetlands', also appear on these Stone Age murals.

We have concrete evidence of ponies in the Northern Isles at a very early period, shown on the Bressay Stone. 'As this monument is admitted to belong to a period before the Celtic Christianity of the islands disappeared' under the shock of Norwegian penetration in the ninth century, 'it may be inferred that . . . the animal was known and probably found in the islands at that period'. We have already seen that Shetland was settled by Norsemen long before they had been heard of in the rest of Britain.

They have been described as sprightly and active as terriers, sure-footed as mules and patient as donkeys, standing at the head of the horse tribe as the most intelligent and faithful of them all.

Apparently the ponies were regarded almost as public property, for a law passed in 1612 forbade the 'ryding ane uther manis hors without licence and leave of awner', under penalty of fine; 'quhasoever sall be tryet or fund to stow or cut ane uther man's hors taill sall be pwinischit as a thief at all rigour in eximpill of utheris to commit the lyke'.

Acts were also passed regulating the right of grazing on the infield land. Regulations were even made for the scatholds, or hill pastures, as in the following decree, passed at Burrastow, Walls, Shetland:

Act anent wyld horses.
The quhilk day (27th June, 1617) it is statute and ordanit be the said Sherif deput with consent of the haill comunes convenit at the said Court that ther sall be na wyld horsis kepit confrome to ane Act maid of befoir and that na man sall put thair horsis without dykis uncloggit in tyme cumoing fra the last day of Maij to the tyme the cornes be put in the yeard under the paine of xls *toties quoties* as they sall be apprehendit or takin in the contrar.
(Acts and Statues of the Lawting Sheriff and Justice Courts of Orkney and Shetland).

'Wyld'; that word again. Of all hill ponies, the herds on the hills of Shetland are about the most sociable and amiable. In the winter especially, when they come down to the ebb 'ta nibble da bleeds o waar', they cannot help meeting people, and will take the opportunity to cadge a cod's head or two off the fishermen. Yet the 'Sherif Deput' knows what he meant when he wrote 'wyld'—unbroken breeding stock.

In his *Brief Description of Orkney, Zetland, Pightland-Firth and Caithness* (1701) the Rev. John Brand writes: 'They have a sort of little Horses called Shelties, than which no other are to be had, if not brought thither, from other places, they are of less size than the Orkney Horses, for some will be but 9 or 10 Nevis or Handbreaths high, and they will be thought big horses there if eleven, and although so small yet are they full of vigour and life, and some not so high as others often prove to be the strongest, yea there are some, whom an able man can lift up in his arms, yet will they carry him and a woman behind him 8 miles forward and as many back; Summer or Winter they never come into an House but run upon the Mountains in some places as flocks, and if any time in Winter the storm be so great, that they are straightened for food, they will come down from the Hills when the Ebb is in the sea, and eat the Sea-Ware (as likewise do the sheep). They will live till a considerable age as 26, 28 or 30 years, and they will be good riding Horses in 24 especially they'll be more vigorous and live the longer if they be 4 years old before they are put to work. Those of a black colour are judged to be the most durable, and the Pyed often prove not so good; they have been more numerous than they now are, the best of them are to be had in Sanston and Eston also they are good in Waes and Yell, those of the least size are in the Northern Isles of Yell and Uist.

'The Coldness of the Air, the Barrenness of the Mountains on which they feed and their hard usage may occasion to keep them so little, for if bigger Horses be brought into the Country, their kind within a little time will degenerate; and indeed in the present case we may see the Wisdome of Providence, for their way being deep and Mossie in many places, these lighter Horses come through when the greater and heavier would sink down; and they leap over ditches very nimbly, yea up and down Mossy braes and Hillocks with heavy riders upon them, which I could not look upon but with Admiration, yea I have seen them climb up braes upon their knees, when otherwise they could not get the height overcome, so that our Horses would be but little if at all serviceable there.'

Two years later we have seen that Martin Martin concurred with Mr Brand, and that Charles Cordiner found ponies in Orkney in 1780.

In 1812 a Capt. Henderson refers to Orkney ponies: 'A great many brood mares were kept by the farmers [in the West of Scotland], who sold the young stock when about 14 months old to travelling dealers. The dealers used to take these young ones to the Orkneys, and usually exchanged them for five and six year old ponies bred in the Orkney islands, which they sold at a profit in the Caithness markets in the late summer. This interchange of blood could not but be beneficial to the breed.' Capt. Henderson does not mention *what* the interchange of blood was: what sort of ponies were to be found in the Orkney Islands. But the *Statistical Account* makes a precise statement. Under Mainland of Orkney, Parish of St Andrew: 'There are few horses bred in these parishes, or in any part of Orkney, most of them being brought from Caithness and Strathnaver,[1] when a year old, and are then called staigs.'

Shetland ponies were first used in the pits in the north of England (where they replaced women and children!) about 1850, and they were much in demand. What a contrast to freedom on the hills! From three

---

[1] North coast of Sutherland.

to five years old their value was £4 10s. though their price varied with the price of coal. As time went on the ponies increased in value.

Youatt writing about 1820 tells us that: 'The Shetland pony, called in Scotland a *sheltie*, an inhabitant of the extremest northern Scottish Isles, is a very diminutive animal—sometimes not more than seven hands and a half in height, and rarely exceeding nine and a half.

'He is often exceedingly beautiful, with a small head, good-tempered countenance, a short neck, fine towards the throttle, shoulders low and thick—in so little a creature far from being a blemish—back short, quarters expanded and powerful, legs flat and fine and pretty round feet. These ponies possess immense strength for their size; will fatten upon almost anything; and are perfectly docile. One of them, nine hands (or three feet) in height, carried a man of twelve stone forty miles in one day.

'A friend of the author was, not long ago, presented with one of these elegant little animals. He was several miles from home, and was puzzled how to convey his newly acquired property. The Shetlander was scarcely more than seven hands high, and as docile as he was beautiful.

'"Can we not carry him in your chaise?" said his friend. The strange experiment was tried. The sheltie was placed in the bottom of the gig, and covered up as well as could be managed with the apron; a few bits of bread kept him quiet; and thus he was safely conveyed away, and exhibited the curious spectacle of a horse riding in a gig.'

> Nor do these islands aught contain
> Worth mention, save peculiar strain
> Of horses so exceeding small,
> Yet active, hardy, strong withal,
> So curious deemed that the Fair
> Prefer them when they take the air
> To Phaeton or to car attached
> A pleasing sight when aptly matched.
>
> *Tour of Dr Prosody to the Shetlands*, 1821.

A lady who published in 1840 a sprightly account of a brief visit to Shetland thus describes the smallest pony on record, as having been reared by Mr William Hay of Hayfield: 'I expected to observe Shetland ponies galloping in every field, but they are chiefly running wild among the distant, unenclosed hills, where, in most instances, the fore legs are manacled together.[1] Nothing is trusted to the honour of a Shetland pony, but they are all shackled in a most uneasy manner, hobbling along like rabbits,[2] which inconvenient contrivance ruins their paces afterwards. When well fed from an early age, they grow nearly to the height of a donkey, but some years ago Mr Hay reared a perfectly well-formed pony, which measured only twenty-six inches high. Not so tall as a moderate-sized hobby horse! I have heard sportsmen talk of a horse

[1] 'Cloggit', as the old lawting ordinances said.
[2] The *Shetland Pony Stud Book* observes that ponies are never hobbled in this way in Shetland 'nowadays' (i.e. in 1891).

that would canter round a cabbage leaf, but here was one literally capable of doing so. The very largest men ride these tiny creatures at full
speed, looking from a distance as if they had merely hooked on a pair of
additional legs, being scarcely a foot off the ground, and yet racing
rapidly along. How would a regiment of cavalry look mounted—or
lowered rather—on these stout little chargers.' [1] *Shetland and the Shet-
landers*, Edinburgh, 1840.

The *Shetland Pony Stud Book* was published in 1891: the earliest
recorded birth is that of No. 22, Lion, foaled in 1864, Dun, 36 inches.

In the *C. G. A. Magazine* for June 1961 a letter appears containing
the following information: 'The Shetland pony is still used to some
extent in its native land, particularly in the island of Unst. Here they
are frequently used for bringing in the peats, and sometimes for hay and
potatoes, etc., as pack ponies. Incidentally more ponies are bred in
Unst than elsewhere in Shetland and an annual sale is now held there
in October. The Shetland pony can be any colour, and the parti-
coloured ones are not due to a former cross with another breed. The
Department of Agriculture for Scotland provides grants towards 18
premium stallions in the Islands, the Shetland Pony Stud Book Society
providing the balance and taking care of the scheme, by which better
foals are now being bred. 14895.'

Sir Walter Gilbey, who was a great equine historian, writes in 1903
of the attempts to increase the size of the Shelties. 'About the middle of
the last century', he says, 'Norwegian pony stallions were introduced
into Dunrossness, with the result that a distinct variety was established
and still continues; this is called the Sumburgh breed; [2] in size the
ponies range from 12 to 13.2 hh.

'Another variety known as the Fetlar breed owes its origin to the
introduction by Sir Arthur Nicholson of a Mustang stallion named
Bolivar previous to 1850; the Fetlar ponies run from 11 to 13 hh. and
are described as remarkably handsome, swift, spirited but less tractable
than the pure Shetland.'

These are of course experiments, and it may be questioned if they
are of value to the Shetland as a breed or whether many of their progeny
survive now.

Several pure Shetland studs were established, amongst them the
Marquis of Londonderry's on Bressay; his object was to help improve
the pure breed of Shetland pony. A well-known breeder, whose stud
was in Kent, won a great number of prizes, including Madison Square
Garden, with some excellent ponies at the beginning of this century.
During the last fifty years many foreign buyers have bought shelties and
have founded studs on the Continent and elsewhere.

[1] In the same year 1840 the *Statistical Account* recorded the most general
colour in the Islands as 'dark mouse grey'.

[2] Sumburgh is the oldest continuously inhabited site in all Shetland—
Jarlshof, excavated by the Ministry of Works. Among the Iron Age remains
(B.C. or A.D. 100) were found bones of Shetland ponies.

The Western Isles. Mr MacDonald, in *Highland Ponies*, says: 'All Highland ponies are descended from common ancestors, but they have differentiated into separate types, each with certain characteristics of its own. The differentiation may be attributed to four main causes: firstly to environment, secondly to their treatment by man, thirdly to selection for particular kinds of work, and fourthly to the attempts made at different times to improve the breeds by the introduction of crosses of more or less alien strains of blood.

'Apart from the characteristics impressed upon the breed by environment and by the various purposes for which the ponies are kept, the most valuable qualities possessed by Highland ponies are their sturdy constitution, their keen intelligence, and their concentrated vitality, all of which are common to the entire breed.'

These ponies can be divided into two sections: the Island and the Mainland—and they are markedly different. No less than eleven islands off the west coast of Scotland have (or had) their types of ponies. Some of these islands we have already visited. They are Skye, Uist, Barra Rhum, Mull, Arran, Lewis and Harris, Tiree, Islay and Jura.

On other islands, on the one hand Arab blood was introduced, and on the other Clydesdale!

Including one or two studs on the Mainland, the Islands must have kept their ponies 'pure' almost until the beginning of the nineteenth century, and they were bred according to the work which they were required to do (and on Mull, for instance, there were again two types: the Gocan and the Galloway). The light-legged Barra pony used for carrying creels of peat was a different sort to the famous ponies of Arran and the renowned 'Herd Laddie' of the mainland Atholl stud.

It is recorded that Lord Forteviot, as Mr John Dewar, M.P., drove a beautiful pair of black ponies.

One of the most noted sires was 'Rory o' the Hills', foaled in 1897, whose great-granddam was a well-bred Clydesdale mare. Rory eventually went to Mull. Rory's grandsire mated to the small native mares seems to have been most successful, for 'stout, sturdy ponies were bred, and there were many mouse dun and dark cream colours among them.'

Of *Lewis* in 1836 the *Statistical Account* of Scotland says: 'The blackfaced cattle, horses and sheep are of rather a diminutive size. They are too numerous by one-half; a small tenant that pays annually £3 sterling will keep seven or eight head. The farmers and tacksmen keep a larger breed of horses for riding and for the cart. But in general the horses are not much higher than Shetland ponies. They are firm and strong, fit for the mossy soil and rocky shore . . . many of them are of beautiful symmetry. Mr S. M'Kenzie of Lewis sent four of them to his late Majesty George IV as a present and as a specimen of insular strength and symmetry in small compass, "multum in parvo".'

The island of *Harris* provides us with a connecting link with the prehistoric finds of Kent and Essex mentioned early on in this book. In his book *The Influence of Man on Animal Life in Scotland*, Professor Ritchie writes: 'We can safely assume that the bones of a very small horse, found in the ancient underground "Pict" or "Erid" house at Nisibost in Harris, are those of the earliest known representatives of the European race. Perhaps from the same ancient line were descended the horses, whose remains were found by Mr Symington Grieve in the upper strata of the Crystal Spring Cavern in Colonsay, where they had evidently been used as food, for the bones of young animals were more plentiful than those of adults.

'The Hebridean ponies are commonly of a brownish-black or foxey-red colour, though there are occasional duns and greys and one race, that of *Uist*, like the ponies of the *Faroe Islands*, is distinguished by a striking silvery mane and tail. They bear a coat of thick rough hair, are of small size, 12.2 to 13.2 hh. and, in the old almost extinct race of Barra, have fine limbs and rather large heads with straight profile and flat nose.' Professor Ewart considers them to be 'a remnant of a very old and once widely distributed variety, the origin of which is never likely to be revealed'. But its connection with Scandinavia at least is undoubted. Faroe is the half-way house between Shetland, Iceland and Norway, and this type closely resemble the Fjord pony of west Norway.

In 1549 Monro noted that amongst the Western Isles there 'layes ane little ile, half ane myle lang, callit be the Eriche, Ellannaneache, that is in English, the Horse isle, guid for Horse and other store, pertaining to the Bishope of the Iles'.

Some Arabian blood was introduced in 1898 by Professor Cossar Ewart, but the crofters did not make much use of the stallions. Earlier, in 1714, the Chief of Clanranald, who was killed at Sheriffmuir in 1715, had imported Spanish blood which did improve the *South Uist* ponies. Probably the same Galician blood that had been crossed into the Connemara ponies. *South Uist, North Uist* and *Benbecula* are separated only at high tide.

'Even in the year 1764, not only the form, but the cool fearless temper of the Spanish horse could be discerned in the horses of S. Uist, especially in those in the possession of Clanranald, and of his cousin, MacDonald of Boisdale. At that time, those ponies, both by build and disposition were thought to be the best horses in the Highlands and, although of low stature, they were judged more valuable than other horses of the same size.'

In 1811 Macdonald writes in his *Survey of the Agriculture of the Hebrides*: 'The Hebridean Breed of horses resembles that which we find in almost all countries of the same description of climate and surface. It is small, active and remarkably durable and hardy . . . the horses range freely . . . and are then hunted after like so many wild beasts, and each tenant or proprietor endeavours to secure his own, which he has not seen for many weeks before. They are driven into enclosed pens or fields, frequently into bogs and morasses, before they can be laid hold of, and sometimes they are injured severely in the process. Their manes are then cut, the hair laid up for rope work or other purposes, and the young horses are gradually broken in for the labour and cruel hardships of the winter.'

A pair of Norwegian stallions were introduced in about 1890: they added considerably to the number of ponies with silver manes and tails. A Clydesdale, too, seems to have been a successful sire. He was known as 'Bain's stallion' was 15.2 hands and belonged to a contractor from Ayrshire who went to Uist to help build the new school houses in 1872. 'Sollas', a son of 'Bain's stallion', was the sire of 'Moss Crop' and 'Isleman'.

Macneil of *Barra* also used Arabian stallions, and a Gaelic song goes: 'Macneil's milk-white steed with flowing mane and tail and surpassing in fleetness the stags of the forest.' At the end of the nineteenth century, few of the *Barra* ponies exceeded 13 hands, and Skye people used them for driving in pony traps; they were attractive-looking ponies with small heads and some 'attained great speed in a pacing gait.' Through crossing with *Uist* ponies this old type is said to have died out.

We have already mentioned Dr Johnson's visit to the Hebrides; he says of the *Rhum* ponies: 'They are very small but of a breed eminent in beauty', like the one the Laird of Coll bought for the top price of one-and-a-half-guineas.

Now the *Rhum* ponies were also known as Black Galloways; and some were sent by Lord Arthur Cecil down to the New Forest. They were noted for their hazel eyes—and this is still a feature of the original Rhum pony strain.

Unfortunately it is almost impossible to trace just how old the strain of *Rhum* ponies is: several writers say 'very ancient'. Most of the ponies were dun and some had silver manes and tails, and in the middle of the nineteenth century were very wild and almost unbreakable. They lived to over thirty years old; Lord Arthur Cecil wrote of some stallions taken to Hatfield which were so savage they had to be gelded. 'They could trot 12 miles in fifty-five minutes and jump anything under the saddle.'

Mrs Kathleen Warren of the New Calgary Stud contributes the following interesting observation on the present-day *Rhum* ponies. 'Today the ponies of *Rhum* could hardly be described as being of "eminent" beauty, but they are probably the most interesting Highland ponies in existence at the present time. . . . Most of them are around 12.2 to 13 hh. and are true pony type. There are a great many golden duns and creams among them, with seal points and legs, and tremendous manes and tails which are covered with an outer layer of silver hairs and also the hair over the coronets and fetlocks. This silver colouring is peculiar to the *Rhum* ponies. There are some which are a sort of chestnut, though more of a cream colour, and have silver manes and tails.'

Mrs Warren further adds: 'In an old book on Deer Stalking, that I found in the Hall of Kinloch Castle on the island, were pictures of small black ponies carrying deer over country similar to that of the Isle of Rhum and these must surely have been some of the original blacks. Some years ago the Highland Pony Society decided no longer to recognize the two types of Highland pony, i.e. the Western Island type and the Mainland type. As a result of this step being taken the old Western Island pony is fast disappearing.'

The island of *Mull* produced another very ancient strain, in fact two: the Gocan (the small island pony), and the Galloway. The former is said to have disappeared some sixty years ago, and the Galloway has since vanished. During the last century an American trotting horse, called 'Yankee', brought over in a sailing ship, sired a grey stallion which became the sire of 'Macneil's Canna', who was responsible for some good ponies on the island. The word Gocan, according to a Mr Morrison of Kengharair, comes from Gocan na Cuthag—the ground lark. These ponies were small and determined: 'they could keep going on the road for any distance'.

Two old-fashioned roadster horses were introduced about 1870, 'Lord Douglas' and 'Tom Thumb'. A brother to the former 'Douglas' was a celebrated trotter and *their* sire was the famous chestnut stallion in the west of Scotland, 'Lord Douglas' Horse'. This horse was bought out of a cab in London; he stood on the island of Arran, but his merits were not fully appreciated until some time after he was put down.

One of the best known studs on *Mull* was the Calgary, and in 1905, in the *Transactions of the Highland and Agricultural Society*, Mr T. Dykes says, quoting from a letter from Mr Mackenzie, the owner of Calgary: 'The line I am going on is to try and get better backs and shoulders on the Highland ponies. I like the Clydesdale as much as any, but the cross was not a success. I am crossing Highland mares with "The Syrian", a well-bred and good type of Arab. I am putting the fillies of the cross back to "Islesman". Putting "The Syrian" to very small ponies 12.2 to 13 hands I got the foals too small, but putting him to strong Highland mares, about 14.2 hands, I have had some grand ponies and all I have sold averaged £40 each. I am quite sure the Arab blood has made the *Mull* ponies what they were in the old days, and I do not see why they should not go back to them again.'

It is not our intention to pursue our inquiries into the twentieth century, but the above was quoted to show how popular the old blood of the Arab was in the Western Isles.

One of the best known ponies on *Arran* who came from the Rosehaugh Stud was 'Herd Laddie', the grand sire of the Highland pony 'Jock', which belonged to King George V.

In 1811 there were around 1,500 ponies of the Gocan type on the island of *Tiree*, then unfortunately the Clydesdale was introduced and the native breed disappeared.

In 1638 Duncan Campbell of *Islay* wrote to his brother Colin of

35. The small West Highland pony probably owed its survival in the nineteenth century to its convenience as a sporting vehicle, especially after the royal family took up residence at Balmoral.

Galcantray asking him: 'I wyshe if you may Cromarties old Spanish horse provyding he be of a reasonable prys'; and Cosmo Innes, speaking of Scotland during the Middle Ages, says: 'Somewhat more care is shown in the breeding of horses. Long before this time the Lairds of Glenorchy [1] had introduced English and foreign horses for their great Stud in Perthshire, and the example was followed by Cawdor.'

The Mainland. We have mentioned the Bressay Stone found in Shetland, on which a rider mounted upon a small pony has been engraved. But at many places on the mainland of Scotland numerous stones of a like nature have been found. They are presumed to be some time prior to the Norse invasions.[2] In *Sculptured Stones of Scotland* we find enumerated as follows: 'Among the scenes pictured on the cross-slabs are men on horseback, sometimes armed with spears and round shields. At times they are engaged in the chase of the deer or in the boar-hunt. The horses are generally drawn with much spirit. We can see the ornaments of the bridles and reins, and the peaked saddlecloth,[3] on which the rider sits without stirrups. The horses are represented sometimes with flowing and at others with docked tails . . . a chariot drawn by two horses with plaited tails like those on Assyrian sculptures, driven by a man in front, and with two figures in the chariot . . . a figure, apparently

---

[1] Glenorchy was once a great centre for breeding ponies. In 1554 there was a dreadful snowstorm, recounted by the monastic chronicler of Finlarig: 'There was no thaw till 17th of January. It was the greatest snow storm that was seen in the memory of man living. Many little wild horses and mares, kye, sheep and goats perished and died for want of food in the mountains and other parts.'

[2] Mainly because the riders have no stirrups.

[3] Or treeless pad or pilch.

of a female, on horseback, with plaided dress. Many of these pictures seem to portray actual occurrences. It seems plain, for instance, that the picture on a stone at Meigle of a boar in the act of devouring a prostrate human figure, and of a chariot on the same slab, is a representation of a real event known to the artist, while the pictures of hunting scenes and kindred subjects probably represent some remarkable passing incident of sport, or at all events scenes which are going on around him.'

The most illustrative of these stones are at St Madoes, Fowlis Wester, near Crieff, at Balletheron, and at Fordoun, and in the churchyard at Aberlemno; and here strangely we have two types of docking, that which we are accustomed to see on hunters of the early part of this century, or on a docked hackney where the hair is left fairly long; and on another stone, the horses are docked and their tails resemble those of the deer in the same picture; they were therefore cut off close to the rump or shaved. And the chariot horses have full long tails which appear to be braided. Of the horses with long tails, they are not full and flowing as in wild ponies, but are well kept and pulled.

We see that docking was not, as we have always been told, necessary to keep the tails free of the reins when driving, but was apparently done for some other reason.[1] The horses—and indeed many are not *ponies* at all, for they are all shapes and sizes—are shown with a variety of different-shaped heads and even with lop-ears! There are some number of horses portrayed and they are all clean legged.

At Kirriemuir there is a truly magnificent stone showing two horses, ridden by gentlemen with beards, sitting on comfortable-looking pad saddles, hunting the stag with a dog and each armed with a spear; but both are mounted on full-sized coursers or hunters, the top one being up to so much weight that he could almost be a Great Horse—and this was probably several hundred years before the advent of William the Conqueror. The horses are wearing ornamented bridles, and one horse's saddle is held in place with a crupper. Most of the horses carrying riders are ambling, although two appear to be walking or trotting as are the chariot horses, one or two are cantering.

We mentioned Professor Ritchie's observations on the ponies of *Barra,* and in connection with the antiquity of horses in Scotland generally he has this to say: 'Whether the primitive horses whose remains have been found in the Forest Bed of Norfolk, ever made their way to Scotland, it is impossible to say, for the glaciers of the Ice Age have long since scoured away possible evidences of that highly probable invasion; but ten bones of small horses were discovered during the cutting of a railway near Crofthead in Renfrewshire in a series of deposits five feet below a layer in which were found remains of the Giant Fallow Deer or "Irish Elk" (*Megaceros giganteus*) and of the Urus (*Bos taurus*

---

[1] It could be (*a*) practical, the hair being periodically harvested and spun into harness and ships' rigging; (*b*) religious: the Ibo horse-cult of West Africa today involves cutting off the horse's tail.

primigenus). There can be little doubt that the horses represented in this deep deposit entered Scotland during one of the milder inter-glacial periods which broke the continuity of the Ice Age.'

Other bones and deposits may possibly represent the domesticated herds of Neolithic man. Professor Cossar Ewart designated the Croft-head bones as belonging to the *plateau* type or North Atlantic pony.

We shall probably never know whether the Neolithic wanderers who first inhabited Scotland found only the *plateau* pony awaiting them—or whether there were already other types present here. But the problems of transporting horses by sea were probably more than Neolithic seamanship or horsemanship could solve. Be that as it may, perhaps the old *Uist*, *Barra* and *Rhum* ponies, and the other ponies of the Hebrides are not so distant from that ancient type.

There seems to be no logical reason why we may not assume that the Romans took horses up to the Antonine Wall, which ran from the Firth of Forth to the Clyde, and even in those days, and for long afterwards, cattle-raiding and horse-stealing were the recognized *forte* of Pictish aristocrats. No doubt a few good stallions found their way 'over the Wall' and even at this stage began the process of improving the stock of the Celtic–Atlantic mares.

As we have said, judging from the extraordinary variety of horses depicted on the stones, they were plentiful and much used in Scotland, both during the Roman occupation of Britain and when it had ceased.

In the year 1406 James I bade that no horse under three years old should be sent out of Scotland; and in 1567 James VI forbade the export of horses. It is also on record that in 1540 Henry VIII sent the Scottish king, by his ambassador Sir Ralph Sadler, a number of Spanish jennets and Barbary horses; this was in response to an application for 'trotting geldings' the previous year, when as we have seen James V personally asked Henry for twenty-four horses. Notoriously, Spanish jennets were pacers, not trotters at all!

But as early as 1535 James V passed a law to increase 'the size of the Scottish horses and more particularly those of the ancient forests, of which Atholl is one of the oldest'. His predecessor had received from Louis XII of France 'a present of a choice collection of the best French breeds'.

There were accounts of 'wild horses' in Scotland in 1527 and again in 1618; most likely these were horses which had been introduced during the Norse invasions which after all lasted from 800 to 1263. There were legends of yellow horses with bristling manes and flowing tails, and this rather suggests horses of Scandinavian origin.

But Professor Ritchie has this to say: 'The oldest reference to Scottish horse breeding of which I am aware, is contained in the Charter of Kelso whereby, before A.D. 1200, Gilbert de Imfraville granted the monks of Kelso a tenth of the foals bred in his forest and studs. The horses were bred by being let loose in the forest, where foals ran wild for three years,

212

until they were broken in. The best horses were selected and kept apart in the parks about the Baron's castle.'

These perhaps were some of the latter-day 'wild horses'. At any rate they were the stock which a succession of Scottish kings improved upon and which subsequently may have developed into the ponies of the Isles and the garrons of the Mainland which we know today.

In his book *Thoroughbreds and other Ponies*, 1903, Sir Walter Gilbey quotes Mr Munro Mackenzie: 'After long study and observation I have come to the conclusion that the original Highland Pony was a small animal from 12.2 hh. to 13.2 hh. such as is now seen on the Island of

36. The small West Highland type enabled the nineteenth-century landowner to shoot grouse in slippers and spats. It is obvious from the posture of this laird that he is about to fire without dismounting.

Barra. . . . One strong reason I have for this conclusion is the greater number of ponies that were bred in the Highlands in old times. In a record I have of my own property (by no means a large one) I find that in the year 1770 nearly 80 ponies were kept, and taking into consideration the very large stock of cattle kept at the same time, the ponies must have been very small and hardy, as the cattle would be sure to have the best part of the ground.

'Highland ponies may be divided into three classes: First, the small ponies of Barra and the outer islands, standing from 12.2 to 13.2 hands. . . . Second, what might be called the high class riding pony of the Western Highlands and Isles, 13.2 to 14.2 hands. These have almost died out but they had a strong cross of Arab blood. . . . The third class is what are called the Garrons, they run a good deal bigger than the former classes. Some are found up to 15 hands. They are more the horses of Perthshire and the central Highlands than of the West Highlands and Isles. I am of the opinion that they were originally bred from small ponies crossed with larger horses brought into the Highlands with troops during unsettled times. They have good game heads, bold eyes, shoulder a bit straight and back long, with the best legs and feet, a good tuft of hair on the heel, and often a very well set on tail.'

'The Highland garron is the largest (14 to 15 hands) and strongest of all pure breeds of ponies in the country and is admirably adapted to the work of carrying the sportsmen to the hill and returning with heavy loads of deer, up to 18 stone in weight, from the wild forests of the Scottish Highlands' (Board of Agriculture and Fisheries).

We must not trespass too far into the twentieth century, but the following story of the capacity of a Highland garron of the Atholl breed to carry weight deserves attention. This was a grey gelding, just over 14 hands, who appeared in a travelling circus—he was a 'real Atholl type—low and long, with great strong loins and quarters and strong fore-arms and bone'. 'He acted', says Mr MacDonald in *Highland Ponies*, 'the part of what is known as a "back-rider"; that is to say, with his back well dusted with resin (invisible) to prevent the rider's feet from slipping, he galloped round the ring carrying various performers in all kinds of ways. He concluded his "turn" by carrying seven full-grown people (five women and two men) at a free and light gallop round the ring. Taking the average weight of the seven riders at $8\frac{1}{2}$ stones, this pony was carrying at least sixty stones, and he did not seem to feel that this was causing him the slightest exertion.'

Earlier in the pages of this book (page 176) we referred to second sight in horses, of sweating violently or suddenly starting, e.g. shying. Many years ago my grandfather owned a horse which was driven in a dog-cart; on a dark night at a certain spot at the bottom of a hill he would shy violently and then proceed to gallop the two miles home. There was no stopping him. None of the other horses did it, but the story went that people had seen a ghost at this place; there was otherwise no accounting for the horse's fear.

To end this chapter on Highland ponies, we will bring forward one point which may account for the weight-carrying capacity of the ponies in the above accounts—and we shall mention a breed that has ceased to exist, a fact which is to recur often as we proceed through the regions of the native pony.

We know that in many places Clydesdales were used to cross with the Highland pony, and it is interesting to note the following written by Mr Dykes in the *Transactions of the Highland Agricultural Society* for 1905: 'Up to 40 years ago, grey mares of ancient and undiluted Clydesdale type were commonly to be found stabled in all the country inns in Kilmarnock and Ayr on Market days—hardy, useful, short-legged sorts, which might still have been preserved but for the fact that there were no stallions of their size and activity and type available. Some of these old-fashioned gig pony Clydesdale greys found their way into the north, and no doubt had much to do with forming the modern mainland ponies.

It is not strictly speaking "pony" blood, but it was brought there when it was wanted, has done much good, and may do a lot of good yet if properly mated.'

The *Highland Pony Stud Book* was started in 1891. It is interesting to note the colours of those ponies registered in 1960.

Total Registered					Dun colour
36 mares	.	.	.	.	26
11 stallions	.	.	.	.	7
6 geldings	.	.	.	.	4
13 Appendix A	.	.	.	.	7
3 Appendix B	.	.	.	.	3
69					47

$66\frac{2}{3}$ per cent of total were dun.
About 9 per cent (6) black, dark brown.
About 18 per cent (13) white, grey.

CHAPTER TWELVE

Galloway, The Dales and The Fells

> 'Sho's a gran' galloway is yon, Misther Dent. Wan
> t' fost prahze at Bowes Show. An' they coom frev all
> ower England to Bowes Show. Aye, all ower England
> —Kendal, Sedbergh and Kirby Stephen.'
>
> Swaledale farmer to co-author's
grandfather, c. 1880.

IN THE south-west of Scotland the local ponies were once known, at any rate to the English, as the Galloway breed. In *The Horseman's Honour or the Beautie of Horsemanship*, edition of 1660, Gervase Markham says: 'For the horses of Scotland they are much less than those of England, yet not inferior in goodnesse; and by reason of their smallness they keep few stoned but geld many by which likewise they retain this saying, *that there is no gelding like those in Scotland*, and they, as the English, are for the most part amblers. Also in Scotland there are a race of small nagges which they call Galloways or galloway nagges which for fine shape, easie pace, pure metall and infinit toughness are not short of the best nagges that are bred in any country whatsoever; and for soundnesse in body they exceede the most races that are extant, as dayly experience shows in their continuall travels, journeyings and fore-huntings.'

Even earlier we read that when Edward III invaded Scotland, 'the common people of the country all rode little hackneys and geldings' (Froissart).

Berenger says in 1771: 'This kingdom has been famous for breeding a peculiar sort of horses called Galloways. From the care and attention paid at present to the culture of horses it is to be expected that it will soon be able to send forth numbers of valuable and generous breeds destined to a variety of purposes and equal to all: the country being very capable of answering the wishes of the judicious breeder, who need only remember that colts require to be well nourished in winter and sheltered from the severity of a rigorous and changeable sky.'

215

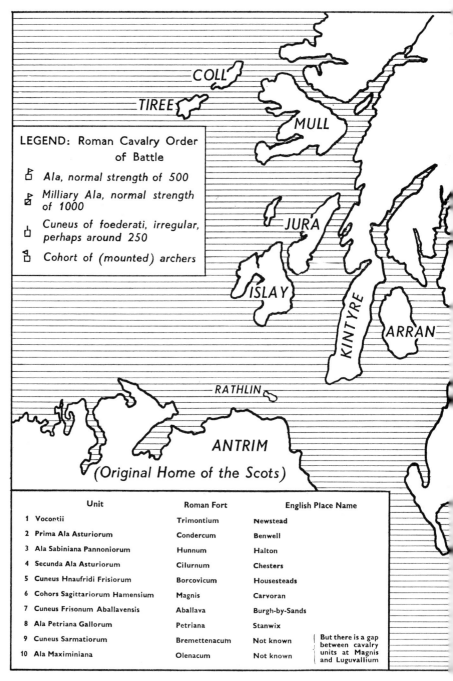

	Unit	Roman Fort	English Place Name	
1	Vocontii	Trimontium	Newstead	
2	Prima Ala Asturiorum	Condercum	Benwell	
3	Ala Sabiniana Pannoniorum	Hunnum	Halton	
4	Secunda Ala Asturiorum	Cilurnum	Chesters	
5	Cuneus Hnaufridi Frisiorum	Borcovicum	Housesteads	
6	Cohors Sagittariorum Hamensium	Magnis	Carvoran	
7	Cuneus Frisonum Aballavensis	Aballava	Burgh-by-Sands	
8	Ala Petriana Gallorum	Petriana	Stanwix	
9	Cuneus Sarmatiorum	Bremettenacum	Not known	But there is a gap between cavalry units at Magnis and Luguvallium
10	Ala Maximiniana	Olenacum	Not known	

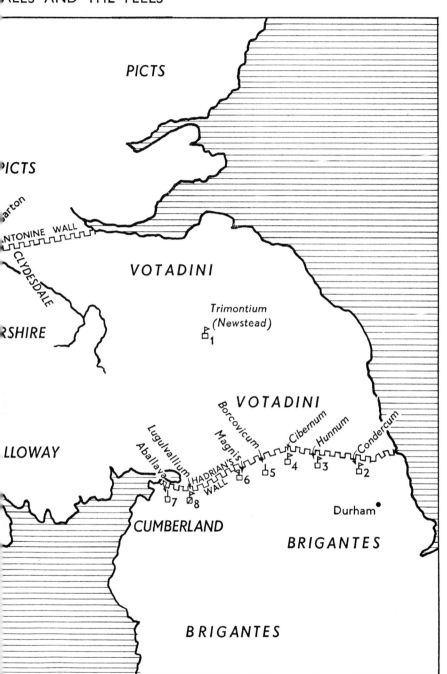

Youatt, 1820, writes: 'The pure galloway was said to be nearly fourteen hands high, and sometimes more; of a bright bay or brown, with black legs, small head and neck, and peculiarly deep and clean legs. Its qualities were speed, stoutness, and surefootedness over a very rugged and mountainous country.'

It was also said that the Galloway was a diminutive horse resembling the Welsh Cob, and the breed gradually diminished when the law of 1605 'deprived the moss-troopers and other predatory border men of a method of livelihood which involved the use of hardy and enduring horses'. (See above at the beginning of 'Stuart Times', page 150.)

Extracts from Samuel Johnson's Dictionary, 1755:

Hobby: An Irish or Scottish horse: a pacing horse: a garran.

Garran: First remarks that the literal meaning of the word is simply the Gaelic for 'gelding'. Then a 'Highland horse which brought into the North of England takes the name of *Galloway*'.

Galloway: A horse not more than fourteen hands high, much used in the North.

Sir Walter Gilbey, in *Thoroughbred and Other Ponies*, 1903, writes: 'Before 1800 and during more recent years the Galloways cannot be described either as horses or ponies: they played an active part in agricultural work in the lowlands of Scotland. In localities where no roads existed, and wheeled traffic was impossible, galloways were used not only for riding but for the transport of agricultural produce; as they lacked the weight and strength to draw the two-horse plough, ploughing continued to be done by oxen, but the sledges were drawn by galloways, which were also used to carry corn and general merchandise in pots and panniers.

'The purposes for which they were used indicated the desirability of increasing their height and strength, and with this end in view cross-breeding was commenced somewhere about the year 1800 and continued for fifty years. The old Galloway after this period almost disappeared from all parts of the mainland, and survives only in such remote situations as the Island of Mull.'

We know now that the cross-breeding was by the Clydesdale, which also caused the disappearance of the galloway on Mull. So the breed vanished from the banks of the Solway Firth, but as we shall see it was not entirely lost but 'passed on' into another breed.

About two hundred years ago a Dr Anderson thus describes the galloway: 'There was once a breed of small elegant horses in Scotland, similar to those of Iceland and Sweden, and which were known by the name of galloways; the best of which sometimes reached the height of fourteen hands and a half.

'One of this description I possessed, it having been bought for my use when a boy. In point of elegance of shape it was a perfect picture; and in disposition was gentle and compliant. It moved almost with a wish, and never tired. I rode this little creature for twenty-five years, and twice in that time I rode a hundred and fifty miles at a stretch, without stopping, except to bait, and that not for above an hour at a time. It came in at the last stage with as much ease and alacrity as it travelled the first. I could have undertaken to have performed on this beast, when it was in its prime, sixty miles a day for a twelve-month, running without any extraordinary exertion.'

In 1754 Mr Corker's galloway went one hundred miles a day for three successive days, over the Newmarket course, and without the slightest distress.

Also a galloway, which belonged to a Mr Sinclair, of Kirkby Lonsdale, performed at Carlisle the extraordinary feat of a thousand miles in a thousand hours.

We have seen that the word Galloway was used to describe a definite breed of Border pony, and the Black Galloways on *Rhum* were different to other island ponies; but the word itself appears to signify a lighter sort of pony, more active, alert and possibly less docile than the usual run of Highland ponies. In this case, as with Gocan, it is the word which expresses the temperament, rather than the locality which has given rise to the name of a breed or special type.

Mrs Murray Usher, of Kirkcudbrightshire, writes: 'Mr John McG. Wilson, Kirkmabreck, Creetown, who is a very knowledgeable farmer of the older generation, tells me, "Yes, there was a distinct breed, now I fear extinct as far as the bounds of Galloway are concerned. They were right hardy workers who could take their place among the heaviest breeds in almost any work on the farm and in some of the lighter jobs were superior, being much smarter. Around 14 hands, well coupled and almost tireless. I do not know of one anywhere; twenty-five or thirty years ago I had one till he died of old age. There was nothing striking about them except their movement which was easy and rapid with great staying power, could run twelve to fifteen miles or more without breaking trot."

'On further inquiry he says, "*Colour of pony*, the one I had was common brown with dark legs which got near black down to the hoofs, that were tough and blue. A small half-moon spot of white on forehead. This pony was bred in Wigtownshire sired by a stallion which was a real typical one of the recognized true breed which undoubtedly then existed. There are none of them now. In any case I never saw more than half a dozen. No one need doubt but that they were a disinct breed of great value to hill farmers for driving or working on the land and easily kept. Although I could not define the areas where they survived and vanished I think you are right in assuming that the hill farms in the north of England would be a natural place to find them at the time that they were in south Scotland."' (Gatehouse-of-Fleet, June 1959.)

Earlier it has been mentioned that the Norse for 'fresh' is *teitr*, being the origin for *tit*, and an important point which south-country people may not realize is that in the popular speech of Yorkshire and Durham and some other northern areas today, 'gallowa'' just means anything under 15 hands of whatever origin. This had been so since the eighteenth century when the special *galloway* races began. At first animals from Galloway ran in them but they soon became the preserve of dwarf thoroughbreds; and the language of the north for *blood pony* is not *gallowa'* but *tit*.

If we are to try our hand at an explanation of the word of which even Samuel Johnson 'could not tell what was the original', then we may appropriately add our quota here, since all explanations must logically be based on the earliest recorded spelling—the Lowland Scots *powney*. It must be a diminutive of some kind. In medieval English, north or south, diminutives in -nay or -ney are not uncommon. Cockney is one such. That leaves the first syllable.

Among the sum total of features that go to make up the elusive whole which the judges call 'pony character', the ears and what lies before and behind them are important. In the ears and the forelock and the upper part of the crest reside those qualities of impudence and innocence, of delicacy and toughness, which distinguish the expression of the pony from that of the horse. In all the dialects of Lowland Scotland, that part of the anatomy between the eyebrows and the nape of the neck, in men as in horses, is called the 'pow'—spelt in English poll. This could be an affectionate diminutive bestowed by the breeders themselves on the creature with the characteristic pow. Alternatively it could be a diminutive of contempt, bestowed by the French-speaking owners of larger horses. (In Scotland, French continued to be the second language of the upper classes much longer than in England.) The French for foal is *poulain*. Poulenet, pouleney, would give rise to pouney since the consistent tendency of *l* is to disappear after *u*, and (phonetically at least) before *n*. For example, Fowberry and Lincoln. The name would imply that the speaker did not believe—or affected not to believe—that the creature could really be full-grown.

Dales and Fell. These two pony breeds are classed together, because whatever their differences of appearance now, everything indicates that they sprang from the same parent stock. There is no trace of doubt either that the parent stock of the Dales and Fell ponies was the same as that of the Welsh or for that matter the Highland. It was the indigenous pony of Britain—whether it was harnessed to the Celtic chariots of East Anglia or carved on Pictish gravestones. But this indigenous pony was itself not a uniform type.

What *is* interesting is how the pony types varied over the centuries— here an infusion of 'alien' blood, there sparse and not very nourishing keep; the desire of their possessors that they should gallop, pull carts, carry packs; fashion; necessity; and greed. These and many other factors 'made up' a pony breed and eventually differentiated the one from the other.

For instance, an explanation which was recently given us for the present difference between the Dales and Fells contains unfortunately too much truth to be overlooked. The Dales, having become an altogether bigger, rounder and plumper sort of pony, owes his 'change' to the fact that unhappily, in the not too distant past, he was 'bred up for meat'.

On page 52 we get a faint inkling that horses may have been handed over to the local British inhabitants when the Romans left, and a few pages later we have a real glimpse of a possible breed, for it is a positive fact that the Cuneus Frisiorum *was* stationed at Housesteads during the last stages of Roman rule. And the West Frisian horse today, although several inches bigger all round (due to better keep) has a dead image in both the Dales and Fell ponies. Readers need only to compare photographs of the two. We suggest that it could be possible that the horses of the Cuneus Frisiorum crossed with the local breed on 'demobilization'. There are thirteen place names in England which denote Frisian settlement, along with that of Angles and Saxons in the Dark Ages after the fall of Rome.

The Frisian is a trotter. The Fell pony breed produced some renowned trotters, but before that it evidentually produced some useful pack-ponies. Although the *most* famous pack-horses finally took Yorkshire as their native county, we can well imagine that the men who used Fell pack-ponies did not necessarily confine their activities to their own locality. Quite the opposite. They most certainly ranged far and wide over the country. We have positive proof of this from the Adwalton Catalogue, where we find that ten chapmen (travelling salesmen, and from their activities here, evidently horse-copers as well) sold, between them, more than half the animals on offer! Chapmen and 'potters' and tinkers knew, as the farmer of Birkdale Tarn quoted at the the head of this chapter did not know, that there was more to England than Kendal, Sedbergh and Kirkby Stephen. They had seen it, and swopped horses up and down it, from Kelso to Barnet.

But earlier than this, by about one hundred years, we have seen extracts from that interesting and illuminating document from Jervaulx Abbey, when requisitioned horses were dispersed after the battle of Flodden, and we find that 129 out of 163 were trotting horses. We suggest that our readers should turn back and consider once again the account of the battle of Flodden (page 133).

We are sure that the resemblance of the Frisian breed of horses to the Dales and Fells, and much later to the chapman horse, is not accidental or a mere figment of the author's imagination; for readers are at liberty to consider the written evidence for themselves.

It is not mere coincidence either that the Dales and Fell ponies do occasionally have white markings, and although these ponies are usually of a dark colour, grey is also known. Returning to the Flodden Roll, we see that 40 per cent were greys and many were 'bausonn'd', e.g. with white markings.

It is significant that most of the great northern abbeys bred white horses. The Cistercian abbeys of Jervaulx, Fountains and Rievaulx, and the Praemonstratensians of Easby bred white horses and cattle, and the colour of their stock served as a trade mark. These monks were of course white-robed. All the entries on the Flodden Roll belonged to the tenants of Jervaulx. At the Reformation this white stock was dispersed, at first causing a general 'wave' of whiteness, which then gradually disappeared under the dominant darker colours.

Writing over fifty years ago Sir Walter Gilbey says: 'An authority resident at Harrington who gives much information concerning the ponies of the Fell-side holdings and moors, states that there are several strains, and the appearance and character of each differ in various districts under the various local influences of climate, feed, etc.; little or nothing is known of the origin of these ponies.

'The resemblance to "Shelties" borne by those of certain localities until about the middle of the 19th century, suggested that they were descended from a mixed stock of galloways and Shetland ponies; but then endeavours were made to improve them by careful selection and mating; and the resemblance, which did not necessarily imply possession of the merits of the Shetland pony, has in great measure disappeared.'

In earlier times a Fell farmer probably owned only between four and six acres of arable land and these ponies were easily able to draw a light plough. They also carted peat and hay. Up to the beginning of this century the Fell-siders made no attempt to improve their 'wild' stock, which lived on the hill-sides and during winter received only a little additional hay. Mr William Graham, in a letter to Sir Walter Gilbey, quoted in *Thoroughbred and Other Ponies*, 1903, writes: 'Up to about fifty years ago great interest seems to have been taken in pony or galloway cob breeding throughout the whole district of the Eden valley, in the villages and hamlets that lie scattered all along the foot of the Pennine range of hills. Previous to the days of railway transit the ponies and small galloway cobs were employed in droves as pack-horses, as well as for riding, and many men now living can remember droves of from twenty to thirty continually travelling the district, carrying panniers of coal and other merchandise between the mines and villages.

'The village of Dufton, in which the hill farm Keisley is situated, was quite a centre of pony breeding, and for many generations the Fell-side farmers in the district have been noted for their ponies; they bred them to the best Fell pony stallions, most of which were trained trotters of great speed. Each of the three mares originally purchased to found the Stud at Keisley were got from well-known locally bred dams and grand-dams, and all were selected to match each other in character and style.[1] The mare from which two of them were bred was from a very old strain by a stallion pony called Lingcropper (ling is a kind of heather), a

[1] The secret of improving a breed or of obtaining special qualities.

record trotter; and all the three mares were themselves by a pony called Blooming Heather, another well-known pony stallion of a few generations younger.'

These notes were supplied by Mr J. S. Dargue of High Scalesceugh, Carlton, Carlisle, a descendant of the Dargues of Bow Hall, Dufton. The present Mr Dargue's father was seventy years old when he was born and died at the age of ninety about fourteen years ago. The Dargues were the breeders of a famous strain of Trotting Fell ponies, and Mr Dargue has one mare left of this breed which has been in their family for 160 years. His great-grandmother came from Murton Hall, and when she married a Dargue of Bow Hall she brought this strain of ponies with her; the Dargues had ponies before that, but this is where the very good strain came in. The ponies were mainly grey, a colour which has practically died out. They were rather lighter in the bone than a typical Fell pony as they were bred specially for trotting.

The following advertisement appeared in *The Field*, 1866:

'For sale, a dark grey pony, 5 years old, 13.2 ins. Can trot a mile in three minutes, carrying 12st. Goes well in harness. The property of J. Dargue, Bow Hall, Dufton.'

Another pony, Strawberry Girl (see P66), 13.2 hands, was bred by the Dargues, for whom she won several trotting races in 1881–2. She trotted a mile in 3 min. $\frac{1}{3}$ sec.

One of the same breed, a brown Fell pony, was sold to a butcher in Dufton before the 1914 war, and was taken hunting, and although under fourteen hands could leave all the hunter-type horses behind. This used to exasperate a Mr John Rigg of Appleby, who was always mounted on good horses. When war broke out Mr Rigg became remount officer, and had his revenge by commandeering the Fell, although it was under the required height.

In the early 20's they sold a pony to the Boardale Pits for £60–£70, a huge price in those days. Showing how the prices slumped in the early 30's five ponies were sold to Bowman of Penrith for £5 each.

Famous names in the Bow Hall breed were: Union Jack, Peepings Swell, Blackthorn 1057 (sold in Spain), Daybreak, Black Bess XIV 3988, Moor Hen II 3989 and Kate III 2252.

'When the Stud Books were first started, they were called Fell or Brough Hill Ponies. This was because Brough Hill Fair was the biggest sale of these ponies. Smaller sales were held in different parts of the north, and dealers would buy ponies at these, and take them in large droves loose, to Brough Hill. They are still called Fell galloways, rather than ponies, in these parts,' writes Miss P. Crossland, the hon. secretary of the Fell Pony Society.

The backbone of such functions as Brough Hill Fair in Westmorland were and still are the tinkers, or 'potters', as they are known in the north. For centuries, too, the Scots drovers swarmed down the green roads across the Pennines, either riding behind the mobs of black kyloe cattle or leading or driving a pack-horse with the sacks of oatmeal on which they lived, instead of squandering bawbees on bread and cheese which might be better invested in ale.

In 1792 Lord Byng complains that he could not get served in a Ribblesdale pub, because it was crowded to the doors with 'plaids and philabegs' (*Torrington Diaries*). We think they must have been the chief distributors of the Galloway pony.

37. The Kyloe steer, by Thomas Bewick. In the background a drove escorted by one mounted highlander, one walking highlander and one dog.

Lingcropper strain of Fell Ponies

'By tradition, the first Lingcropper was found on Stainmore, in Westmorland, "cropping the ling" and carrying a saddle, his rider presumably having been killed in one of the Border raids. (Some people say in the '45.) This stallion was the founder of a strain of exceedingly good ponies. The fact that his rider was presumed Scottish does not necessarily mean he was a Highland pony. He could have been a Galloway! The next pony of note to bear the name was the Lingcropper who ran the mails from Penrith to Keswick, a distance of eighteen miles, for twelve years without a break. As well, he sired a great number of very good ponies. The late Mr Charlton's well-known Linnel Lingcropper was a descendant on his mother's side. She was Linnel Heather Bell, bred by the late Joseph Relph, of Birkett Bank, the noted sheepdog handler and breeder of ponies. This mare's mother, Heather Bell, by Lingcropper Again, bred a number of very good foals. Jack's Delight, mentioned in the accompanying letter from Mr John Relph, was another son of Lingcropper.'

Mr Relph says: 'Jack's Delight was owned by Joseph Relph of Southernby (my great-grandfather), he was shown four times and took first each time, he was advertised for three years to trot any Galloway in the world.[1] I think a lot of Fell ponies strain back to him. Large numbers of ponies were kept by farmers, some were used as pack-ponies and

[1] The world, by Birkdale Tarn standards, comprises the North Riding, Westmorland, Durham, Lonsdale and Cartmel.

some for pit work, some very fast ones were used as hackneys. I haev heard about a pony which got on the railway lines at Troutbeck and galloped in front of the train the ten miles to Keswick—I fancy he was half pony!' [1]

Miss Crossland further adds a note on:

Shepherds Meets

'These were and still are held at certain places each year, where the farmers take all the stray sheep which they have gathered among their own. In the old days, of course, the shepherds would ride to the meets on their ponies. The best known meet was that held on the top of High

38. The Old English road horse, by Thomas Bewick.

Street, the range of fells running between Bampton and Ullswater, and a very central place for all the surrounding district. (It must have been exceedingly bleak on a bad day!) On High Street are the remains of the Roman road which ran from Troutbeck (Westmorland) to Penrith. Here were held the pony races, each shepherd probably matching his mount to out-trot the others. The Shepherds Meets moved down to Mardale, and when this village was submerged by Manchester Water Co., they were once more moved to Bampton.'

A north-country team of author and illustrator uses the term pony without explanation or apology. This is R. Beilby and the famous wood-engraver Thomas Bewick in their *History of Quadrupeds*, 1791. The book was first published in Newcastle, and no doubt the original 'subscribers' would be country gentlemen in the northern counties. But Beilby speaks only of Welsh, Shetland and Highland ponies, rather as

[1] Mr Relph's great-grandfather maintained that the ponies in old times much resembled the galloway and highland ponies, and that there were many duns and greys in former days, both in the Fells and Dales ponies.

if he did not consider the northern English breeds to be ponies at all. In this same book Beilby speaks of the palfrey under the name of the Old English Road Horse (the New English Road Horse, from his point of view, would be the Norfolk Roadster). His remarks are practically an obituary of the palfrey, speaking of it in the past tense but not in unflattering terms. It 'was strong and vigorous and active and capable of bearing great hardships, was rather low, seldom exceeding 14 hands: his body round and compact, his limbs strong and his head thick'. This is a fair description of the Elizabethan palfrey pictured on page 158, but probably meant to apply to the last survivors of the ambling type of Dales or Fell pony still to be found in remote parts such as Cheviot or Stainmore in Beilby's youth.

In his book *The Different breeds of English Horses*, c. 1820, Youatt rather significantly does not mention either the Dales or the Fell pony, but he does tell us about another breed which had disappeared. 'A great many ponies of little value used to be reared on the Wildmoor Fens, in the neighbourhood of Boston in Lincolnshire. They seldom reached thirteen hands; the head was large and the forehead low, the back straight, the leg flat and good, but the foot, even for a Lincolnshire pony, unnaturally large. They were applied to very inferior purposes even on the fens, and were unequal to hard and flinty and hilly roads. The breed became generally neglected, and at no very distant time will be almost extinct.'

As we know, this Lincolnshire breed is extinct; it contained the typical signs of degeneration in the large head and low forehead. But the large feet show an effort at survival—small feet would have sunk into the boggy fenland. We have already seen that horses living on the steppes or plateau lands are inclined to narrow, small feet, and that horses living in forest or marshland acquire considerably larger feet. But large feet, like large heads, are not a quality to be encouraged. Professor Ewart's remarks are worth noting, since we are considering the complete disappearance of a breed—the Lincolnshire ponies—which were not such distant neighbours of the Dales and Fells, who just over a century ago might well have remarked to themselves: 'There, but for the grace of God, go I.'

'Heavy horses on short thick legs ending in broad hoofs are usually supposed to be more primitive than slender-limbed horses. It should, however, be borne in mind that the broad hoofs—which imply big fetlock joints and wide metapodial bones, are in fact highly specialized structures, which, like other structures of this kind, are difficult to maintain in a state of efficiency. Further, it need hardly be pointed out that the large hoofs of cart-horses are, to a very considerable extent, the product of artificial selection.'

So by a turn of fate, while one breed died out, the other survived and improved, on the one hand retaining its native characteristics, and on the other infusing its blood with that of the descendants of the Norfolk

Roadster and Thoroughbred, and producing a new and extraordinarily active breed in the modern Hackney Pony.

To prove our remarks that ponies or horses can be changed as the dictates of necessity or fashion demand, it is worth recording that in 1872 Mr Christopher Wilson of Kirkby Lonsdale began to improve 'the material at hand, having built upon that foundation a breed which at the present day [1903] stands unrivalled for shape and action. Mr Wilson selected his breeding mares from among the best ponies of the districts, and put them to the pony stallion Sir George, who won eight first prizes at the shows held by the Royal Agricultural Society. Sir George was by Sportsman, a brown stallion bred in Yorkshire and descended through Phenomenon, a Norfolk Hackney in a direct line to Flying Childers, the speediest racehorse of his time. The female off-spring from the selected mares and Sir George were in due time mated with their sire and threw foals which showed elegant and true Hackney characteristics in far more marked degree than did their dams, as might be anticipated in animals three-parts instead of one-half bred.'

Sir Walter Gilbey then goes on: 'Their height was kept down to the required limit by turning out the young stock after the first winter, upon the rabbit warrens and moorlands of Rigmaden to find their own grazing among the sheep and rabbits, as their material ancestors had done. This system not only succeeded in its direct object, but went far to preserve that hardiness of constitution which is by no means the least valuable attribute of the mountain pony.'

The third direct cross from Sir George produced a mare, Georgina V, which had constitution and stamina, and also *more bone* than her dam or granddam. Mr Wilson once wrote to Mr MacDonald, quoted in *Highland Ponies*: 'The old Galloway was the same as the Fell pony, only it showed a little more breeding. The Fell pony in my part of the country is from 14.1 to 14.2 hands in height and is used for all kinds of farm work —in fact it is a cart cob in miniature. The Arab crosses will not stand the winter out of doors. I saw a lot of them in the Island of Harris, but they could not remain out in winter as do the Fell ponies. No doubt the Arab cross sweetens their heads, but they lose the bone and constitution. My "Sir George" ponies used to lie out all winter, and I only took them up about three weeks before sending them to the Islington Spring Show, where I frequently won with them. I am quite sure that the Hackney would be a more suitable cross for the Fell pony to breed troopers from than the Arab. The resultant ponies would be much hardier. I don't, of course, mean the pampered-up Hackney.'

Because of the success of his breeding the 'Wilson pony' became famous as a trapper. We shall later see that a son of Sir George went to Dartmoor; and it is worth observing that the official description of points for the Dartmoor is identical with that given for the North Wales pony, with certain amendments and additions and excepting for height.

We shall not delve further into strains of Hackney ponies except to mention that Mr Wilson also owned a pony called Little Wonder whose sire was Confidence (d'Olys), dam a Welsh mare!

There is no doubt that the Fell pony and the Welsh pony were the foundation for the modern Hackney pony; that Sir George came of a line of the old Norfolk Cob and the Thoroughbred Flying Childers who was by the Darley Arabian. In the next chapter it will be seen that another of Flying Childers's descendants was Mambrino, who with Bellfounder helped to found the trotters of America.

Whether we entirely agree or not the following remarks by Lord Arthur Cecil, written over fifty years ago, are worth considering. He says: 'No real distinction can be drawn between them [the Highland] and the Fell pony. We have seen that the Highland pony is even to the fore as far south as Kintyre, while we know the Galloway was the beast of burden of all that great promontory which terminates in the Mull of Galloway. The present writer has heard of them even in later days in Ayrshire, Dumfriesshire and Wigtownshire, and Burns refers to them— indeed, "Grey Meg" in "Tam o' Shanter" was probably a Galloway. Thus we see the Highland pony bred more for speed and called a Galloway extending down to the Solway Firth, which is the northern border of the Fell pony. Now, we know that, even in the present day, horsemen are not particular how they get a good one, or where it comes from, provided it *is* a good one, and it is not to be thought that they were any more particular in earlier days. We may very well be sure that if "Kinmont Willie" had a good pony, "Jock Eliot" would have been delighted if he could have got hold of it, and raised a breed from it. We may equally well conclude that "Kinmont Willie" would have glorified himself considerably if he could have rooked his shrewd Caledonian antagonist out of a good beast. Thus, as both animals existed under the same conditions and in adjacent counties for exactly the same purposes, it must be concluded that there was little or no difference between them. That the two kinds have diverged slightly only shows that as ages have gone on the Clydesdale, with his clean hard bones, has come in throughout Ayrshire and Dumfriesshire and caused a gap in the necessity for the pony. The Fell pony, on the other hand, driven by cultivation to his mountain fastnesses in the border counties of England, has decreased slightly in size and quality of bone, though probably the measurement of bone is even greater. The main point of difference, however, between the Fell pony and the Highland pony is that while they are about equal in point of cleverness on their legs, the Fell pony has been developed into a very fast trotting animal, retaining this characteristic from his near neighbour the Galloway.

'This is also probably the case on account of the well-known sporting proclivities of the inhabitants of the counties of Cumberland, Westmorland and Yorkshire, where these ponies are found, and far back in the nineteenth century, indeed at the very beginning of it, names occur in their pedigrees, such as "Ayrshire Champion" and "Highland Robin", which go to prove the transition through Galloways to the Fells, while nearly all of those now known to exist come through a pony named Merry Driver, descended from a pony named Old Grey Shales [see P67], which was foaled in 1819.[1] This being so it is not unlikely that these Fell ponies formed a foundation for the roadsters which have since developed into the hackney.'

Indeed, the very word Shales is a connecting link, for Marshland Shales (page 238) holds an important place in Hackney pedigrees; and there are numerous other Shales, Black, Brown, Scott, Dodd's and above all Shales the Original or Old Shales—a pillar of the *Hackney Stud Book,* who was by Blaze by Flying Childers. Equally there is an odd link in the name Merry Driver, for a horse called Driver was sired by Old Shales!

Dales Stud Book: Section of the *N.P.S. Stud Book,* started in 1917, and this system remains today.

Fell Stud Book: Started as a section of the *Polo Pony Stud Book (N.P.S.* since 1913), 1899, and continues.

[1] Lord Arthur Cecil says 1755, but this was the date of Shales the Original. In any case the pedigrees are correct.

CHAPTER THIRTEEN

The Eastern Counties and the Roadsters

He was a good plain husbandman, and rode to mill
with his corn under him, and brought home the meal
again under him. (Description of Clement Paston of
Paston, in Norfolk (*fl.* 1350) by one of his descendants.)

THERE is no native breed, as such, which now belongs to the eastern
region of England, and yet several breeds are 'native' to this part of
England. At the time of Queen Boudicca the Iceni were great horse
breeders; indeed, after her defeat, her chieftains were ordered by the
Roman General Severus to return to their horse-breeding and to refrain
from meddling in politics!

The First Thracian Cavalry of the Roman Auxiliaries was stationed at
Colchester; we show the tombstone of the *duplicarius* Longinus mounted
upon a useful pony (P10); and as we are well aware of the great number
of chariots which were put in the field against the Romans, we may
presume that a cavalry regiment which was stationed in such a well-
known horse-breeding area most probably used local remounts. A
quantity of bones and harness has been found in Norfolk and Suffolk,
and the ponies used in the war-chariots were famous for their handiness.
'Occasionally fragments of chariots have been found in British sepulchres. About 1815, a barrow near Market Weighton [1] in Yorkshire was
opened, in which was a cist containing the skeleton of a man. Near the
head were the heads of wild boars. Inclining from the skeleton, on each
side, had been placed a chariot wheel, of which the iron tire and ornaments of the nave alone remained. The wheels had been about 2 feet
11 inches in diameter, and each of them had originally rested on a horse,
the bones of which were found under or adjoining them. Near to the
horses was found a pair of bits made of iron and plated with bronze. [2]

---

[1] In the East Riding. This place was a classic nineteenth-century centre of
Roadster breeding. Market Weighton was in the territory of the Parisii (a
Belgic tribe), on whose northern frontier were the Brigantes, who were also to
be found in southern Ireland and northern Spain.

[2] For comparison a Ralli trap, build by Wendover fifty years ago, has a wheel
diameter, from rim to rim, of 4 feet 3 inches.

'A second barrow, in the same neighbourhood, also yielded the remains of a charioteer. The skeleton was found to have rested on a shield; on each side had been placed a chariot-wheel and bridle-bit, which were all of iron. The diameter of the wheels was about 2 feet 8 inches.

'Other remains of chariots in sepulchres have been found at Stanwick in Yorkshire, at Hamden Hill, Somerset, and at Le Teifenau, near Berne in Switzerland.' (*Sculptured Stones of Scotland.*) More recently similar remains have been found at Vix, in Burgundy.

As well as the evidences of chariots, we have the portrayal of wild ponies on the silver plate from the Mildenhall (Suffolk) collection.

It is, however, strange that horses seem to be absent from the pages of eastern counties local history until after the Conquest. The fact that they are not particularly mentioned does not justify the conclusion that there was no local breed; unassuming and unambitious it may have been, but the sturdy ponies of the Iceni cannot have died out or have been eaten up by the Anglo-Saxon invaders. Because the very rivers provided the means of invasion for every marauder who was fed up with his home politics (or starved, since bad harvests and flooding of grazing by sea-water were one cause of the Angelcyn's migration), it may have been the reason for the horses keeping themselves to themselves. Having no vast forest in which to hide, one can imagine that they may have disappeared, with their owners' knowledge, into that rather inhospitable area known as the Fen country. This divides Norfolk and Cambridgeshire from Lincolnshire—in those days it was undrained, unsettled, very wild marshland.

The first glimmer that this could have been the case is the mention of the old Fen trotter and about the same time the Lincolnshire trotter. In the early Middle Ages a number of genuine breeds came to light and we are especially made aware of the trotters. We would only observe that trotting appears to be a peculiarity of horses bred on marshland, and that it was peculiar, *at that time*, to horses coming from the eastern regions of England. A trotter appears on the seal of King Stephen, another carries the Reeve in Chaucer's *Canterbury Tales*—she was a good mare and a dapple grey cob—and the Reeve was a Norfolk man. It seems to us that it was not by accident that Chaucer mounted his pilgrims on specified animals; and as the Reeve rode a mare and manages an estate, we can be fairly certain that she was not the only mare 'back home.' Certain Norfolk manors in Domesday (1086) already show an abnormally high proportion of *runcini* among stock listed.

Elizabeth I's order for mustering Dymlances and Light Horsemen enacted that every dymlance should be mounted on a trotting stallion or trotting gelding.

Unlike other native breeds of ponies where they can be traced almost progressively forward through the ages, in this case one has to trace backwards, beginning with the modern Hackney, and the Suffolk Punch, and the now extinct Lincolnshire Fen pony, all comparatively 'modern' breeds, having no actual connection with each other, and yet, as we shall see, possessing ancestors who were very nearly related—ancestors which are shared both by pony and light horse and heavy horse breeds of today.

Almost overnight the whole locality begins to bristle with special breeds of horses—which in turn died out, after having passed on some of their blood and their qualities in the foundation of yet another breed. That is the astounding thing about the eastern counties breeds: sometimes nothing remains of the original stock or of what succeeded it, and yet some of the most famous horses in all Britain were bred of native stock and themselves founded world-famous lines.

Like the Arab enthusiasts, who would have you believe that the Arab is a species unto itself, having sprung ready made, most probably, from the lap of Epona, a number of modern pony enthusiasts like to think that *their* pet breed has existed with the personal perfections which it boasts today from time immemorial. In East Anglia, and I do not suppose the eastern half of the north midlands is an exception, we say that a stranger must reside in a parish for at least twenty years before he ceases to be a stranger!

With this same aloofness which they show the stranger, who obviously did not have any parentage in which they could be interested, the breeders of eastern counties horses cheerfully admit that their breed did not have ancestors either. In fact, like the Arab, they just 'happened', and not so very long ago. One can obtain a long list of what the ancestors were not, to be told at the end that it was due to So-and-so's Old Horse; all we can say to that is that the Old Horse had a remarkably busy time.

The disadvantage of working backwards is that one has to form opinions in order to proceed further backwards; and if one begins to dish out one's personal opinions as the gospel truth, then the whole structure is liable to crumble.

An example can be seen in the stud card of Young Active (39). The most careful scrutiny reveals only the slightest indications as to his probable ancestry—except that he bred coach-horses. The picture at the top of the card is nothing to go by; we have seen half a dozen similar pictures representing other stallions. It simply shows the sort of mettlesome coaching sire that breeders liked. Yet the name of Young Active's grandsire helps a little, for Ruler, it will be later noticed, is also the ancestor of the Welsh sire True Briton, and Ruler was a well-known Yorkshire Coach-horse. We should also remember that the Yorkshire Coach-horse became a breed—apart from the Cleveland Bay—about 1790, therefore some forty-two years earlier. But a writer of the time, between 1796 and 1810, had a very good word for Yorkshire horses and especially for a stallion known as Trotting Jalap, by *Jalap* by Regulus by the Godolphin Arabian, dam a grand-daughter of Flying Childers. This horse is especially referred to as a most valuable sire of Yorkshire trotting stock. We have seen that Jalap appears as an ancestor of Young

Active, and also how closely interwoven is trotting blood with coaching blood, having Thoroughbred and Arab ancestry.

It is interesting, too, that we meet here that which is to baffle us all the time, 'Mr Bell's noted horse of Lichonfield', 'Luke Walmsley's York Horse', but no mention of who or what the dams were. But these

YOUNG ACTIVE,

THE PROPERTY OF JAMES MELL, OF CROWLE,

Will COVER MARES this Season 1832,

AT ONE GUINEA EACH MARE.

YOUNG ACTIVE was got by Symmetry, the property of the late Lawrence Stephenson of Cherry Burton ; his dam own sister to Prince Regent ; his grandam by Ruler. Symmetry was got by Mr. Halliday's Active, his dam by Mr. Corney's Old Horse, his grandam by Mr. Bell's noted horse of Lichonfield, his great grandam by Jalap.

Mr. Halliday's Active was got by Old Active, the property of Thomas Sawden, of Lund ; Old Active was got by Mr. Bell's horse, of Harpham Moor ; Mr. Bell's horse by Luke Walmsley's York Horse ; and the York Horse by Luke Walmsley's old horse Success.

Ruler the great grandsire of Young Active, for symmetry of shape and colour, his stock is unequalled, having never got a chesnut foal, which is singular in a blood horse.

YOUNG ACTIVE is a good bay, stands 16 hands one inch high, for action and breeding as a coach horse he stands unrivalled. If ever he gets a black or chesnut foal, the ᵔ₁ey shall be returned. He has proved himself to be a very sure et.ᵗer.

WHAL¹ ᵖRINTER, KNOTTINGLEY.

39. Stud card of Young Active, 1832, from the collection of Mr Ernest Hutton.

facts were too well known to the men of those days and a hundred or two hundred years previously to need recording. They did not need recording because that sort of good horse had always been in the district; and if great-grandfather's memory erred as to the matter of size or height, or whether or not *his* grandfather had used a stallion which had belonged, 'so he always understood', to one of Cromwell's troopers—a rare good sort, which probably had some of that trotting blood which Good Queen Bess insisted on when mounting her cavalry.

That was the type of the Chapman horse; they carried packs, of course, but they trotted as did the squire on his rouncy when he led his master's destrier. That rouncy would be a good sort too, a really strong cob, which could trot out when he had to. And he did have to years later, when one of the packmen got hold of him and went into the Fell district. As we have seen, it was not unknown for a chapman to barter his own horse, perhaps for a couple of good pony mares, whose off-spring would soon up-grade into a pair of good pack-mares or geldings.

So, in fact, can breeds of horses come about, especially in a part of the country which was as busy throughout the ages as the eastern side of England. So, too, can they die out, as the famous Chapman horse died out, or rather grew up into the more famous Cleveland Bay, with which we will deal in another book.

We have seen, from the description of William Fitzstephen in 1171, 'that pack horses with stout nimble legs' and 'horses suitable for squires' which trotted were available at the Friday horse-market at Smithfield. Then we find an interesting Proclamation issued by Richard II in 1386. There was a scarcity of horses in the early years of his reign, and prices rose. In the Proclamation, which was published in Lincoln-shire, Cambridgeshire and Yorkshire, breeders were forbidden to ask the high prices which they were demanding.[1]

Horses were also hired from 'hackneymen' and these had to brand their horses or mark them to prevent unscrupulous hirers from stealing the horses and selling them in a distant town.[2]

In the Regulations of the Establishment of Algernon Percy, fifth Earl of Northumberland, 1512, we have already seen the various types and sorts of horses in his stable, to wit, 'Item, chariot hors to stand in my lordis stable yerely. . . . Seven great trottynge horsys to draw in the chariot and a nag for the chariot man to ride—eight.' Sir Walter Gilbey adds: 'The chariot of this period was a four-wheeled springless cart with a hood or tilt over it; the interior was furnished with carpets and seats as luxurious as the art and skill of the time could supply.' Such conveyances had been in use since Richard II's time (see the earlier reference to the Luttrell Psalter) without much development in 150 years.

In the reign of Queen Elizabeth I, Sir Thomas Chaloner, Ambassador at Madrid, said that 'England had none but vile and ordinary horses and that . . . if Englishmen . . . chose to devote attention to breeding, they could rear better horses than they could import'. And yet Gervase Markham, whose works were written during Elizabeth's reign, says: 'When the best Barbaries that ever were, were in their prime I saw them overrun by a black hobbie at Salisbury; yet that hobbie (master Charlton's black hobbie) was more overrun by a horse called Valentine,

---

[1] Of course this was quite useless. A typical unenforceable statute such as medieval kings and parliaments resorted to in order to 'control' the economy. But the laws of supply and demand take no account of such ordinances, then or now!

[2] Sir Walter Gilbey, *Horses Past and Present*.

which neither in hunting nor running was ever equalled, and yet was a plane bredde English horse both syre and damme.'

Sir Walter Gilbey goes on to tell us that, 'in January 1636, Charles issued a Proclamation forbidding the use of coaches in London and Westminster unless they were about to make a journey of at least three miles; and he required every owner of a coach to keep four horses for the King's service.

'This prohibition of private hackney coaches was not the outcome of desire to encourage horsemanship; for, in 1637, he granted to his Master of the Horse, James, Marquis of Hamilton, power to license fifty hackney coachmen in London and the suburbs and convenient places in other parts of the realm. This licence, which was granted in July 1637, suggests favouritism, as, according to a contemporary publication (*Coach and Sedan*), there were in 1636 over 6,000 coaches, private and public, in London and the suburbs—surely more than were needed.'

In 1659 there is definite mention of a stagecoach in the diary of a Yorkshire clergyman. They plied between London and Coventry, London and Aylesbury, and London and Bedford and possibly elsewhere. But owing to the roads—or lack of them—horses of the Great Horse stamp must have been used.

Also after the Civil War the Lincolnshire Trotter was emerging; and we read that King William III in an Act of 1694 granted licences to 700 hackney-coaches, four-wheeled carriages, in London and Westminster, and that no horse, gelding or mare under 14 hands was to be used in a hackney or stagecoach. (In 1710 another Act was passed to the same effect.) But it was to be another hundred years before John Macadam (1756–1836) did anything about the rather dreadful roads, which made it possible for highwaymen to enjoy an unlawful and dangerous means of livelihood! Macadam's system of road-making was generally used by 1819.

The Darley Arabian was foaled in 1702. And in 1715 Flying Childers, by the Darley Arabian—who had the greatest influence in developing more than one breed of pony or horse—was foaled. 'After his Turf career was over', writes Sir Walter Gilbey, 'Flying Childers stood first at 50 guineas, then at 100 guineas, and for one season at 200 guineas.'

In the middle of the seventeenth century, when flying coaches from Oxford to London covering their fifty miles a day were introduced, the 'caudator temporis acti' of the day croaked till he was hoarse and foretold red ruin on all sides. But it was during William IV's reign that coaching and coach-horses were at their best; it did not last long, for soon railways sounded the knell. But at that time journeys were made at the rate of 10 to 10½ miles per hour from London to the other great cities.

The proprietors reckoned the needs of a coach at one horse per mile 'one way'. A coach running from London to York, 200 miles, required about 200 horses; from London to Edinburgh, 400 miles: 400 horses; from London to Exeter, 175 miles: 175 horses. Sometimes as many as twenty-five coaches ran daily in summer from London to Brighton alone. As the distance is about sixty miles, in one day therefore 1,500 horses were needed. According to Nimrod (Charles James Apperly), the average working life of a horse in a fast road coach was about four years.[1]

In 1761 Henry, Earl of Pembroke, in his *Military Equitation,* refers to the 'wretched system of horsemanship prevailing in the army', and refers to the 'common method of putting a man on a rough trotting horse, to which he is obliged to stick as best he can. Most of the officers, when on horseback, were a disgrace to themselves and the animals they rode.' We imagine these horses were the descendants of the squire's rouncy—cobs, with what we now call hackney action. And palfreys, amblers and pacers are 'out'.

Here we reach a very interesting stage of our inquiries, for two types of trotting horses come on to the scene; evidently there is the cob with hackney action, to which one is obliged to stick as best one can, and there is the roadster type, which was *ridden* considerable distances in trotting matches.

The Norfolk Roadster. For many years prior to 1700 posts were carried on horseback, and fast trotting horses became increasingly in demand. Soundness of constitution, hard legs, speed and endurance were indispensable. These were horses capable of travelling long distances and a quite usual feat was to be able to trot fifteen or sixteen miles per hour carrying an average-sized man. There were trotting matches as early as 1710, and these continued until 1750, when they were quite usual. Our illustration (P69) shows Phenomena.

PHENOMENA

The Celebrated Trotting Mare, Aged 25 Years, May 1813

This Celebrated and Matchless Mare, which has been for Years the Admiration of the Sporting World is now the Property of F. C. Daniel Esq., of Mile End, who keeps Her as one of His Hackneys and we congratulate Her . . . being so Fortunate to trot into private Hands. This famous Mare which is under 14 hands ½ was bred in May 1788 at Malton Park in Norfolk, by the late Sir Edwd Ashley then Member for the Cambridge . . . bred mare and Othello her Sire, She trotted April 1796 on the Highgate Road 17 miles within 1 hour, was then the Property of C. Herbert Esq., and afterwards bought by the late Duke of Leeds for 1800 Gns . . . the Parties are not generally known but to the Sporting World, it may be right to state some of her most Wonderfull Performances.

Independant of . . . she succeeded, She was matched in June 1800, then, 12 Years old, by Mr Robson to trot 17 miles within 1 hour on the Huntingdon Road and which She performed with ease in 56 minutes. An Act unheard of in the annals of Sporting History. The Performance was doubted by some and very large Bets were offered that she did not perform the same Distance

[1] *Horses Past and Present.*

in the same time, viz. 56 minutes. Mr Robson accepted the Challenge and in July following, within one Month from Her amazing Performance, she again trotted the 17 miles, a few seconds under 53 minutes. Which is unparalled in Sporting Inteligence.

She was afterwards matched for 200 Guineas to Trot 19 miles within the Hour, to which Her Opponents paid Forfeit. This was in Consequence of its being proved by several stop-watches that during the last Match She did 4 miles under 11 minutes! Which alarm'd the Sporting Gentlemen, who one and all declar'd She literally Flew and were of Opinion She could trot 20 miles within the Hour! They would have nothing more to do with Her. When this Beautifull and Valuable Creature was 23 Years Old Feb: 1811, She Trotted 9 miles in 28 minutes and 30 seconds and within the last few months when in Mr Boswell's Possession, She won four Extraordinary Matches in One Day. Notwithstanding the Hardships with which this Prodigy of Nature has been treated, She still retains and shows a Beautifull Symetry, scarcely to be seen on any Animal of Her Species although She is in Her 26th Year and having performed such Herculean Tasks. She is Fresh, Clean in Her Legs and Credit is due to Her Possessor for getting Her into such High Condition, when it is well known a few months since She was a mere Skeleton, Proof of an excellent Stamina, Strong Constitution and good Nursing, we hope Mr Daniel is a Philanthropist and we understand He has a Claim to that Title, having by a peculiar Invention of His Own been the means of saving the Lives of some of our Brave Tars at Sea, and we hope for His own Credit, as well as for Humanity's sake, he will not let such a Pheno-menon be Inhumanly treated. But that he will by Gentle and Kind Treatment, prove Himself Old Phenomena's Life Preserver.

As far as we know Phenomena left only one descendant behind her. This was the bay mare, by the blood horse Walton, which bred Mr William Jacob's Phenomenon, sire of Norfolk Phenomenon (Taylor's) by Norfolk Phenomenon (Bond's), a red roan or sorrel horse, by Norfolk Cob, out of a sorrel mare.[1]

Here we would emphasize the colour, sorrel or red roan, which appears most frequently in the very early pedigrees of both the Norfolk roadster and the Suffolk Punch; in both cases it seems to have been the colour of the 'old breed', it invariably produces the chestnut colour; and sorrel is the colour of the Danish/Schleswig/Jutland breed. And it is a colour which is practically unknown in any other breed in the British Isles.

'Quite unjustifiable doubts have been expressed regarding the staying powers of the breed [roadster]. In 1820 a horse trotted one hundred miles in a few seconds over 11 consecutive hours on the Ipswich Road, carrying 12 stones for the first, and 7 stones for the second fifty miles. In 1822 a blind mare covered forty miles in 3 hours 43 min. In the same year Mr Dryson's Wonder trotted 3 miles in 8 min. 43 sec., carrying 15 stones 14 lb.; and in 1832 Nonpareil was driven 100 miles in 9 hours 56 min. 57 sec.; the first 20 miles were trotted in 1 hr 57 min., and in $3\frac{1}{2}$ min. she started again, completing 40 miles inside 4 hours. She

---

[1] This horse eventually went to Scotland, having sired a number of excellent horses.
The illustration P68 shows Ambition, another sorrel horse.

accomplished the above performance without showing the slightest symptoms of fatigue, commencing to feed as soon as she got back to her stable.[1]

Just in case our readers doubt the possibility of these feats we would point out that in those days horses were *fed* and got fit; both arts today are fast dying out.

There is a portrait by Cooper, R.A., of a trotting horse painted about the year 1820, which is referred to as 'a specimen of that useful kind of

40. Marshland Shales, 1824.

horse which is equally adapted to draught or saddle'. The hackney in those days, 1700–1800, was *much* more heavily built than nowadays. Before the railways came farmers rode their hackneys to market, and very often their wives rode pillion behind. The distances too were quite considerable, so we may suppose that with rider, pillion passenger and saddle, the horse could easily be carrying 33 stones! Moreover we learn that a number of big stallions standing 16 hands were immediate descendants of Marshland Shales (40); and mention is made of sires standing 17 hands.

In the two pedigrees opposite we see mention made of the dams as just 'mare' or 'So-and-so's mare'; this happens in all the pedigrees of horses in our eastern region, no matter what breed. Even the great Flying Childers's grandam was just 'mare'. These mares were, in the language of the

[1] *The Horses of the British Empire.*

PEDIGREES OF MARSHLAND SHALES AND BLAZE

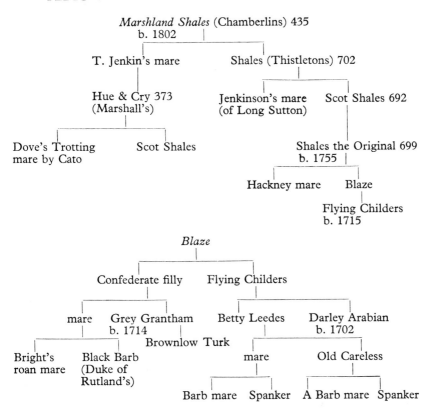

Nottinghamshire Gervase Markham, 'plane breede English hors both syre and damme', or as Thomas Blundeville of Norfolk observed in 1565, after writing about various breeds such as the Spanish jennet and the Irish hobby, he constantly refers to 'our mares', which is perhaps just as tantalizing as 'the old breed', except that we are now beginning to understand what both mean. He says that for remount purposes one should use the Flanders mares, because they trot, also those of our mares which are of high stature and trot 'as *some* of our mares do'. In all probability *these* were the mares, or rather their descendants, who were mated to Blaze and Shales the Original, and are referred to in the pedigrees as Bright's roan mare, Trotting mare, Jenkinson's mare (of Long Sutton), a Yorkshire trotting mare—or just 'mare' with no appendages.

In vol. iv of the *Welsh Stud Book* (1905), J. Marshall Dugdale has this to say of Blaze: 'As the sire of this Shales (the Original) Blaze must be always looked upon as the principal figure in the first chapter in the Genesis of Great Trotters. It is worth noticing that among the progeny of Blaze, we find the name of the celebrated horse Sampson, foaled in

1745, and who in early annals was described as "the largest-boned blood horse ever bred". His dam, like many dams, may have been rather a subject of discussion, but we have not to do with that here. Amongst other measurements handed down to us we find he was $8\frac{1}{2}$ inches below the knee, a very useful claim to excellence in any well-bred horse. The celebrated grey, Mambrino, was the grandson of Sampson, and the imported Messenger, son of Mambrino, founded, as is well known, the great line of American trotters. Blaze thus occupies a position elsewhere than in England as the founder of a great race of Trotters.

'The sire of Blaze was Flying Childers or Devonshire Childers, as he was called in the *General Stud Book* of about 1800, wherein he was described as: "Generally supposed to have been the fleetest horse that was trained in this or any other country". At one time', continues Mr Dugdale, 'there was a rival claimant to this title of Thoroughbred father of all the road horses. A few at one time laboured under an erroneous impression, that to a certain horse called Blank, by the Godolphin Arabian, but bred on several similar lines to Blaze and nearly related belonged the honour. . . . In this paternity case, judgement declared with one accord for Blaze, and the saddle was put on the right, and I believe the best horse. The dam of the Original Shales was described as "strong commonbred mare", while the dam of that great trotting sire and son of Original Shales (Driver or perhaps Scot Shales?) was defined as a "well-bred hunter".

'Those who read the pedigree will not fail to notice a little uncertainty in the case of both the third dams on the one side. What sort of mare it was that was mated with the Brownlow Turk, or what were the characteristics of Bright's roan mare: on this subject history is silent. But if these few stones in the edifice are lacking, there is plenty left to show us how they did things in the days when good King George III was king. These were indisputably the lines on which the great road horses of yore were bred.'

Well! Mr Dugdale had evidently not read his Blundeville, or he would probably have agreed that they were just 'one of our mares'.

Messenger was imported to America in 1788. A grey horse, he was bred at Newmarket in 1780. He raced with great success on the flat, but an interesting fact is that there is no suggestion that he was a trotter. However his sire Mambrino seems to have had that ability, as his owner Lord Grosvenor, as was the fashion in those days, 'offered to match him once for 1,000 sovereigns to trot 14 miles in the hour'. This was probably about 1770. There was much controversy about Mambrino's lineage, he was by Engineer, by Sampson, who was said to have been by a coaching stallion, by a Lincolnshire black cart-horse. But Sampson won a lot of races over four miles.

This was the horse chosen to be the father of the trotters, and in pedigree he went back to the Godolphin Arabian three times, also three times to the Darley Arabian, and inherited in a closer degree Matchem, through Turf to Regulus,[1] the sire of Eclipse's dam, and in almost direct line to Place's White Turk, 1660.

It would be interesting to follow Mambrino's progress across the Atlantic. But it was said that when Messenger, the father of the trotters, passed over the gangway of the ship which took him from England to America, it meant 20,000,000 sovereigns to the people of the United States of America.

Another well-known Norfolk Trotter was Bellfounder, who was also exported to America.

Stud Card of:

BELLFOUNDER

The Wonderful Norfolk Trotter

Imported July 1822, from England.

To cover (this season 1823) at 20 Dollars.

This celebrated horse is a beautiful bright bay with black legs, 7 years old, standing 15 hands high. His superior blood, symmetry, and action exceed every other stallion. He is allowed by the best judges in Norfolk to be the fastest and best horse ever sent out of the country. He has proved himself a sure foalgetter, and his stock for size and substance are not to be surpassed. They are selling for the highest prices of any horses in Norfolk.

Bellfounder was got by that well-known fast and high-formed trotter Old Bellfounder, out of Velocity by Haphazard, by Sir Peter out of Miss Hervey, by Eclipse; grand-dam was of good north country blood, but not thoroughbred. Velocity trotted on the Norwich road in 1806, sixteen miles in one hour, and she broke fifteen times into a gallop, and as often turned round, won her match. In 1808, she trotted 28 miles in one hour and forty-seven minutes, and has also done many other great performances against time.

Bellfounder at five years old trotted two miles in six minutes, and in the following year was matched for 200 guineas to trot nine miles in thirty minutes, which he won easily by 32 seconds. His owner shortly after challenged to perform with him seventeen miles and a half in an hour, but was not accepted. He has since never been saddled or matched.

Old Bellfounder was a true descendant from the original blood of the Fireaways,[2] which breed of horses stands unrivalled for the saddle either in this or any other country, Bellfounder is strongly recommended to the public by Mr S. Souch of Chelmsford, and by Mr Woodford, Moorlands, London.[3]

In the *Hackney Stud Book* during the first fifteen years there are enumerated—including a number of Black, Grey, Marshland—no less than 135 horses with the prefix or suffix Shales.

The foundations of the modern Hackney were laid by the old Norfolk Cob or Roadster; in some pedigrees there is also Fell and Welsh blood. As we have seen, the Norfolk roadster evolved as a breed, by the infusion

[1] *Horses of the British Empire.*
[2] Fireaway blood also appears in every Hackney or Hackney Pony pedigree today.
[3] The above was taken from *Horses of the British Empire.*

TO COVER THIS SEASON, 1835,
At One Guinea and a Crown the Groom,
THAT WELL-BRED HORSE
YOUNG MOUSETRAP
THE PROPERTY OF
THOMAS FOW, OF WINTRINGHAM.

Young Mousetrap was got by Mousetrap, his dam by Mr. Jenkinson's old Fireaway, grandam old Atlas, great grandam old Servington. Mousetrap was got by old Mousetrap, his dam by Pagan, grandam by old Atlas. Old Mousetrap was got by young Marsk out of Gentle Kitty. Young Marsk, was got by Marsk, dam by Blank, grandam bay Starling, by Ioulton Starling, out of Mr. Holmes' Miss Mersell, by Croft's Partner, and was the dam of Trunnion. Gentle Kitty was bred by Mr. Hutton, and got by Sylvio, son of Cade.

Young Mousetrap is a beautiful blood bay with black legs, stands 15 hands 2½ inches high ; and is allowed, by judges, to be the fastest trotter in the county, of his age. From his superior shape, beauty, and action, he his calculated to get Hackneys and Hunters—and his Stock falls very large and promising.

He will Travel in the Neighbourhood of Winterton, Barton, Brigg, Kirton, and Market-Raisen.

The Money to be paid the last round.

☞ MARES MISSED LAST YEAR, ONLY HALF PRICE.

Palmer, Printer, Kirton.

TO SERVE MARES THIS SEASON 1833,

THAT CELEBRATED ROADSTER COLT
WILDFIRE
The property of John Bromby, Aldborough.

At £1 10s. each Mare, and 2s. 6d. the groom's fee, to be paid the first time of serving.

WILDFIRE is a good dark Chestnut, stands 15 hands 2 inches high, and was got by Confidence, dam by Wildfire ; g. dam Mr. R. Ramsden's Wildfire, by Kenby's Meratiles was got by old Meratiles, whose sire was R. Ramsden's Performer, Mr. R. Ramsden's Wildfire, was got by Mr. Kirby's Wildfire, of York, which horse beat the celebrated black Trotting Mare of Mr. Shales, on Sunbury Common, winning 200 guineas. He is sire of that famous horse Nonpareil, Theompson, for which Mr. Theobald refused 1200 guineas.

Old Wildfire's dam was by Skyscraper ; g. dam Marshland Shales, which trotted 17 miles within the hour carrying 12 stones, beating Mr. West's noted horse Driver for 200 guineas.

This Colt will travel a small circuit on Trent side, Kirton Lindsey & Scunthorpe.

All Mares tried by this Horse are payable, except by consent of the groom ; the money to be paid the last time round. No business done on Sundays.

Ackroyd, Printers, Brigg.

CARELESS,
THE PROPERTY OF
R. R. GRAVENOR,
EAST LOUND,
WILL SERVE MARES THIS SEASON,
1861,
At £1, 10s. each, and 2s. 6d. the Groom.

CARELESS is a beautiful chestnut, rising 3 years old. He was got by Young Prickwillow, belonging to Mr. Godfrey, of the Levels, who was sold at three years' old for 100 Guineas.

Careless was out of a splendid mare by Old Don Juan.

Young Prickwillow was by Old Prickwillow, out of a fast trotting mare by Wildfire

The Money to be paid the last Round

W. Alock, Printer, Baxter-gate, Doncaster.

1835.

AT THE BARRACK FARM, WOODBRIDGE,

At £2 2s. each Mare and 2s. 6d. the Groom.

SUNBEAM,
(819 HACKNEY STUD BOOK.)

The property of Mr. J. Grout, Bull Hotel, Woodbridge.

SUNBEAM is a beautiful dark Chestnut Horse 15. 1½ h.h. 5 years old, bred by Mr. HENRY MOORE, Burn Butts, Cranswick, Hull

Sire, Bourdass' Denmark (177) ; Dam, Empress, by Triffit's Fireaway (241.).

SUNBEAM has capital knee action, and is strongly made, very fast, good temper, and rare constitution.

J. LODER, PRINTER, WOODBRIDGE.

TO COVER THIS SEASON, 1833,
At £2 5s. each Mare,
THE CELEBRATED TROTTER
GREY SHALES,
The Property of J. Golden, Esq. Carnby.

This Superior Horse was bred by Mr. West, of Newton, and got by Mr. Chadd's Champion Shales. He is allowed to be the fastest trotter in England ; his Grandsire Old Marshland Shales, trotted 17 miles in one hour, carrying twelve stone, beating that noted Horse, Driver, for 200 Guineas, and afterwards stood Champion of England.

GREY SHALES' dam is a superior grey mare, got by Old Pretender, whose sire was Jenkinson's Old Fireaway, which, trotted 3 miles in 3 minutes, and was afterwards sold for 1000 guineas;—grandam by Cribbage, whose sire was Wincup's Trumpeter, whose sire is Lord Clermont's Trumpater, who is the sire of Sorcerer. Sorcerer is the sire of Snowleshin, Mowl, Sorcery, Maid of Orleans, &c.

GREY SHALES is descended from the first blood, and the fastest trotter in the Kingdom. He is 9 years old, stands 15 hands 3 inches high; and for symmetry, action, and breeding as a Nag, there can, among Judges, be but one opinion. He has in one round proved himself a certain and handsome stock-getter; and has travelled four seasons in one round. As a proof of the value of his Stock, 100 Guineas have been refused for his two year olds, and from 20 to 30 for his foals.

GREY SHALES trotted Mousetrap for £20 a side, 10 miles on the Newark road, carrying 12 stone, and beat him two miles in ten.

Grey Shales will travel in the neighbourhood of Kirton, Butterwick, Winterton, Brigg, Barton, Great Limber, Habsen, and home on Saturday Nights.

JAMES HOLLAND, the person employed, has strict orders not to trit the horse for any person.

Y. STARK, PRINTER, GAINSBURGH.

Commander in Chief.
The Property of THOMAS FOW, of Winteringham,
WILL SERVE MARES THIS SEASON, 1837,
At One Pound Eight Shillings each.

Commander was got by Conqueror, his dam by Runaway, grandam by Mr. Rounding's Colt, (which was sold to go abroad in 1798,) a son of Mr. John Harrison's noted horse Granby, of Kelsey Hill, great grandam by Mr. Stickney's noted horse.

Runaway was got by Escape, his dam by Saeralaear, his grandam Misfortune, Buzzard's dam by Qui'en's out of Match'em, great grandam by Snap, great great grandam by Regulus, great great great grandam by Bartlett's Childers, great great great great grandam was sister to the two true blues by the Honeywood Arabian, out of a Byerley Turk Mare, &c. &c.

Conqueror was got by Mr. Crapp's Admiral, which was sold to go abroad when nine years old for 300 Guineas, his dam by Mr. Agars' Rainbow, which was sold for 300 Guineas when 17 years old, grandam by Coachman.

Admiral was got by General Benefit, his dam by Mr. Gowdlass's Turk, of Hutton Cranswick, gran dam by Mr. Lumplugh's old Volunteer, great grandam by Mr. Sawden's Old Horse of Lund, great great grandam by Mr Dundey's noted Old Horse.

General Benefit was got by Coachman, his dam by Mr L. Stephenson's old Horse of Cherry Burton, grandam by Mr Bell's old Horse of Leckonfield, great grandam by Mr Freeman's old Horse. Coachman was got by Mr Agars' Young Rainbow, which sold for 300 Guineas. Rainbow by Dart, Dart by Old Rainbow, Old Rainbow by Mr Dundey's noted Old Coach Horse.

Commander was bred by Mr. Harrison of Kelsey Hill, near Hedon, and was late the property of Mr J. Burkhill, of Winterton Cliff; is rising 3 years old, a good bay, with black legs, and stands 16 hands high ; he has proved himself a sure foal-getter.

SEASON, 1918.

THE PRIZE-WINNING HACKNEY STALLION

Wandale Polonius 13125.

2nd Prize and Reserve for the Junior Championship Hackney Show, Newmarket, 1918.

The property of Ernest E. Hutton, Westerham Hill, Kent.

"Wandale Polonius" is a very fine dark chestnut colt, foaled 1915, standing 15.3 on the best of limbs with quality and great action. he is very like his sire Polonius and is one of the last of that great sire's get.

PEDIGREE.

Sire, Polonius 4931.
Dam. 15217 Lady Elms by The Marquis 6122. -
G Dam. 17279 Elms Princess by Prince Henry 3rd. 5759.

A limited number of mares at £7 7s. 0d. each and 5s. groom's fee.

For nominations apply to owner.

Telegram : Hutton, Biggin Hill.   Telephone : No. 5 Biggin Hill.

1887.
"CONFIDENCE,"
THE PROPERTY OF AND BRED BY
HENRY MOORE,
BURN BUTTS, CRANSWICK, HULL.

Registered in HACKNEY STUD BOOK, 163.

CONFIDENCE is by Denmark (Bordass') 177 ; by Sir Charles (Beal's) 708 ; dam Poll the 3rd 274 by Fireaway (Shaw's) 242 ; by Fireaway (Betts') 239 ; g. dam Poll the 2nd, by Black Rattler (Harrison's) 82 ; by Performer (Ramsden's) 547 ; g. gr. dam Poll the 1st by Performer (Ramsden's) 547 ; by Pretender (Wood's) 596.

He has won the following Prizes :—

1883, 1st Prize of £20 in All aged Hackney Class at Manchester, being then only 3 years old.

1884. 2nd Prize at Sutton.

1885, 2nd Prize in First Class at the Hackney Stud Book Society's Show in London, being only beaten by the champion horse of the Show.

CONFIDENCE is a light chestnut 7 years old, stands 15 hands 2 inches high, and is free from all blemish and hereditary disease, with fine symmetry and superior action.

CONFIDENCE will be in the neighbourhood of Sutton, on Mondays ; will stand at the White Horse, Carr Lane, Hull, on Tuesdays ; at Market Weighton on Wednesdays ; Driffield on Thursdays ; and travel short distances near home the rest of the week.

CONFIDENCE will serve a limited number of Mares at £3 each, and 3s. the Groom. Mares taken in to grass at 7s. 6d. per week. Corn, if desired, at market prices.

The Money to be paid to the Groom at Midsummer.

EXPRESS Co., DRIFFIELD.

---

41. Early stud cards of harness horses, mainly of the nineteenth century, from the collection of Mr Ernest Hutton.

of Thoroughbred via Arab and Turk, and Barb blood, crossed with 'our mares'. But 'our mares' of a closely defined region!

In the early part of the nineteenth century too many of the best stallions and mares were bought up and exported to the Continent. In 1829 three foreign dealers bought upwards of 300 mares at Horncastle Fair. This went on at sale after sale, year after year. Before a committee, appointed to investigate, in 1844, Mr Richard Tattersall said that America and the countries of Europe had been purchasing the best stallions and mares that money could buy in England during the last hundred years and more. Mr J. East (firm of Phillips & East) said, 'that the French agents buy the very best mares they can get; you cannot get them to buy a bad one'.

Sir Walter Gilbey, in *Horses Past and Present* (1910), goes on to say that it was a pity this committee, which had been formed to assess the state of the equine world, 'did not ask questions as to the number of mares purchased for France, Germany, Russia and Austria, and also inquire the use to which the mares are put in those countries. The answers would have been instructive, for it is now well known that fifteen out of every twenty of them were heavyweight Hunter mares— many of them stale for riding to hounds, but in every other respect suitable for breeding.

'These foreign buyers had no prejudices; they bought the mares with the view of breeding stock of the type most suitable for the requirements of their respective countries; the mares had plenty of Thoroughbred blood in their veins, and it remained for breeders to select stallions of the right stamp. Hence the demand from all continental countries for Hackney sires which began sixty years ago and has continued ever since.' Sir Walter Gilbey was of course referring to 1850 or thereabouts, but, as we shall see, the question *which* foreign army was getting the advantage of our breeding was still exercising the minds of a royal commission in 1897.

So once again we see how commercialism ruined one of the finest and most valuable breeds of horses which England has ever produced.

'There is no doubt,' writes Herman Biddell, an authority on the Suffolk, 'that Blakes Farmer [a famous Suffolk Punch sire, foaled 1760] was a trotting horse. He appears to have been a chestnut and not much above cob size'. Referring to Mr Gleed's bung-tailed horse foaled in 1805, Biddell says: 'The horse himself gives the idea of a trotting cob. But he was a full-sized horse with the massive shoulders, the muscular development, the rounded hind quarters and the handsome crest and clean legs which are handed down to the present race of show horses.' A picture of him was painted by Hobart of Bildeston in the first half of the nineteenth century.

Mr George Ewart Evans (in *The Horse in the Furrow*) writes to us as follows: 'The probable reason for the early use of the horse in ploughing in Suffolk was the lightness of the soil in the Sands—in a large part the hinterland of Orford. I collected a little information about the use of lightish horses in ploughing "common yards" . . . these were called Suffolk Cobs (the poor man's Punch); they had, it appears, a Punchy look.'—In fact the Suffolk Cob differed but little from his neighbour the Norfolk Cob of the same period—and indeed he could be compared to the Welsh Cob, who, in his turn, as we shall see from the chapter on Wales, is 'closely allied to the Welsh Cart Horse', and all

42. North Star, 1861.

these horses, before the peculiarities of special breeds took shape, were 'plane bredde horsys', descended from 'our mares'.

There was yet another infusion into the 'old breed'. 'Like Blake's,' says Herman Biddell, 'the first of the line was a trotting horse; and this trotting horse was the son of a race-horse, a thoroughbred which appears to have been brother to a well-known racing stallion belonging to the Duke of Grafton, a grandson of Eclipse.' He was known as Barber's Proctor, the old Shadingfield Horse foaled in 1798.

In 1855 the Butley Abbey horses were sold, among them Duke, who 'was purchased by Mr Fisher Hobbs, to take into Essex, where he travelled [in a van!] for several years. But he was nine years old and somewhat dilapidated then. His price was 255 Gns. When he won at Windsor his stable companion Ripshawe was second. Those were the days when the item of action was little thought of. "Run on with No. 407", said one of the judges. "What d'ye want to trot him for? You mayn't run such horses as *these*!" and the merest apology for a trot was all they got out of him, for Charles Row, like everybody else at the Abbey, always took his time.'

Thus the legend grew that Suffolks could not trot, although they possessed the same blood which made the Norfolk Trotters on the Thoroughbred side—and on the distaff side they must have been descended from the Great Horse mares (who also trotted—we have before us instructions upon how to teach the Great Horse to trot to the best advantage!), and in part they may have been descended from 'our mares', which were probably a lighter, more cobby type, and un-doubtedly an ideal foundation from which to get first-class horses.

CHAPTER FOURTEEN

Exmoor, Dartmoor and the New Forest

'The small horses (in the whole upwards of 400) are not taken into winter keeping, nor to more sheltered grounds, during the severest winter, when the snow covers the Forest (of Exmoor) to the depth of many feet . . . the Forester has an annual sale for the small horses. . . .' Billingsley's *General View of the Agriculture of Somerset*, 1795.

THERE seems little doubt but that the Exmoor pony may be considered as a breed [1] indigenous to Britain, the descendant of the *Plateau/Celtic* or, as we have called it in the beginning of this book, the North Atlantic pony, and probably very nearly related to those ponies which pulled the chariots of the Celts.

We know that in a period of two hundred years horses can be so improved that they will grow at least a hand and a half, or, as Admiral Rous has shown, since 1700 many breeds, and especially the Thoroughbred, have grown $6\frac{1}{2}$ inches. And in the development of the small Exmoor of 12–13 hands to the short-lived Exmoor Cob, and the now practically extinct Devonshire Pack Horse, we have a typical example.

Among all the Domesday manors in the county of Devon, Brendon had the greatest number of *Equae indomitae* running on the common; there were 104 unbroken mares, which probably means three-year-old and upwards and would correspond to a total stock of about 400 of all ages and both sexes. And less than half of Exmoor is in Devon.[2]

In his *History of Cornwall, c.* 1603, Carew says: 'The Cornish horses are hardly bred, coarsely fed, and so low in stature' that they were liable to be seized on as unsuitable, according to the statute of Henry VIII, by anyone who caught them depasturing the commons.

At the end of the Civil War one of the first Acts of the Republican Government was to make a survey of all the Crown property throughout

---

[1] All the sub-species *Equus* migrated to the British Isles—none originated here.

[2] The whole of the Royal Forest lay in Somerset. Badgeworthy Water forms part of the county boundary. But nearly half the area designated as Exmoor National Park is in Devon.

the country. When, in 1651, the commissioners arrived on Exmoor, they made a perambulation of it in the medieval manner, and estimated the extent of the Royal Forest at some 18,000 acres.[1] The bounds of the Forest indicated by their report did not quite coincide with what we now call Exmoor, nor with what was then loosely called Exmoor, but near enough. What they did report was the existence of fifty-two suitors, mostly very small freeholders and leaseholders, with grazing rights on the Royal Forest. Each of these affirmed that he and his predecessors had been entitled, time out of mind, to depasture or agist on the Forest as many horned cattle as his enclosed lowland holding would maintain (and this must have been very few, since most of these holdings were worth only 10s. or 12s. or 14s. by the year) and sevenscore sheep and five mares and colts. This is not to be taken as five head, either mares or colts. The mare-and-colt is one unit; how many followers there were to a mare would depend on the time of year and the state of the market. In the disturbed years since first the Parliament had taken up arms against the King, it is unlikely that the Michaelmas horse fairs had functioned regularly all the time. While the war had driven up prices of big military horses and encouraged their breeding, even under hazardous conditions, it need not have produced a like boom among small moorland horses. In the early autumn we might reckon one foal to a mare, and either one yearling or one two-year-old unsold owing to lack of markets. Say an average of two 'followers' per mare. Between them the suitors could run two hundred and sixty brood mares, with say five hundred and twenty young stock. A reasonable proportion of stallions is one to twenty mares; thirteen stallions (there were probably rather more), making a grand total of about eight hundred head, a figure that compares fairly closely with the numbers on the moor today. The commissioners observed that in fact there was not keep for fifty-two times sevenscore sheep, and that none of the suitors kept anything like that number. But they made no such reservation in the case of the horses.

In contrast to the annual drift at Michaelmas laid down by Henry VIII, we learn from this report that the suitors of Hawkridge and Withypool had to drive the Forest nine times a year. Much of Exmoor had come back into royal hands since the Reformation, before which time the Abbot of Taunton had held a considerable acreage. But his was a black-robed order, and the monks probably left no legacy of white stock on Exmoor. One Cistercian house did formerly hold part of the moor, but it was the Abbey of Neath, far away in Glamorgan, and probably these monks did not farm the moorland holding for themselves or supervise its husbandry at all closely.

In the early days there were no roads of any kind on the moors, and therefore wheeled carts would have been useless, and the sled and the pack-horse were used for transporting agricultural produce.

[1] In 1795, some 19,900.

The sleds were drawn by oxen, and ponies were used to carry corn, etc., in pots and panniers. At the beginning of this century it was said that pack-horses might have been met with some fifty years previously, in the western and southern districts. They were the larger ponies of the Dartmoor and Exmoor breed, and were indispensable to the farmers.

William Marshall, the highly industrious, best-selling author of the Rural Economy series, gave the West Country the full treatment in 1796. His *West of England* included Dorset, Somerset, Devon and Cornwall. Besides some highly intelligent remarks on the pack-horse in trade and agriculture, which we will examine in another book, he mentions frequently what he calls the 'Mountain Horse'. By this he means the ponies of Dartmoor, Exmoor and Bodmin Moor, which he regards as all one breed. Among other things he says: 'At the foot of Hingston, one of the highest of the Western Mountains, I observed two Cornish mares and foals, the smallest I have ever seen: the mares not more, I apprehend, than eleven hands high.' Hingston Down has figured before in this book, in the table of equestrian place names in Chapter 3 above. It is among the oldest English (as distinct from Cornish) place names in Cornwall and means 'stallion farm hill'. Strange that the little mares should have caught his eye here of all places. Note that Marshall only says 'pony' when speaking of Scottish animals, no matter how small they may be.

In 1816 a Mr Collyns recounts that he 'bought an Exmoor pony for 23*s*. [a fair price in those days] at Simonsbath. When haltered, that is caught and secured for the first time in his life, he proved to be two years old, he was only 11 hh.' Mr Collyns's nine nephews and nieces learned to ride on this pony, and when twenty years old it carried a man to hounds, 'in such a manner as to excite the surprise and the envy of many a sportsman apparently better mounted.[1]

In 1820 Youatt writes: 'The Exmoor ponies, although generally ugly enough, are hardy and useful. A well-known sportsman says, that he rode one of them half-a-dozen miles, and never felt such power and action in so small a compass before. To show his accomplishments, he was turned over a gate at least eight inches higher than his back; and his owner, who rides fourteen stone, travelled on him from Bristol to South Molton, eighty-six miles, beating the coach which runs the same road.

'The horses, which are still used in Devonshire, and particularly in the western and southern districts, under the denomination of Pack-horses, are a larger variety of the Exmoor or Dartmoor breed. The saddle horses of Devonshire are mostly procured from the more eastern counties.

' . . . Hay, corn, straw, fuel, stones, dung, lime, are carried on horseback; and in harvest, sledges drawn by oxen and horses are employed. This was probably in early times the mode of conveyance throughout the kingdom. . . .

[1] *Thoroughbred and Other Ponies.*

'There is on Dartmoor a race of ponies much in request in that vicinity, being sure-footed and hardy, and admirably calculated to scramble over the rough roads and dreary wilds of that mountainous district. The Dartmoor pony is larger than the Exmoor, and, if possible, uglier. He exists there almost in a state of nature. The late Captain Colgrave, governor of the prison, had a great desire to possess one of them of somewhat superior figure to its fellows; and having several men to assist him, they separated it from the herd. They drove it on some rocks by the side of a tor (an abrupt pointed hill). A man followed on horseback, while the captain stood below watching the chase. The little animal, being driven into a corner, leaped completely over the man and horse and escaped.'

At the beginning of this century there were at least two famed herds on Exmoor, those bred by Sir T. Dyke Acland, who sold his property to Mr Knight, removing his ponies to Dulverton. As we shall see, Mr Knight 'bred up' some of his ponies; but today the Acland (Anchor) herd retain supremacy as they alone preserve the characteristics of the old strain; standing between 11.2 and 12.2 hands high, they are dark brown with black points and have the mealy tan muzzle and 'toad eye'.

The then Sir Thomas Acland states in the *Livestock Journal* of 28th May 1886 that his father, prior to 1815, had about 500 Exmoor ponies running wild on Exmoor and that a famous and possibly mythical stallion, Katerfelto, was supposed to have infused some fine Spanish or Arab blood into them. Before the disafforestation of Exmoor the Aclands were foresters from 1767 to 1814, and the survey and valuation made at the latter date shows 640 horses agisted on the Forest, of which 180 stallions and mares and 300 colts and fillies belonged to the Crown's lessee, Sir Thomas Acland.

The Rev. John Russell declared that no hunter was any use without Exmoor blood in him, Thoroughbred sire, dam by a Thoroughbred out of one of these little Exmoor ponies. 'Such a bred one would stay for ever, be as intelligent as a dog, the pony strain would ensure that, and he would last as well—Parson Jack Russell would have said twenty years at 2 days hunting a week.'[1]

Mr Knight used a Dongola [2] horse—a Barb of about 16 hands—but was not entirely satisfied with the results. But his policy was to breed up the Exmoor to a certain standard of height and power. His son, Sir Frederick Knight, continued the policy, and by 1860 had 'got them to such a pitch of perfection as to make everyone talk about Exmoor Cobs.'

Mr Knight died in 1850 and the first sale at Bampton Fair was held in 1854. In 1863 Sir Frederick owned around 400 ponies, including nearly 100 brood mares. The *Sporting Magazine* has an account of a sale at Reading in that year: 'Seeing that Mr Knight's half hundred

---

[1] G. S. Lowe, *The Horses of the British Empire.*
[2] Dongola is in Western Sudan.

Exmoor ponies walked in their neat and blue trimmed halters 140 miles "direct from the hills" to Reading, the least we could do was to go and meet them there. The lot were bigger and better looking than they were in '61, nearer 13 hands and very much better broken. Three men are now constantly with them, both riding and driving all the year through; and the purchasers are no longer in a dire state of perplexity as to how they are to coax them home by fair means or foul.

'Their journey occupies 9 days to Reading, three of which are spent in a good grass field as an interlude. . . . Prices have gone up steadily in 3 years to £13 19s. 6d., which is £1 7s. 6d. more than they made last year and fully 3 gns beyond the average of '61. . . . The top price of the year was 34 gns, and it was hardly to be expected that three such grand ex-sires could be found as "The Sparcombe" pony, Pandarus and Palmerston, which averaged 37 gns the last time they were sold. . . . The foals by a 14 hands 1 inch son of Old Port (the first-born of Beeswing) from a Devonshire Pack mare are so promising that Mr Knight intends to have him back next season from the tenant to whom he lent him.'

In 1900 the 'Knight' ponies were bigger than the 'Acland', which were described as a 'wonderfully thoroughbred looking and handsome pony with fine lean head, intelligent eye and good limbs', but he was a shade too small for general purposes. It is recounted that an interesting sight was 'the display of jealousy by the stallions when two droves of ponies were brought up for inspection. Each kept his harem crowded together apart from the other, "rounding in" his mares with the greatest fire, keeping, at a far distance in the hills, the weaker sires who might be suspected of designs upon the drove.'[1]

The Katerfelto story is typical, in the maddening vagaries of its chronology, of the literature of pony breeding. G. S. Lowe in *The Horses of the British Empire* (1907), writes: 'There is a romantic story founded on fact in connection with such improvements on Exmoor. Katerfelto, the title of one of Whyte Melville's best novels, was a sort of spectre horse constantly seen on the moors, but no one knew where he came from. After being talked about for some time, it was decided to catch him, and in doing so the horse took an extraordinary leap, which has ever afterwards been called Katerfelto's leap (similar to Captain Colgrave's attempt!). Caught he was, and kept by an ancestor of the Froude family at East Anstey. Old men who lived forty years ago [2] can remember him, and so it may be that a hundred years have passed since Katerfelto appeared in the flesh. He has been described as a dun stallion of about 14 hands, with a black list down his back,[3] and of a blood-like appearance. He may have been therefore a racing Galloway for what anyone knows, but the story that passed into history [4] was that

[1] *Thoroughbred and Other Ponies.*
[2] i.e. who were alive in the 1860's.
[3] A highly uncommon colour scheme in the Arab, or in the Barb.
[4] Or legend.

a freebooter or political offender rode him up the country to Porlock, turned him loose, and escaped by sea to a foreign refuge. Anyway Katerfelto was running with the ponies for two or three years, and it is probable that the present breed inherit much of his blood. "The Druid" gives a different account of Katerfelto from this, and wrote that Katerfelto's dam, stolen by some gipsies, proved in foal to an Arab, but I had my version from the late Mr Froude Bellow and I fancy it is the correct one.'

However it is true that an Exmoor stallion of that name was the winner of the first prize for pony stallions at the Devon County Show. Exhibited at the Royal Show, Plymouth 1890, a stallion called Katerfelto, 'Entered by the Directors of Convict Prisons, Government Farm, Princetown, Devon, "Katerfelto", bay, was foaled in 1880, bred by Mr F. Smyth, Wistland Pound, Barnstaple, s. John Trot.'

According to MacDermott's *History of the Forest of Exmoor*, in the whole history of Exmoor as a royal forest the word pony was unknown and Exmoors are 'Horse Beasts' or 'Widge Beasts' until about 1710.[1] In 1777 the words 'Exmore [*sic*] Naggs' are used in the Foresters' Stock Accounts. In 1805 this became 'Exmore Horses'. But this change should not be taken to imply an increase in size.

Dartmoor

A well-known Dartmoor breeder is at a loss to explain the preservation of a greater uniformity of type on Exmoor than on Dartmoor in terms of the usual reason for such uniformity, which depends on the degree of isolation of the breeding area. We agree that this is the most potent factor in preserving an unmixed or 'unimproved' type, but we submit that over the centuries the isolation of Exmoor, although it is the smaller region of the two, has in fact been greater.

There are today three large towns within reach of Dartmoor in less than one day's journey on foot—Plymouth, Torquay, Exeter. Of these the last was already a considerable place in Roman times (Isca Dumnoniorum). Plymouth flourished as a port in the Middle Ages. So did Dartmouth. Torquay is admittedly of more modern growth.

There is no town of comparable size to Exeter within the same range of Exmoor, or any North Devon port to compare with Plymouth. We may perhaps equate Bideford/Barnstaple with Dartmouth over most of their history, but Bideford is nine miles beyond Barnstaple, *away* from the moor. Tavistock, on the fringe of Dartmoor, was once of greater importance than now, as is proved by the large (for the west country) acreage of ploughland it returned in the Domesday survey.

But the question of communications across the moors is perhaps of greater weight than access to them. The most direct route from Exeter to Plymouth is straight across Dartmoor by Moreton Hampstead and

[1] But 'widge' had vanished from the local speech by the time F. T. Elworthy's dialect dictionary *West Somerset Words* came to be compiled in 1886.

Two Bridges, whereas the only important road over or past Exmoor is that from Bristol to Bideford. However this skirts the northern fringe of the moor by Porlock and Lynton. No mileage is saved by way of Exford and Simonsbath, and for centuries this route meant literally fording the Exe.

In many ways the isolation of northern Exmoor has increased in the last century due to the decline in seaborne traffic across the Bristol Channel and along its south coast; this was once considerable, but the trading coasters which still plied within living memory are now a thing of the past, and all that remains of the passenger traffic is irregular day-trips from Swansea to Ilfracombe, Lynmouth and Minehead in summer.

King John valued the deer population of both moors highly enough to retain them in his own hand while disafforesting the whole of Devon in 1203, but as the progress of agriculture advanced, game as an item of food for the court became less and less important and the interest of the Crown fainter and fainter, until in 1818 the Crown was glad to part with Exmoor as a liability.

Travellers with an eye to economic potentialities, from Defoe to Cobbett, report Exmoor as a dreary unprofitable waste, while they are less severe about Dartmoor. Perhaps the failure of successive mining ventures on Exmoor was a further deterrent to outsiders.

Princetown was chosen as the site of a huge prisoner-of-war camp, which became the convict prison of today, not so much because of its isolation as because, even at the time of the Napoleonic wars, it was fairly handy to Plymouth, where the Navy landed its prisoners. These, drawn from captured ships, were far more numerous than military prisoners from French and satellite armies. But the existence of the prison itself has brought a constant traffic, and a certain resident population of officials, first from the Admiralty and later from the Home Office, that had been totally lacking on Exmoor.

In the reign of Henry I (1100–35), when Dartmoor was a royal forest, one of the king's squires took a stallion to the royal manor of Gillingham for the purpose of covering the king's mares. This king also received two Arabs as a present from eastern Europe; one of them was sent on to King Alexander I of Scotland.

Sir Walter Gilbey tells us that in 1903 'the Dartmoor pony's good points are a strong back and loin and substance. For generations past the farmers appear to have been in the habit of taking up a few mares for riding and breeding purposes; to these diminutive dams a small Welsh cart stallion is put, and the result is an animal hardy and serviceable enough for ordinary farm work. These form a small minority.

'For the most part the Dartmoor ponies still run wild, shaggy and unkempt on the waste land where they breed uncontrolled, on which they are foaled and live and die; often without having looked through a bridle. No stallions of alien blood appear to have been turned out with these herds, but mares got by crossing the Exmoor and Dartmoor strains have been put to small blood horses with good results. Early in the [nineteenth] century a Mr Willing of Torpeak made successful experiments in crossing the Exmoor pony with the smaller variety peculiar to the Dartmoor "tors". In 1820 Mr Wooton used to buy mares of this cross and put them to small racehorses standing in the district.'

In the chapter on 'Galloway, the Dales and the Fells', we mentioned Mr Christopher Wilson's Sir George. A breeder on Dartmoor obtained a brown stallion by Sir George out of Windsor Soarer, which he put to selected mares. Only the best of the young stock were kept. The colt foals at two years old were put to the mares got by the brown stallion. The experiment was successful, browns, black browns and chestnuts being the colours of this improved breed, which sold well.

It is to be observed generally that those 'imported' sires whose progeny sell well have in the long run least influence on local breeds, because their issue is sold 'up the country' before they in turn have time to breed.

The Field of May 1876 has this to say: 'Instead of deteriorating the stock improves yearly, and the care which is now taken to infuse pure blood [1] without harming the essential characteristics of the original denizen of the moor has succeeded in producing an animal of superlative merit fitted for any kind of work, whether for the field, road or collar. It must be observed that the "moor" should apply to Exmoor and the Bodmin wastes as well as the Forest of Dartmoor, Dartmoor Forest itself being within the precincts of the Duchy of Cornwall. The moor pony or galloway of 14 hands is often in reality a little horse; and when it is stated that Tom Thumb, the well-known hunter of Mr Trelawny, was a direct descendant of the celebrated Rough Tor pony of Landue, and that Foster by Gainsborough, carrying for many years fifteen stone and upwards, was from a moor pony near Ivybridge, the assertion is not made without bringing strong collateral proof of the validity of the statement. These animals possess many other qualities of the Thorough-bred—speed, activity, and any amount of stay, with legs of steel; they can jump as well as the moor sheep, and much after the same fashion, for no hedge or fence can stop either one or the other.'

In *Horses of the British Empire* we read: 'The first origin of these Devonshire Pack Horses was possibly the pony, and the ordinary horse of their times used for agricultural purposes. By 1700 there was a regular family of pack-horses bred to themselves and fostered with some amount of care. A very common sign-board for the public houses in the oldest village was "The Pack Horse". Trotting matches were not infrequent during the seventeen hundreds for the honour and glory of the thing, or for small sums, or even for gallons of beer or cider. At one

---

[1] The modern theorist would use the term 'pure blood' to indicate the 'original denizen'!

time they had all the roads to themselves as travelling sires, but as fox-hunting began to take its place, and fast coaches appeared upon the scene, the Thoroughbreds shared the patronage of customers, and also a few Arabs.'

In 1637 there was a pack-horse service from Bampton to London.

G. S. Lowe continues: 'There were then, doubtless, further improvements in the Pack Horse, but still some of the old yeomen were jealous in the matter of crossing with other blood, and it is still a question whether the Cottagers of about 1810 were crossed at all. They were extraordinary animals, as no day's hunting could be too long for them, and they were as good on the road as in the field. The type was about 15.1 for the stallions, long and low, deep through the girth, shoulders not quite of the orthodox order but still long and fairly slanting, a trifle of lowness in the wither being the fault, and then with very short legs and plenty of bone, nearly always dark browns or bays, with very seldom much white about them bar a slightly blaze face, which was not uncommon.'

Show card of Cottager, early in the nineteenth century, describes the celebrated Pack Horse stallion by Old Cottager, dam a great trotter, will travel, etc., over the following districts at £2 a mare. Cottager is open to trot any other horse in the country, 16 miles, or will do that distance within the hour on the road, or to gallop and jump four miles on a steeplechase course. Money always ready.

'The father of Sir Frederick Knight bought some manors on Exmoor, and some of the ponies were then crossed with Cottager..At four years old the produce had drawn attention to themselves. About 1824 there was a Mr Wreford who bred race horses, on meeting Mr Knight he said, that he understood that Mr Knight had been crossing his ponies with cart horses. Mr Knight replied that he had been using a pack horse, and told his sons to get out two of the four-year-old ponies and give Mr Wreford a gallop. The latter was riding a Thoroughbred mare who had won races, and possibly he was giving the boys some weight, but he was never in it. In a mile and a half they could have beaten him by a hundred yards. There were many similar cases, but gradually these good horses were lost, and the last of the Cottager line, a horse called Safeguard, belonging to a Mr Soper, was sent to Australia in 1885 or 1886.'

The Late Goonhilly

The Cornish horses generally are hardly bred, coarsely fed, low stature, quick in travel, and (after their growth and strength) able enough for continuance, which sort prove most serviceable for a rough and hilly country. But very few of them (through the owner's fault) retain long this their natural goodness, for after two years age they use them to carry sacks of sand which boweth down and weakeneth their backs, and the next summer they are employed in harrowing which marreth their pace, two means that so quail also their stomachs and abate their strength as the first rider findeth them overbroken in his hands. Howbeit now from naught they are almost come to naught, for since the statute 12th of Henry the Eigth, wich enableth every man

43. Cornish pack-horses carrying sand, by J. Rowlandson, about 1790.

to seize upon horses that pastured in commons if they were under a certain
size, the sheriff's officers . . . have of late time accustomed to drive those
waste grounds and to seize on those not voluntary statute-breaking tits, so as
nature denying a great harass and those [officers] carring away the little, it
resteth that hereafter, not the dam's foal but the dam's trotters are trusted
unto . . . ordinary husbandmen should do well to quite breeding of horses and
betake themselves to mules for that is a beast that will fare hardly, live very
long, draw indifferently well, and carry great burdens, and hath also a pace
swift and easy enough for their mill and market service. By which means, look
what is abated from the usual number of hackneys should with a gainful
recompense be added to their goodness, for not long since it happened that
one brought over a he ass from France because of the strangeness of the beast,
who following his kind begat many monsters, viz. Mules, and for monsters
indeed the country people admired them: yea, some were so wise as to knock
on the head or give away this issue of his race, as uncouth mongrels.

From 'The Survey of Cornwall' by Richard Carew of Antony, 1602.

Richard Carew of Antony was the sheriff of the county of Cornwall in
1586, and knew what he was talking about, since in that year there was
a mobilization of the militia, which showed up painfully the quality of
horses available for the defence of the county that lay most open to
Spanish invasion. Later it was his officers who 'drove the waste grounds'.
Many interesting points arise out of his observations. For instance, we
see that the undesirable runts were indeed removed from some Cornish
commons but he says nothing about their destruction. Of course not;
the procedure has obviously been what local authorities followed in
regard to vagrants and sturdy beggars under the Elizabethan Poor Law;
flog them into the next parish in the case of the parish constable, or into
the next county in the case of the sheriff's officers. There is only one

44. Cornish Pack-horses, 1788, by J. Rowlandson. The one on the left carrying hay, on what were known as 'Long Crooks', was recognized by the late Miss Calmady-Hamlyn as the type of Goonhilly Pony familiar in her youth.

next county for Cornwall, which meant that Dartmoor was favoured with the leavings of Bodmin Moor and Goonhilly Downs at about 7*s*. 6*d*. a head, which no doubt appeared in the account books on the credit side under 'disposal of carcasses' and on the debit side under 'expenses of officers driving Bodmin Moor', which I have no doubt was a thirsty job.

It is noticeable that Carew uses the word *tit* in a wrong sense, but not surprising, since it was not really current in his part of the world, so very far away from the Scandinavian sphere of influence. He has heard the word and thinks it just means a small animal, whereas it means a lively one. By 'nature denying a great harass' he means that conditions do not allow a large breed (not a numerous stock, which is what his words would imply were it not for the contrast of the 'little' which the officers

45. Cornish rural scene of 1812 (Rowlandson). The fact that horses are available for the dairymaids to drive the cows out to pasture shows that they are plentiful, if of indifferent quality.

carry away). His last remark about the ass is surprising because Cornwall and west Devon are now the only two English counties that support any considerable number of donkeys on commons, etc., and so we tend to think that they have 'always' been there. In fact they have only been there intermittently, and probably the donkey imported from France which Carew reports was not the first ever but the first seen in his lifetime. Quite probably it was one of the giant Poitou breed, since again the sea passage from French Atlantic ports like Nantes and La Rochelle to Cornish ports is short and easy. Its progeny would soon dwindle down to dwarfs in the wet Cornish winters.

The New Forest

If we take into consideration the fact that the Bayeux Tapestry gives us one of the earliest representations of our native ponies—the little mare shown was probably seized not far from Hastings, and may once have been an inhabitant of the New Forest; and from the Anglo-Saxon names, explanations for which have appeared in the early part of this book, such as Studdal in Kent, formerly *Stod-weald*—'the wood of mares'—it seems fairly obvious that wild, semi-wild and perhaps later domesticated herds of ponies were to be found in various parts of the country at all times. Again we have the delightful drawings from Canterbury, and these, too, were the ponies which the artist saw in his own locality.

At one time the Forest extended by way of the Dorset heath practically up to Dartmoor, and there is no reason to doubt but that the early Forest ponies were akin to those of the moors. It is thought that the New Forester may have been descended from those ponies which at the time of Canute were to be found in the district of Ytene. This was afforested by William the Conqueror in 1072, but had always consisted largely of rough pasture that could carry only a very low density of stock.

In 1217 Henry III ordered the warden of the New Forest to give the monks of Beaulieu all the profits accruing from the droves of ponies from that date until November 1220, this gift being for the benefit of the soul of his late father, King John. There were then a sufficient number of ponies to have been a source of annual revenue to the Crown.

There are very few further references to the New Forest pony until the advent of the Thoroughbred Marske, who exercised a similar influence on the Foresters as did Merlin on the Welsh ponies.

In Sir Walter Gilbey's book *Thoroughbred and Other Ponies* the following account is given: 'In 1750 H.R.H. the Duke of Cumberland acquired by exchange a Thoroughbred foal from his breeder, Mr John Hutton. The animal was named Marske and was run at Newmarket; achieving no great success on the Turf, he was put to stud, but up to the time of the Duke's death his progeny had done nothing to win reputation for their sire.

'When the Duke died in 1765, his horses were sold at Tattersall's, and

Marske was knocked down "for a song" to a Dorsetshire farmer. The farmer kept him in the New Forest district, and here Marske, the sire of Eclipse, served mares [1] at a fee of half a guinea.' Eclipse was foaled in 1764, won his first race as a five-year-old in 1769, and made his name in a single season on the turf.

'For four years at least (until Mr Wildman ferreted out the sire of Eclipse and bought him for £20 to go to Yorkshire), the New Forest breed of ponies were being improved by the very best Thoroughbred blood, the effects of which continued to be apparent for many years after Marske had left the district.'

We must remember that the Thoroughbred of that time *averaged* 14 hands; Marske was under 14.2 hands high. There is a picture of the grey Alcock Arabian, 1720, where the height of the pony at the wither scarcely comes up to his leader's elbow!

After Marske left the Forest nothing much was done to continue the improvement until 1852, when Queen Victoria lent the Arab stallion Zorah, which ran with the mares in the Forest for eight years. Sir Walter Gilbey continues: 'When the influence of the Arab sire sent by the Queen ceased to be felt, degeneration again set in, the decreased prices brought by the ponies at the fairs proving conclusively how the breed was deteriorating. To combat evil the Court of Verderers in 1885 hired four well-bred stallions, which were kept by the "Agisters or marksmen for the service of commoners' mares". However this did not help much either for the foals both good and bad were sent for sale to the fairs. And the wild mares were naturally not affected—these continued under the protection of their particular stallion, and in this manner in-breeding continued. In 1889 Queen Victoria again lent two more Arab stallions, Abeyan and Yirassin; a son of Abeyan out of a Welsh mare continued the improvement.' Under Forest conditions, not the most beautiful stallion, or the fastest one, serves the Moor mares—but the dirtiest fighter.

In 1888 a number of *Rhum* ponies, called Black Galloways, to which we have referred, were sent down to the Forest by Lord Arthur Cecil, who says: 'The *Rhum* ponies, which were much thought of by my father, seem to be quite a type of themselves, having characteristics which would almost enable one to recognize them anywhere. Every one of those I bought in 1888 had *hazel* not *brown* eyes; and although only a small boy in 1862, when six or seven of these ponies came to Hatfield, I can remember that they also had the hazel eye. They have, almost without exception, very good hind quarters, with the tail well set up; and it is in this respect that I hope they will do good in the New Forest. On the other hand they have big plain heads which are not liked by the commoners. This defect, however, is rapidly disappearing with good keep, and it does with all breeds of ponies. . . .

[1] But note, this is a very different thing from having a stallion (such as Zorah, above) actually running the Forest. Marske served only *selected* mares, and most of the progeny was no doubt sold away.

'I have noticed all the deer-stalking ponies I could see, on the look-out for some of these characteristics; but with the exception of the hazel eye and a somewhat strong inclination towards blackness of colour, I cannot say that I have seen much trace of the same kind of pony on the mainland of Scotland. This, however, is no doubt rather through cross-ing with other strains than because they have not some of the original blood; and I feel sure that the Galloway of olden days was of the same type, though that term has now come to mean something quite different and in no way connected with the district of Scotland.' Lord Arthur Cecil was referring to the then frequent galloway races; a galloway was almost any breed of small horse of about 13 to 14 hands, which could gallop and was matched. We hear of galloway races on Exmoor, in the north and also in Ireland.

He continues: 'The hazel eye is not uncommon on Exmoor, and occurs in the Welsh pony. It would be a very interesting study to try and trace the tendency to show that colour; it would, I think, throw light on the ancestry of many horses or ponies; or, at least it would reveal many curious instances of reversion.'

The poet Oppian was a great believer in the power of the eye, holding that the eye of the steed should match the eye of the quarry in colour: bluish for bears, yellowish for leopards, fiery and flaming grey for wild boars, and gleaming grey for lions. However, we have never heard that he visited either Rhum or the New Forest!

There was a New Forest Act of 1877 which gave Commoners the power under certain specified regulations: (1) to make drifts on these lands at such time and in such manner as they may think expedient and not at Michaelmas, as formerly: (2) to make by-laws with regard to the conditions as to the time, breed or otherwise, under which Pony Stallions and other Male commonable animals are to be allowed to roam at large on the hills; and the removal from the Forest of the Cattle and other animals belonging to persons not being Commoners in the Forest.

Apart from ponies the Act provides for defunct Verderers, in that, a 'dead Verderer shall be deemed to create a casual vacancy in their midst'.

Since the Bayeux Tapestry, where we found east Sussex ponies, and illustrations done by the monks of Canterbury (see illustrations, Ps 20, 21, 22), we come across a few references to ponies in Kent. William Lambarde, *Perambulation of Kent* (1570), implies that by his time they did not exist: 'Touching domesticall cattle, as horses, oxen, kine and sheep, Kent differeth not much from the others: only it is challenged as singular, that it bringeth forth the *largest of stature* in each kind of them.'

A witness on the New Forest for the Royal Commission on Agricul-ture, 1896, George Edward Briscoe Eyre, landowner, deposed: 'The pony business is a very large business. People begin in early life. If a man can get hold of a mare, perhaps a broken-down mare, cheap, he will turn her out: and if she will live on the Forest at all, she will begin to pay him very shortly. Of course they do not sell their mares; they sell the yearling colts and accumulate the mares so to speak, and so it goes on. There is an immense deal of money made in the Forest by ponies.'

In 1898 Lord Etherington, who owned the Simonsbath stud of improved Exmoor ponies, lent a stallion to the New Forest Association, which was turned out with the wild mares. And Lord Arthur Cecil believed that the Welsh pony stallion of 13.2 hands would be as good a cross for the New Forest pony as any other.

At the same time the Deputy Surveyor of the New Forest, the Hon. Gerald Lascelles, told the Commoners that they had a magnificent run for their ponies. . . . Ponies running out all winter in the mountains of Ireland and Wales, on Exmoor, in Cornwall and on the Fells of Cumberland and Yorkshire had a far worse climate to face, and the same sort of pasture.[1] These ponies would laugh at the hardships of the New Forest.

Although at first there was opposition to the idea of 'bettering the real Forester' the ponies have much improved since the beginning of this century.

We observe that as well as Connemara, Highland, Exmoor, Dartmoor, and Welsh, the New Forest pony has a place in the *Polo Pony Stud Book*.

As readers may know, only a small area of the 60,000 acres is actually covered by trees; mostly the pasture is exceedingly poor, consisting of heather and rank grass.[2] It is quite extraordinary how tame these 'wild' ponies can be. One sees them in twos and threes in the streets of the little towns and villages—and a quite odd sight was a pair of ponies with foal walking sedately along a pavement following a couple of people who were out shopping. We ourselves half expected to see one of the ponies carrying a shopping basket! When one realizes their friendliness and the obvious trust in humanity, it is all the more distressing to read of the disastrous and easily avoidable accidents in which these ponies are involved [3] at the hands of passing motorists. It is quite unnecessary to

---

[1] But a different subsoil. New Forest is on gravel and clay, Pennine fells are limestone.

[2] But also, especially in winter, the ponies browse a lot on trees and shrubs, especially bramble shoots.

[3] *Figures for 1st January 1962 to 28th June 1962 (corresponding figures for 1961 in parentheses)*:

Ponies killed	67 (60)	Ponies injured	11 (18)
Cattle killed	31 (34)	Cattle injured	9 (12)
Donkeys killed	4		
Deer killed	39		
Total killed	141 (94)	Total injured	20 (30)

Total killed and injured, 161 (124).
Total killed and injured in 1960, 230 ponies alone.

Accidents at night, 63 (86). Accidents outside the Forest, 42 (41).
Vehicles involved: Private cars, 81; motor-cycles, 4; heavy vehicles, 80.
Accidents not reported, 26. People killed, nil; injured 7. Local motorists, 26.
In three accidents two animals were killed in each accident.
(Figures supplied by Sir Berkeley Pigott, verderer.)

drive so fast or so inattentively that one cannot pull up for a pony in the road. The ponies of the moors and forests are much older inhabitants of this island than are we; to them we must appear as ill-bred squatters.

In conclusion we have noticed that the 567 brands of the *New Forest Stud Book* rather resemble hieroglyphic signs, having meaning only to the initiated and presumably the Commoners. One wonders—in the secret glades of the Forest, is there occasionally a gathering of the brands—and whether an unbranded filly of one herd is for politic reasons sometimes transferred to the harem of a superior stallion?

The *Dartmoor Stud Book* was started as a section of the *Polo Pony Stud Book* in 1899 (*National Pony Society* since 1913) and continues.

The New Forest Stud Book was started as a section of the *Polo Pony Stud Book* in 1899. In 1910 the Burley and District New Forest and Cattle Society (forerunner of the present society) published vol. i of their Stud Book, containing 118 Stallions and 356 Mares. After this date all registrations were included in the *N.P.S. Stud Books* in a New Forest Section, till 1959, when the present society produced vol. i of its own book. This contains 131 Stallions, 312 Mares and 39 Geldings.

It is proposed to produce a Stud Book each year now on the same lines as the 1959 volume.

The Exmoor Stud Book, part of the National Pony Stud Book since 1899, will be independently published for the first time this year (1962).

CHAPTER FIFTEEN

Wales

I am Taliesin,
I sing of pure lineage,
I will endure till the end.
The Festival (Cwyndawd).

IN WRITING both this and the subsequent chapter on Ireland, we have been very conscious of a disability: for we do not speak either Welsh or Irish. Since we are both professional linguists in other fields we feel, more keenly than most authors, the hampering effect of this lack of knowledge and of the constant necessity to rely on other people's translations. Still, we have thought it better to press on regardless of this drawback, the more so since we have observed other writers boldly pronouncing and expounding though even less able than ourselves to vouch for their historical sources. It is open to those better versed in the more ancient languages of these islands to correct us if they will, but quite apart from that, we suggest it would be a great service to a particular aspect of our history if some horse-breeder who knows either of these two languages or Gaelic were to render into English some of the relevant material which up to now is only to be read in the original language. The same course is open to any fluent speaker of these languages who knows one end of a horse from the other.

In delving back into the past, one finds the words 'Arab' or 'having Arab blood' used far too frequently and ambiguously. The *Welsh Stud Book* refers to the Romans crossing the Mountain ponies with Arabs. But in fact at the time of the Roman occupation of Britain the Arab was not a breed of horses as such; he may equally well have been a Persian, Libyan, Syrian or Barb, for Arabia itself had no indigenous breed. There is no breed of horses which was originally native of and peculiar to Arabia. True, the nomad Arabs proved themselves past masters at breeding horses, but in the first place these horses came from other countries, far to the north-east, perhaps from Transcaspia through the agency of the Hittites at the beginning of the Bronze Age.

However we need not get excited about this, for whatever heavenly descent we would like to ascribe to the Arab, the undoubted fact remains

262

that he, like 75 per cent of our native ponies, is descended from the *Plateau* or *Steppe* varieties or crosses of these. The purity of the Arab breed lies in the fact, which is of considerable importance, that he has been selectively bred for at least a thousand years longer than any other breed. But of course the Romans, maintaining a garrison of anything up to twenty regiments of cavalry in Britain, will have had a stake in remount breeding.

The Romans never seem to have referred to Arabs, neither did the Greeks before them, and they give us twelve breeds, which were well known to them and which they recommended for various purposes. We think it quite likely that it was not until the twelfth century that the first recognized Arabs were brought into this country; until then most probably Barbs from North Africa had been imported. Harun al Rashid of Bagdad may have given Charlemagne some Arabs. And Charlemagne's descendant Hugh the Great gave Athelstan some 'equos currentes'.

By 'Arab' we mean any hot-blooded race of western Asiatic or possibly North African origin. In our opinion direct importation from the Near East was extremely rare until the eighteenth century. Up to that time it mostly took the form of exchanges of gifts between monarchs, but then so did all trade originally. After the conquest of Sicily by the Arabs from Egypt some considerable number of horses, bred wholly or partly from Arab stock in Italy, began to reach western Europe. But the greatest number of oriental horses to reach these islands came as a direct or indirect result of the Muslim conquest of Mauretania, or Barbary, and Spain; during the wars between the Muslims and Christians in Spain, large numbers of horses changed hands, and at its high tide the Muslim host penetrated as far into France as Tours. But for the victory of Charles Martel in 732, Moorish warriors mounted on Barbs might have ridden along the southern shore of the English Channel. The greatest number of Barb imports to England came in the last quarter of the seventeenth century. For a short while, during the reign of Charles II, Tangier was an English colony.

It is a curious fact that research into the ancestors of the Welsh pony brings one face to face with the same expression as does research into the origins of the East Anglian breeds of horses—that is the magic reference to 'the old breed'. But whereas the 'old breed' of the East Anglian order proves difficult to define exactly, in Wales we are in a much happier position. Although the *Welsh Stud Book*, first opened in 1902, rather glides over the 'old breed' in order to establish a modern breed, yet we are in the extraordinarily interesting position of being able, in this year of grace 1962, to compare visually a ten-year-old cob with the Powys cobs of Henry I's day.

It is just on 773 years since we read of the first mention in the history of our native ponies, that they were being bred for the purposes for which they were needed. Our informant is the historian Giraldus

46. View of Llanberis, with ponies in foreground, 1788.

Cambrensis, who was Archdeacon of Brecon; and we have already read his account of the studs which he found south of Lake Bala and of the breeding of the Powys cob.

In the Middle Ages several different types of horses were known in Wales: the Palfrey, the Rouncy and the Sumpter, the sumpter being a pack-horse. At that early period they may well have been one and the same, although used for different purposes. Lastly there was the Working Horse. Quite possibly later it was this working horse crossed with the imported Andalusian horses referred to (P73) which produced the Powys Cob; and we have no proof that these cob-like characteristics died out in the succeeding generations. Rather we should assume that they survived.

Perhaps at some period the Powys Cob took on the guise of the Welsh Cart Horse, only to reproduce his cob qualities when given the chance.

The Mountain Pony, of course, would have no difficulty in producing the rouncy or the sumpter; the ponies themselves have, like all mountain ponies in Europe, the essential qualities for pack-animals. But with the introduction of Barb blood, we can well imagine also that crossed with a good sort of pony an extremely well-mannered and well-made palfrey would result. In fact the essentials for a palfrey are already found in the Section B ponies of the present *Stud Book*. Or would be, if Section B ponies could pace instead of trot!

Except for the medium of their representation, on the one hand drawn and the other photographic, it is impossible to believe that over 700 years separate these cobs!

Volume i of the *Stud Book*, 1902, says: 'Although the Welsh ponies and Cobs have of late been very terribly neglected and the original beauty and distinctive character in many districts spoilt by injudicious crosses for the purpose of gaining size, still there are evident signs of awakening appreciation of the pure old blood, which has all the time been carefully guarded by men who value it as much as Eastern breeders do the high caste [1] Arab. There are several distinct types of these Ponies and Cobs: the small hardy original Mountain type, those somewhat larger bred on the lower grounds, those more of the Cob type and lastly the larger Cob. Although quite distinct in appearance and height, still they have the same family likeness, true pony character, air and action, which latter is remarkable for its freedom and dash.'

47. Leading hay, near Carnarvon Castle, 1774.

Further referring to the Church Stretton herds, the *Stud Book* continues: 'It is of great importance that this original Mountain Stock should be carefully preserved, as it is undoubtedly the foundation from which the larger ponies and cobs inherit many of their most valuable qualities and character.'

Although four *types* of ponies are given, there are only two *kinds*: 'Those specially adapted for riding and those specially for harness. By selection, animals of each section can be bred for either work, and families which will breed true to type will be established'.

Now a writer in the *Live Stock Journal* has this to say: 'I have always maintained that the Welsh Cob and the Welsh Cart Horse are closely allied. With his winter coat and silky feather, the cob looks just like a little cart-horse. The Welsh Cart Horse, before the infusion of Shire blood, may almost be called a distinct breed.

[1] We do not know who invented this odious expression. It is still (1962) too common today. Caste is an Indian, specifically a Hindu institution, quite meaningless in an Arabian, or in any Mahommedan context.

'They were active and powerful, of moderate size—perhaps when compared with the modern cart-horse even of small size—but very compact, and with remarkable pluck, being able to move heavy weights in the hilly country of Wales which would have been thought beyond their power. Their legs and feet were sound, and their bone hard and flinty. Their heads were free from all coarseness, and they had none of that sluggish look which is noticeable in the Old English Cart Horse. It is on this account that the mares of this breed were the dams of so many

48. Snowdon from Capel-Cerig, about 1780. Cob and slide-car in foreground. Compare this and two preceding pictures with P49.

good "light horses" of all sorts when mated with Thoroughbred or hunterbred stallions.

'Now the reason for all this is not far to find; the Mountain Pony is undoubtedly the original foundation. It is the Mountain Pony which gave the life and dash, together with their pluck and hardy constitution. The farmers who cultivate land in close proximity to the enclosed grazing land of the mountains generally bring the ponies down to the lower slopes, or to grassland adjoining their homesteads, during the winter. The stallions are rarely taken from the herd, and there are seldom any precautions taken to keep the other horse stock on the farm from mixing with the mountain herd. It can easily be understood how the pony blood has become infused with the cart-horse, and a sort of indiscriminate mixture from time to time has been the means of evolving the better type of old-fashioned Welsh Cart Horse as described in the early part of this letter; and by further judicious crossing the cob has been produced. The Mountain Pony, of course, has been kept true to type from the nature of its surroundings—the ground they live upon and climatic influences. It has been the rule of the "survival of the fittest" which has eliminated any alien blood of the cart-horse or any other coarse strain. The Welsh Cob as it used to be before the modern Stud Book Hackney was introduced was the further crossing this "cob-pony" cart-horse with well-bred sires. In those days [in the nineteenth century] the term "Hackney" was applied to any horse which was not a cart-horse, and in Wales and Shropshire, at all events, had no reference to the Norfolk horse or any special breed. When an animal's pedigree was asked for, or any description of the sire, the answer would be, "Oh, indeed, he was by a Hackney", meaning it was not a cart-horse. I mention this as the expression "Hackney" so frequently occurs in old writings that, unless carefully considered, the impression is formed that the pedigree Stud Book Hackney is meant, which is altogether misleading.'

This term 'Hackney' was derived from the 'hakenay' which was the late medieval all-purpose animal—from the French *haquenée*: a light saddle horse, other than a palfrey.

We read in the laws codified by Howel the Good in the tenth century that a foal until a fortnight old was worth fourpence; from the fifteenth day of his age till one year 24 pence ($1\frac{3}{5}$ oz. silver); when a year and one day old he was worth 49 pence and stood at that value till he began his third year, when he was valued at 60 pence. When in his third year he was broken in, and his value depended on the work he was fitted for. A palfrey or a sumpter was valued at 120 pence (8 oz. silver), and a working horse to draw a cart or harrow 60 pence (4 oz. silver).

It was not permissible to use horses, mares or cows for ploughing for fear of injury; oxen only might be used. Any entire male animal was worth three females; thus a wild stallion was worth ninescore pence to the mare's value of threescore pence.

The value of each part of the horse was strictly specified by these laws; the worth of his foot was equal to his full value. For every blemish one-third of the total worth, including his ears and tail. Possibly cropping and docking were then in vogue (we have already seen from the illustrations in *Sculptured Stones of Scotland* that docking was most certainly practised even in the ninth century).

Another clause says that the tail of a filly for common work is worth the total value of the animal. As was the practice in Scotland and Ireland until nearly the end of the eighteenth century, the harrow was often secured to the tail (see page 279) as in Connemara. Sore backs were apparently known a thousand years ago, for the code goes on to say that the man who borrows a horse and frets the hair on his back has to pay fourpence; if the skin is broken to the flesh eightpence; and if skin and flesh are broken to the bone sixteenpence. Borrowing without the owner's permission: fourpence for mounting, fourpence for each rhandir (league) he rode the horse. He had to pay a fine to the owner's lord as well.

It was apparently customary to fetter or clog the horses when they were turned out to graze. Trespass by day in corn by a clogged horse cost one penny and by night two. If the horse were kept free it cost only half—perhaps because the horse had escaped or possibly that trailing clogs more damage would be done to the corn. But stallions were free and there was no fine for his owner for any damage which he might do to the crops.

In the history of breeds of horses it is strange how often one exceptional horse or pony appears to save the strain or strongly influence the breed, as Marske did the New Forest, as Flying Childers did in his two lines—the Thoroughbred and the Norfolk Roadster. And now in Wales, in the early part of the eighteenth century, we meet Merlin. A gentleman who may have been related to the Watkin Wynn family bought Merlin, a famous little Thoroughbred racehorse who had broken down on the turf. Merlin was turned out on the Ruabon hills, Denbighshire, and apparently suffered not at all from exposure, and his influence for good was quite marvellous; after a few years 'the stock of his district showed such marked superiority over that from other parts of the country that the value of the young ponies greatly increased. In course of time the impression made by Merlin became so notable that his stock and their descendants were recognized as a distinct strain, and, known by the name of "Merlins", commanded much higher prices in the market than other ponies.'

In about 1820 Youatt writes: 'Pony hunting used to be one of the favourite amusements of the Welsh farmers and peasantry, a century and a half ago, and it has not, even now, fallen altogether into disuse. The following story of one of these expeditions is founded on fact: "A farmer named Hugo Garonwy lived in the neighbourhood of Llweyn Georie. Although he handled the small tilt plough, and other farming tools in their due season, yet the catching of the merlyn, the fox and the hare were more congenial pursuits; and the troubles and thumps which he received, and from which no pony hunter was exempt, served but to attach him to the sport. Rugged, however, as the Merioneddshire coast and its environs were, and abounding with precipices and morasses, he sometimes experienced worse mishaps—and so it happened with Garonwy.

'"He set out one morning with his lasso coiled round his waist, and attended by two hardy dependants and their greyhounds. The lasso was then familiar to the Welshman, and as adroitly managed by him as by any gaucho on the plains of South America. As the hunters climbed the mountain's brow, the distant herd of ponies took alarm—sometimes galloping onwards, and then suddenly halting and wheeling round, snorting as if in defiance of the intruders, and furiously pawing the ground. Garonwy, with the assistance of his servants and the greyhounds, contrived to coop them up in a corner of the hills, where perpendicular rocks prevented their escape.

' "Already had he captured three of the most beautiful little fellows in the world, which he expected to sell for 4L. or 5L. each at the next Bala fair—to him a considerable sum, and amounting to a fourth of the annual rent which he paid for his sheep-walk. There remained, however, one most untameable creature, whose crested mane, and flowing tail, and wild eye, and distended nostril, allowed that he was a perfect Bucephalus of the hills; nor indeed was it safe to attack him in the ordinary way. Many of the three-year-olds had been known to break the legs of their pursuers, and some had been dismounted and trampled to death.

' " Garonwy was determined to give the noble fellow a chase over the hills, and so overcome him by fatigue before the lasso was flung. The dogs were unslipped, and off they went, swift as the winds, Garonwy following, and the two assistants posted on a neighbouring eminence. Vain was the effort to tire the merlyn. Hugo, naturally impatient, and without waiting to ascertain that the coils were all clear, flung the lasso over the head of the wild horse. The extremity of the cord was twisted round his own body, and tightening as the animal struggled, the compression became insupportable, and, at length, in spite of every effort to disengage himself, Garonwy was dragged from his horse.

' " The affrighted merlyn, finding himself manacled by the rope, darted off with all the speed of which he was capable, dragging poor Garonwy over the rocky ground and stunted brushwood. This occurred at some distance from the men. They called in their dogs that the speed of the merlyn might not be increased, but ere they could arrive at the spot at which the accident happened, the horse and the man had vanished. Whether the sufferings of the hunter were protracted, or he was dashed against some friendly rock at the commencement of this horrible race, was never known; but the wild animal, frenzied and blinded by terror, rushed over a beetling cliff, at a considerable distance, overhanging the sea-shore, and the hunter and the horse were found at the bottom, a mis-shapen semblance of what they had been when living." ' [1]

A very similar description has been given, as we have seen, of colt-hunting in the New Forest; and precisely the same method is used, and was used by the ancient Persians to catch wild onager, which they tamed and trained for their war-chariots. (A notice to this effect is to be seen on the onager paddock at Hagenbeck's Zoo, Hamburg).

In its purest state the Welsh Mountain pony is under 12 hands. It is described as an Arab in miniature, with the Arab head and setting on of the tail. 'There are no doubt traces of far back crosses of Arab in many of the best types of the small pony.'

There is the story of some ponies who were shut up in a farmyard,

[1] *Cambrian Quarterly Magazine.*

when one of the ponies jumped the gate, which measured 5 feet 10 inches. 'The pony had an up-hill take-off at the gate, and merely touched the top rail with one of his hind legs, and landed safely on the high road on all his four legs.'

Then there was the 11.3-hand 'Sambo' who at four years old became champion jumper at Olympia, 1887. 'It was said of the pony that his rider would ride him under a bar and afterwards turn round and ride him over it.'

In an article on Montgomeryshire Horses, written in 1900, Mr Halford writes: 'On my first coming into Kerry parish, which is 15 miles long and 22,000 acres in area, there were but six gigs and one four-wheeled carriage in it. Every farmer kept a well-bred mare on which he rode to market and which occasionally bred him a colt. The very small farmer came on a stronger horse, his wife riding behind him, with a basket of butter, eggs or poultry for a make-weight. Many of the stallions were Thoroughbred or as near it did not matter; many of them were brought from Yorkshire for the season. The Hackney of those days had good shoulders and rode well.

'Of late years—and I think partly owing to the formation of the Hackney Society—a different class of hackney has been located near Welshpool.

'Ever since I have known anything of a Welsh Cob, or I may say for sixty years,[1] I have attributed most of its high qualities to the source from which it originally sprang, i.e. the ponies of our mountains, which are indigenous, and some, with their ancestors, have never been touched by the hand of man except for branding. Of course size has been obtained by crossing with larger sires, principally with more of the Yorkshire than of Norfolk blood, until recent years, when we have been influenced by sires which have given pace, but not quality—cobs more suited for harness than for saddle. I have hardly ever known a Hunter, Hack or Cob, where it can be traced back to the Mountain Pony, that it has not excelled in some, if not all, those good qualities common to the breed from which it emanated. The celebrated "Steel Grey", which was only a cob, was bred in this way. . . . This mare was never beaten. She was only 14.1½ hh., good-looking, by "Hesperus". Her record on the race track: March 9th, 1875, 10 miles in 29 min. 45 sec.; April 13th 1875, 10 miles in 27 min. 5½ sec.; July 10th, 1876, 5 miles against time, 14 min. 14 sec. at Lillie Bridge, London—to say nothing of her most successful career on nearly all the trotting tracks.

'I have always thought that a cob to carry a heavy weight, and at the same time to be near the ground, was the most difficult class of horse to breed, if perfect. The black cob which used to carry the late Sir Watkin W. Wynn (a heavyweight, say 17 stone) about the show ground at the different shows of the "Royal" and which old *habitués* may well

---

[1] i.e. since about 1840.

remember, was bred from a small light Welsh Cart mare with a touch of pony blood, and by a Thoroughbred horse.'[1]

Though Welsh Cobs can go as far back as some of us—and perhaps further than most—in producing an impressive family tree, again, like some of us, they become stuck at certain places to prove which ancestor was who. For one thing they indulged in an over-frequency of the same name; the old *Stud Book* abounds in Comets, Flyers and Expresses. These, to quote vol. ii, 'were as handy as Jack Tars and went like great guns, their hocks sending them along. As for their sire the Young Express, he evidently did not creep through life unobserved. He, too, seems to have had his reputation in Bristol and round about it. He seems to have been looked upon as a holy terror in the neighbourhood . . . not because of any noise he made . . . but on account of the pace he went, the dust he raised, and the stones he scattered far and wide as he clattered by with his proud possessor, a sporting butcher, in tow, at a speed the late lamented and long departed John would have envied but scarcely been able to emulate.'

Another sire of good Welsh Ponies was Little Tommy. 'By Stockinger by Stockwell, his grand-dam was said to be a pony. He was a small horse with plenty of bone and quality and when well-mated—for he was more at home with good than bad things—left useful progeny of which there are many about. As little Tommy's career hereabouts dates somewhere near 1882,' says a writer in vol. ii of the *Stud Book* published in 1903, 'I imagine he has gone the way of all flesh, at any rate he must be over-due, for he led a crowded life in the society of many mares, and amid scenes of entertainment and exhibition. Little Tommy's record reads like the history of an admirable Crichton, so varied were his successes. He won prizes both as a hunter and a hackney in the Bath and West of England Show; at Hereford they looked upon him as a roadster, and gave him his reward accordingly. In Radnorshire, at Penybont and Builth, he assumed the role of hunter and romped away with the prizes. Then relying rather on his own athletic prowess and indomitable pluck than the fickle and transient glances of judges, he turned variety entertainer on his own account, and won jumping prize after jumping prize, amongst others, in two successive years at Abergavenny, and on one occasion he claimed superiority over 23 competitors carrying no less than the intemperate weight of 14 stone, in spite of his somewhat inadequate height of 15.1 hands.'

Then there was True Briton (*Hunter Stud Book* 839), 1835, by Ruler, a Yorkshire Coach Horse (1999), probably out of an Arab mare, a 'tremendous good horse and trotter'.

'Whatever else he was,' says the late Mr Charles Coltman Rogers, 'he must have been a top sawyer at the game of impressing his progeny with desirable attributes, and he holds a place, as an immigrant in our

[1] In the *Welsh Stud Book*.

midst, second to none, in making historic a breed of fine trotting roadsters.'

Here is a record of a different kind. 'Old Stager', a chestnut (who became nearly white with age) and a blaze, was foaled in 1865, 13 hands; bred by a Mr J. C. Severn of Penybont, had thirty-four foals. She always lived out on mountain land, summer and winter, with a few other breeding mares; they received some rough hay in the winter. 'Old Stager' lived to be thirty-nine years of age.

If some of their pedigrees glow with foreign-sounding names like Alonzo the Brave, Young Messenger, Fireaway, and Winnal George by the famous Sir George whom we have already met up on the Fells— well! it would not be the first time that a Norfolk horse went west. Mambrino, for example, went considerably farther west and was just as successful. A little 'new' blood does not necessarily cheapen a family tree.

In 1842 C. J. Apperly writes: 'They are never lame in the feet, or become roarers; they are also very little susceptible of disease in comparison with other horses, and as a proof of their prowess of crossing a country, the fact may be stated of the late Sir Charles Turner riding a pony ten miles in 47 minutes and taking 30 leaps is his course, for a wager of 1,000 guineas.'

Coltman Rogers's remarks on mating, which appear in the 1905 *Stud Book*, are worth quoting. From the information which the reader has gathered from the foregoing pages in the historical part of our book, it will be very clear to him that, in Wales, these remarks are most apt.

'How to maintain this Welsh breed of Cobs is another long and vexed question, with all its variable history of vicissitudes, happy accidents, paradoxes, contradictions. There are some lucky few born with a certain knack of knick—they seem to know naturally what animals suit each other, and how to mate them. However, the earth is but ill-sprinkled with the Heaven-born genius, and probably when, as the old jockies said, "The blood did not nick", it was due to want of judgment on the part of the breeder. Sometimes they may appear to break the most well-worn and trite rule with happy impunity. But, be it remembered in many other things besides horse-breeding, in music, painting, architecture, and "Les Beaux Arts" generally, those who have successfully broken rules have been those who know thoroughly the fundamental rules of the game, and where they could occasionally be daringly transgressed. Probably all the successful breeders of the nearest affinities have been intimately acquainted with every authority and experience handed down with regard to the system.

'Often it may happen that the first result of a violent cross carries with it no permanency in descent, especially in the second generation. There arises an incalculable mixture of traits and what has been described as "chaotic constitution". The physiological reason for this is that any species, after several generations, acquires a certain and special adaptation to a particular form of life, and if you mix the constitutions of two widely divergent varieties, you get a constitution adapted to the modes of neither.'

Anyway, in Wales at least, they seem to have been fortunately possessed of that 'knack of knick'.

One of the greatest difficulties which beset our Welsh friends in their desire to breed good ponies, and to keep the ponies free from undesirable elements, was that which bothers all owners with rights on common lands. Namely that any commoner has the right to turn out anything, good, bad or indifferent, on the said common lands. Anyone not possessing the goodwill or common sense not to allow rubbishy stallions to roam could, of course, ruin everybody else's efforts at improvement.

To quote Mr Coltman Rogers again: 'There are, however, to be found two places where the apparent miracle of unanimity has been accomplished and good results obtained in consequence of it, namely on the Longmynd Hills at Church Stretton, and on the Gower Commons, situated on the Peninsula of that name near Swansea. On both these places the one-minded and far-seeing natives have had drifts of ponies, and ordered peremptorily off the scenes all that they did not wish to have about the place, and messing around.' Mr John Hill and the Hon. Odo Vivian were responsible for this state of perfection.

'The result of operations at Gower is quite remarkable reading. After clearing the Common, among other undesirable elements, five sire ponies of such counter personal attractiveness put in an appearance, that none, even among the lowliest cotter born of the rustic population around, could be found who would show any inclination to either beg, borrow or appropriate them. In addition to this despicable quintette, and among the candidates for removal, there turned up a roving and interloping Jackass, the father of many mules. On many other places than Gower we have received similar complaints of the same nature from outraged owners, namely, that the most cherished specimens among these pony mares were at the beck and call of the first sportive vagrant that brayed.'

This state of affairs made necessary an appeal to Parliament for an Act to 'clear the Hills'.

We give now, as a matter of interest, the names of four sires who appear frequently in the pedigrees of the *Stud Book*.

Trotting Comet (*H.S.B.* 834) 'was famous throughout Wales as a sire', foaled about 1836. 15.2 hands. His sire, Flyer, a blind black horse of the ancient trotting species common to his country, was bred near Aberystwyth from a mare by name Black Bess, 'to whom a pretty legend would attach a high-flown and alluring pedigree, but of whose antecedents, truth to tell, but little would appear to be specifically known. The dam of Trotting Comet was a chestnut Cardiganshire trotting mare of some renown.

'The virtual certainty of both of Comet's parents having been of old, germane and well-established form is possibly best indicated by his own phenomenal impressiveness at stud.'

'*True Briton* (*H.S.B.* 839), sire a Yorkshire Coach-horse, known as Ruler, dam Douse, reputed to have been an Arab mare, whom a marauding tribe of gipsies stole and sold to one John Walters, of Llanfair Clydogau, for whom she bred True Briton. The *H.S.B.* has another version and assigns paternity of Douse to True Briton Trotter 840, son of Granby. This version on its face is incorrect.'

Cymro Llwd, a dun 'sired by an imported Arab from a trotting mare, the fastest of her day, by a horse rejoicing in the name of "Old Comet Brown", which is a trifle redolent of Wales.'

Alonzo the Brave (*H.S.B.* 22), a 15.3 bay Hackney, full of the historical Shales blood.

From the foregoing pages it will be seen that many Welsh pony pedigrees, especially those in Sections C and D, rejoice in Norfolk Trotter ancestry; by the same token, many of today's Stud Book Hackneys would not have been entered if they had not been endowed with Welsh forbears.

The Polo pony, though undoubtedly a 'native' breed of these islands, favours no one particular region; he is quite non-partisan and indulges in no chauvinistic claims.

However, even the best bred Polo pony has been pleased to praise the hills of Wales for the hardiness and handiness which he has inherited from the maternal side. Perhaps if they were inclined to be clannish, one would find the well-bred Polo pony sporting a leek rather than a rose— for who can deny that such a pony bears a strong family likeness to the favourite palfrey of an early Welsh knight?

CHAPTER SIXTEEN

Ireland

Within one of the raths at Tailtean, another royal seat
in Meath, a great annual fair was held, which included
the celebration of a sort of Olympic Games, such as
wrestling, running, horse and chariot racing; and
chariot races took place of old at the Curragh of
Kildare.

Dr O'Donovan's *Four Masters.*

THERE was a spot at Tara called the Slope of Chariots, 'and it is distinctly stated in the life of St Patrick,[1] preserved in the Book of Armagh,
that the "Gentile" or Pagan Irish had chariots at Tara before their
conversion to Christianity' (Dr O'Donovan, *The Book of Rights*).

In the very striking hymn said to have been composed by St Patrick
at the time of his meeting with the pagan High King and his Druids at
Tara, he invokes Christ to be with him 'in the chariot seat': that is
when he was travelling by land (Dr Todd's *St Patrick*, from *Horae
Ferales: York Vol. of Arch: Inst:*). We further read that St Odran drove
St Patrick's chariot (*Sculptured Stones of Scotland*).

In 1829, in digging on a moor near Ballindalloch, the skeleton of a
man, and the bones of a horse, were found, along with fragments of
rings and bits of iron, one of them like a great hoop, the whole suggesting
the grave of a charioteer with his horse and chariot (Wilson's *Pre-
Historic Annals*).

Chariots drawn by horses are sculptured on the base of the North
Cross, Kilklispeen, on the base of the North Cross at Clonmacnoise,
and on that of the Cross which stands in the churchyard of Kells.

Dr O'Donovan wrote: 'According to the early Irish annals and other
fragments of Irish history, the ancient Irish had many roads, which were
cleaned and kept in repair according to law.' In *Cormac's Glossary*
definitions are given of the terms used to denote different roads. One of
the roads was made for the meeting of two chariots, i.e. the chariot of a
king and the chariot of a bishop, so that each might pass the other.
According to the ancient Irish topographical work called *Dinnseanchus*,
there were five great roads in Ireland, which radiated in different
directions from Tara; and Dr Petrie says that of 'some of these roads

---

[1] St Patrick christianized Ireland about A.D. 450.

very indistinct traces remain, but they are still remembered by the old inhabitants' (*Sculptured Stones of Scotland*).

A notice of a chariot brought from Ireland occurs in the Life of Samson, Bishop of Dol in Brittany, about the middle of the sixth century. The chariot on the Stone at Meigle, Scotland, is similar to that which belonged to the bishop. It is recognizably of Celtic type—that is, open in front, without the dashboard of the 'classical' model, and could be driven by the charioteer sitting down, not standing up in Mediterranean style.

As we saw earlier in this book, the King of Leinster rides a very active horse to parley with the Earl of Gloucester; a very similar account is given of the Irish Hobby by Blundeville in 1567; and referring back some three hundred years to Giraldus Cambrensis and his *Topography of Ireland* and *How to Conquer Ireland*, 1188, we are able to see that for many countries Ireland produced very good horses—in fact, for well over a thousand years we have these odd glimpses of equine activity. Quite probably one reason why we are not able to find more eyewitness accounts is that the use of horses, and fairly good horses at that, was such a normal and usual thing that nobody considered it worth while recounting.

Richard Berenger, who was Gentleman of the Horse to King George III, writes in 1771: 'Ireland has for many centuries boasted a race of horses called Hobbies, valued for their *easy paces* [1] and other pleasing and agreeable qualities, of middling size, strong, nimble, well-moulded and hardy. The nobility have stallions of great reputation belonging to them but choose to breed for the Turf in preference to other purposes; for which perhaps their country is not so well qualified, from the moisture of the atmosphere, and other causes, which hinder it from improving that elastic force and clearness of wind; and which are solely the gifts of a dry soil, and an air more pure and refined. This country, never-the-less, is capable of producing fine and noble horses.'

From the map on page 123 we are able to see the connection between the Brigantes of Spain and those of Ireland. One need not stretch one's imagination to suppose that this connection was kept up for many hundreds of years, and that Barbs and 'Asturiones' would have been imported from earliest times into Ireland—perhaps during the period when the Brigantes used the seaway horses were exchanged! There is no doubt that the similarity between the Irish Hobby and the Spanish Jennet is very real.

A fact tending to support the view that through most of our history the import of hot-blood horses has been predominantly Barb rather than Arab is that the overwhelming majority of pictures of English light horses down to the eighteenth century show the tail set on low. And the most conspicuous feature of the Barb, that distinguishes it from the Arab, is the low-set tail. This peculiarity extends to the Dongola horse

---

[1] This means that they *still* ambled and paced like the medieval palfrey.

of the south-western Sudan in one direction, and to many Spanish horses with a Barb strain in the other. In Greece, and later in Rome, this tail conformation and the goose rump that goes with it were either unknown or poorly thought of, since Graeco-Roman art shows horses with square quarters, the base of the tail in one horizontal line with the end of the spine, in the accepted Arab style. This type is seen from the Greek bronzes of southern Italy, about 500 B.C., to the Roman pictures and carvings of the second and third centuries of our era. Perhaps this is what led Blundeville to assume that the pure-bred Arab or 'Turk' really came from Greece? But as far as we know good riding-horses were first bred by the Medes in the cool grassy country of western Iran, near Hamadan. This country looks like Montana. From it were exported the famous Nisean horses of antiquity, which even the Chinese sent emissaries to purchase in Han times, second century B.C.

The Greek poet Oppian especially recommends Nisean horses for hunting and for chargers; they are of exceeding beauty and docility, and possess a full light-coloured mane!

Youatt, writing in 1820, tells us that Pinkerton, in the second volume of his *Travels*, gives a curious account of the state of the Irish horses on the island of Raghery, on the northern coast of Antrim, early in the preceding century (1700). A Government survey of the coast was taken at that time.

'"You must know", says the writer, "that it was but the other day that the people of Raghery recollected that a road might be of some convenience to them, so that in our excursion we were obliged to follow the old custom of riding over precipices that would appear contemptible even to a man that enjoyed the use of his legs. It seems that my horse, though fifteen or sixteen years old, had never before felt a bridle in his mouth. He had, however, borne it good-naturedly and well; but we were now come to a difficult part of the road, even the top of a very rugged precipice. He was evidently frightened, and after many attempts to shake off his fear, he refused to proceed another step. The reasoning process in his mind was evident enough, and often amused me afterwards: 'You may have your whim when you cannot do either yourself or myself much harm, but I do not choose to risk my neck for you or for anyone.'" The bridle was taken off, he selected his own path, and the rider was carried over an exceedingly dangerous heap of rocks, with a degree of caution which Mr Pinkerton could not help admiring in the midst of his terror.'

Youatt further adds: 'In some of the rich grazing counties, as Meath and Roscommon, a large, long blood horse is reared, of considerable value. He seldom has the elegance of the English horse; he is larger-headed, more leggy, ragged-hipped, angular, yet with great power in the quarters, much depth beneath the knee, stout and hardy, full of fire and courage, and an excellent leaper. It is not, however, the leaping of the English horse, striding as it were over a low fence, and stretched at his full length over a higher one; it is the proper *jump* of the deer, beautiful to look at, difficult to sit, and, both in height and extent, unequalled by the English horse.' This is the Irish hunter. He continues:

'The common Irish horse is generally smaller than the English. He is stinted in his growth; for the poverty and custom of the country have imposed upon him much hard work at a time when he is unfit for labour of any kind. He is also deficient in speed.

'There are very few horses in the agricultural districts of Ireland exclusively devoted to draught. The minute division of the farms renders it impossible for them to be kept. The occupier even of a good Irish farm wants a horse that shall carry him to market, and draw his small car, and perform every kind of drudgery—a horse of all work; therefore the thorough draught-horse, whether Leicester or Suffolk, is rarely found.'

All descriptions of the native Irish horse or 'hobby', from Blundeville to Berenger, insist on its 'easy paces', which implies in fact an amble rather than a trot. In other words it was a potential palfrey.

In *Historie of Ireland* Edmund Campion says: 'Horses they have of pace easie, of running wonderfull swift. Therefore they make of them great store, as wherein at times of need they repose a great piece of safetie. This broode Rafael Volateranus sais to have first from Asturia, the country of Spain between Galicia and Portugal, whereof they were called Asturcones, a name now properly applied to the Spanish Jennet.

'I heard it verified by Honourable to Honourable that a Nobleman offered and refused for one such horse an hundred kyne, five pund lands, and an airy of haukes yearly during seven years.'

Nothing is said about the size of the ponies in question, but in another passage Campion says of the Irish Wolfhound that it is 'bigger of bone and limme than a colt', by which presumably he means that a full-grown wolfhound is bigger than a new-born colt, which would be just about right for a Connemara pony of modern stature.[1]

Those parts of Campion's book which constitute the Description as opposed to the Historic proper are derived from the author's personal observations about 1570.

An Irish cow was worth about 5*s.* Elizabethan currency, so a hundred kine is about £25. 'Five pound lands' probably means land worth £5 a year, which we could assess at a capital value of £100. Impossible to assess the cash value of a nest full of young hawks. Perhaps £5 × 7 = £35. This amounts then to £160, partly in instalments, 'pay as you hunt', and makes an interesting comparison with the 400 cows which King McMorrogh of Leinster is reported to have paid for a similar horse in 1399, and which works out at some £8,000 in modern currency. Campion's horse would cost about £3,200 in modern sterling.

[1] That could be the reason why King Arthur's (Irish) wolfhound was called Kaball = 'The horse'.

Arthur Young also refers to the practice of horses pulling with their tails (which we have already mentioned in the chapters on the Highlands and Wales). In 1776, on visiting County Cavan he found to his astonishment that 'the people very commonly plough and harrow with their horses drawing by the tail. The people insisted that when the horses

49. Inside car, 1843.

were tired from collar work, all that was necessary to rest them, was to strip off their harness and secure the plough or harrow to the tail'.

At the beginning of this chapter we referred to the chariots of early times. It may be interesting to the reader to have a glimpse of the conveyances used by the Irish in more modern times. From Hall's *Ireland* (1843) comes the following extract: 'The inside jaunting-car is not often to be hired; it is usually private property, and is perhaps the most comfortable, as well as elegant, of the vehicles of the country.

50. Outside car, 1843.

'The outside jaunting-car is that to which especial reference is made when speaking of the "Irish" car. It is exceedingly light, presses very little upon the horse, and is safe as well as convenient; so easy is it to get on and off, that both are frequently done while the machine is in motion. It is always driven with a single horse; the driver occupies a small seat in front, and the travellers sit back to back, the space between them being occupied by "the well"—a sort of boot for luggage; but when there is only one passenger the driver usually places himself on the opposite seat "to balance the car", the motion of which would be awkward if one side was much heavier than the other. The foot "board" is generally of iron, and is made to move on hinges, so that it may be turned up to protect the cushions during rain. This foot-board projects considerably beyond the wheels and would seem to be dangerous; but in cases of collision with other vehicles, a matter of no very rare occurrence, the feet are raised, and the injury is sustained only by the machine. The private cars of this description are, of course, neatly and carefully made, and have a character of much elegance; but those which are hired are, in general, badly built, dirty and uncomfortable.

'The car, or rather cart, used by the peasantry, requires some notice. Flat boards are placed across it, and upon these straw is laid, and often a

51. Wheel car, 1843.

feather-bed. The one described in the engraving has the old-fashioned wheels cut out of a solid piece of wood.[1] These vehicles are now, however, nearly obsolete; their unfitness having been understood, they have given way before modern improvements. In Ireland there are few turnpikes, the repairs of the roads usually falling upon the county; money for the purpose being annually voted by the grand juries. The roads are for the most part good; and of late years, a better system of surveying . . . has led to the formation of "new lines" to nearly every place of importance. The old plan, therefore, of carrying a road "as the crow flies" up and down the steepest hills, through morasses, and along the brinks of frightful precipices, has been entirely abandoned.'

The Connemara Pony.[2] In 1897 a Royal Commission was appointed to report on the state and recommend measures for the improvement of horse breeding in Ireland, with particular reference to the work of the

---

[1] The earliest known wagons pulled by oxen of the Sumerian period, *c.* 3000 B.C., also had solid, fixed wheels.

[2] Connemara is a region of County Galway, western Connaught.

Congested Districts Board. Its report, Cmd. 8652, is a copious document, full of interesting matter and long since out of print. It deals with the supply of draft horses, hunters, ponies and cavalry remounts. The latter had been perhaps one of the springs of the inquiry; it is apparent from the report that the War Office had been failing, of late years, to get enough remounts of the right type from Ireland, because they had consistently paid about £5 a head less than the agents of foreign armies. The commission tried hard, and in vain, to find out on behalf of which power these agents had been buying. All the witnesses were unable, or professed themselves unable, to distinguish between more than two kinds of foreigner—the English and the rest.

52. Irish landlord and Irish tenant, 1852.

A large number of very varied witnesses were examined: landowners, farmers, breeders, stud-grooms, racing men, dealers. The most quoted extract from the report deals with ponies and it will stand quoting again. 'In . . . portions of Galway, Mayo and Kerry, a hardy breed of ponies formerly existed in considerable numbers though unfortunately they are becoming very scarce. This is a valuable breed and has achieved a well-earned reputation.' This is the conclusion of the Commissioners themselves and from it we can see that even at the end of the nineteenth century, according to the witnesses, the breeding area of the best native ponies was not confined to the barony of Connemara but extended to the north as far as Sligo and to the south-west, well outside Connaught into Kerry. In regard to horses generally the Commission found that there was no significant breeding north of the Boyne. Though many references in the earlier part of the present book are from Ulster, it is apparent that Ulstermen of the late Victorian age bought young stock exclusively in the south and the west of Ireland.

Among the witnesses was one Thomas Meleady of Dublin, described as a dealer. We shall let him speak for them all, not because he is the most typical but because he is the most articulate. And well he might be, since talking was three-parts of his trade. After all, his job was to talk the ponies off the farm at about £17 a head, and into the strings of the 'gentlemen and officers' at a substantially larger figure. Other witnesses had to be coaxed to testify and plied with leading questions. Not so Mr Meleady. A stream of information, opinion and advice pours from his lips, couched in English of truly Elizabethan richness and vigour. Unfortunately the ages of witnesses are not given, but from internal evidence Mr Meleady cannot have been much less than fifty-five in 1897, or much over sixty, because 'I am all my lifetime going in trains'. For him the Good Old Times lay not very far back in the past—say somewhere about 1860. His world is one of simple outlines, populated by heroes—'gentlemen and officers' who buy polo ponies; villains—other horse dealers; and misguided innocents who cannot be taught that it costs as much to breed a bad horse as a good one: 'Poor men are destroyed feeding rubbish . . . the bad mares eat the grass from under the good ones.' For him, behind the successive ruin of every horse-breeding district lurks the sinister form of the Scotch Horse—the Clydesdale colt with his voracious appetite and unthrifty frame, his big soft bone and big coarse head, his long back, angular neck and hairy heels. Call Thomas Meleady:

'Well, there is forty years I am going through County Galway, Mayo, Wicklow, Wexford and all parts of the south, as far as Skibbereen; there isn't a county or place I could mention but I was in. I am all my lifetime going in trains.'

Q. 'Can you buy many horses in the west?'

A. 'Sometimes you could, but not of course good ones. Now if you wanted a nice polo pony I remember a time you could get them, you could go down to the fair there and buy ten or eleven out of the fair. Every month I went into Belmullet for the twenty-five years and we never came home with less than ten or eleven good polo ponies out of it.'

Belmullet (pop. now 691) is the most remote and god-forsaken of all small towns in north Mayo. It lies on the isthmus connecting Mullet peninsula with the mainland, at the opposite end of Blacksod Bay from Achill Island, thirty miles from the nearest railway station (then Kilalla, now Ballina).

Q. 'And you say you can't get them now?'

A. 'No, not in that country. I left ne'er a good one in it that I saw.'

Q. 'Do you travel down there now?'

A. 'Not so much. We don't want so many polo ponies, and now they want a different class of polo pony. At that time it was 14 hands and now it is 14.2 hands. *Now* it is a little thoroughbred horse we want like Watchspring long ago . . . a 14-hand-2 pony down there is neither a pony nor a horse now. If you get a good 14-hand-2 pony now round Wicklow or Wexford you want that—but you don't want a half-bred one now—

they are no use, those small half-bred ponies—you must have a thorough-bred pony now. When I went down *there* first there was a breed of ponies in it you could get up and ride them off the grass thirty miles across the mountains as I often did from Belmullet into Ballina, and they would never tire, without a feed of oats, nor did they know what the taste of oats was. . . . I took the weight of them out of it; they had necks and shoulders like thoroughbreds, and the best shape you ever saw, but they are gone out of the country altogether. They used to call them Achill ponies. . . .

'The mixture of ponies with Scotch horses that got into Galway and County Mayo ruined that country, and they are neither horses nor ponies . . . other countries as well, for they sell them as foals to Wicklow and Wexford and ruined *that* country.

'The Scotch horses came there when I was a very young boy.' (In the 1840's?) 'They were easy to tire; heavy-legged horses; the farmers got them cheap and gave them to mares and then the foals were soft, hairy-legged bits of ponies, and no use, not the old Irish class of pony I am speaking of. In the County Mayo, sir, there is a great deal of mares that should not be allowed near a horse at all. What destroyed the ponies first in that country was the Clydesdale mixed up through them.'

He explains that the farmers put the pony mares to Clydesdale colts in order to gain another two inches in height at a ridiculously early age, when they sold the young stock to dealers from the east coast counties. He himself never bought unbroken ponies in Connaught, or any ponies under five years old, and reckoned to pay an average price of £16 or £18 and a top price of £30. He complained bitterly about the price of rail transport to Dublin from Kilalla—not a penny less than 30s. a head. Of course he sees the pony-breeding world from a particular angle which is not that of the breeder or of the Connaught farmer. Nevertheless he was interested in breeding and wanted a system of registration *in Ireland* which was not to materialize for almost another thirty years. He was not concerned with the usefulness of the pony to the western farmers and peasants themselves; only as a potential item of merchandise to the 'gentlemen and officers'. His evidence is valuable for the history both of people and ponies. Since in his day the child's pony was not a significant economic factor, and the elder child's pony hardly existed; his concern was mainly with the polo pony. The Connemara pony of good unmixed stock did not grow over 14 hands. When this height became inadequate for the game the Anglo-Irish officer class lost interest in the breed. His is just the right generation to speak with authority, because it was in the 1860's, when he appears to have been upwards of twenty years old, that the game of polo was introduced into Britain by way of the Army in India.

About the same time we have an echo of Ireland's heroic age, thrown back from the most unlikely sounding-board. A quite aggressively English lady, a Mrs M. B. Pattisson, writing up her tour of Achill Island for *Temple Bar Magazine* in 1896, says: 'We met endless strings of ponies, laden, some with creels of turf, some with "scraws", long wide sods of turf, cut from the heathery grass and used as thatch for the cottages. The ponies were led by girls in picturesque attire, and in some instances the damsels were riding seated behind their loads at the extreme edge of the animals' hind quarters. With apparent precarious balance they trotted along the steep and rugged road, using no rein and making a small switch do the necessary guidance. We saw one girl make her pony kneel down while she sprang up behind her creels.'

If you want to know how this is done, Xenophon will tell you. His *Art of Horsemanship* describes the cavalry drill whereby the trooper made his horse bend at the knees to enable him to mount wearing his armour and carrying shield and weapons, but without stirrups.

Now these Mayo girls came from families whose men, down to the seventeenth century, had ridden in leather cuirasses carrying weapons, but with no stirrups, like Xenophon's Athenian pupils.

Another witness to the Royal Commission, Mr Ussher, C.B., also stated that he lived for twenty-five years in the west of Galway and there was an extremely hardy, wiry class of pony in the district, showing a great deal of the Barb or Arab blood. 'Without exception they were the best animals I ever knew—good shoulders, good hard legs, good action, great stamina, they were seldom over 14 hands 2 inches. I never knew one of them to have a spavin or a splint, or to be in any respect unsound in his wind.' This strong trace of Barb or Arab blood may have been introduced by the Martins around 1833. This is the family to which 'Humanity Martin', the sponsor of the original Cruelty to Animals Bill, and Violet Francis Martin ('Martin Ross') the sporting novelist, belonged.

Another witness referred to the Connemara as 'long and low with good rein, good back and well-coupled'. 'I never saw lovelier mares,' says Mr John Pardon, of the herd belonging to Mr William Lyons, who maintained a special herd for generations (Sir Walter Gilbey, *Thoroughbred and Other Ponies*).

At the time of the famine the peasants were in dire need, and poverty necessitated that they sold their mares, and although the remainder depreciated in quality they kept their characteristic hardness. Another witness stated that he had bred 'one of the best hunters he ever possessed out of a Connemara mare', and another described a mare got by the pure-bred hackney stallion Star of the West from a 'mountain pony'. This mare could cover an English mile in 3 min., over 71 miles in a day and 15 statute miles in 1 hour 10 min. She hunted carrying 10 stone.

It seems, too, that Welsh blood has played some part in the present-day Connemara pony, for the first entry in the *Stud Book*, Cannon Ball, was by Dynamite, by the Welsh Cob stallion Prince Llewellyn. Dynamite seems also to have inherited trotting blood and eventually he went off to America to try his luck there.

About 1870 there was a quite extraordinary pony called Master George, who stood only 12 hands. There was some doubt as to his origin, whether he came from Norway, Iceland or Ireland, the supposition being that he was really a Connemara pony, as no Norwegian or Iceland pony had ever been heard of to travel as fast as this pony. Twice he trotted eighteen miles in the hour and thirteen minutes. In a match at Brentwood he won his first mile in three minutes one second, but such was the rowdyism that accompanied this sport and eventually destroyed it that revolvers were fired at poor Master George in the next heat. A savage rush was made at him and this upset pony, trap and driver, but Master George was equal to the occasion, got up and the trap righted itself, and trotting out fair and square the pony won by himself.

In 1900 Professor Cossar Ewart wrote of the ponies of Connemara that he was struck with their strength, endurance, easy paces, intelligence and docility and with their capacity for work, which would soon prove disastrous to horses reared under less natural conditions. He also remarked on the differences in size, shape and colour, and found no fewer than five types, each one fairly distinct from the other.

Writing some sixty years ago in *The Horses of the British Empire*, Lord Arthur Cecil says that these ponies were used in much the same manner as the ponies of Scotland. They also have good riding shoulders and a 'marked natural proclivity for jumping'. He thinks that on the small islands off the Irish coast they are probably nearer the old type, though not so big as those on the mainland, and it is a noteworthy fact that dun is a common colour, which may serve to connect them with the Scottish ponies.

We ourselves think that there is quite obviously a connection here with the *Celtic*, or, as we have more generally called it in the preceding chapters, the North Atlantic pony and the old primitive breed of the pony of Uist.

The term 'Connemara pony' is of comparatively recent origin. The type was formerly much more widely distributed throughout Connaught (or indeed throughout Ireland) than now. Old authors refer to it simply as the 'Irish horse'. But then, in 1581, a Galway curragh was not called a Galway curragh. It was called an Irish boat, just as this animal was called an Irish horse (or hobby, if the English author wanted to be disparaging). Elizabethan writers (Stow, Spenser, Campion, Fynes Moryson) distinguished between only two kinds of horse in Ireland: the Irish, and the English 'Great' horse brought into the country for military purposes. Earlier British writers (Trevor of St Asaphs in 1399 and Gerald de Barry in 1177) make the same simple distinction. Irish chroniclers themselves in the Middle Ages mention only two kinds of foreign horses, British (Bretnac), meaning probably Welsh, not English, and Spanish. The latter are the famous Spanish jennets, an ambling light horse shipped direct to Galway and Limerick from Galicia. And only one 'native' horse.

The Anglo-Norman invaders first brought the Great Horse which was part of the general chivalry-cavalry scheme of things, ultimately of north French and Flemish origin. Its descendants, more or less unmixed, are the vanishing Irish Draught breed. Other descendants, mixed with thoroughbred and Irish pony stock, are the Irish Hunters.

The Irish themselves down to the reign of Queen Elizabeth I preferred to fight on the native horse because it suited their style of armament and tactics. This is shown in another picture from Derrick's *Image of Ireland*, where English cavalry in plate armour, heavy saddles, carrying shields of almost medieval weight and pattern, are charging mounted kerne wearing no helmets and only mail shirts, carrying no shields and wielding light javelins overarm, while the English are armed with proper lances 'couched' underarm. The Irish further saved weight by using the kind of pilch instead of a saddle, seen in this picture in detail. The English *in the main* are riding heavier horses and the Irish lighter, but this is because the war has been going on for some time and both sides are partly making do with captured remounts, so the distinction has become blurred.

The horse in the illustration, page 156, was in Ulster, but the type was then universal in Ireland. Like everything else of native design, the curragh, the costumes, the bards, the harpers, the cattle-thieves, etc., the native pony was pushed farther and farther west from the times of Essex and Cromwell onwards.

Following advice from the Royal Commission in 1897, selected Thoroughbred and Roadster stallions were sent over to Ireland, and it was questioned whether it was desirable to establish Hackney sires in a country so famed for its Hunters; but it was generally acknowledged that the bone and substance of the Hackney were eminently desirable in many districts to improve the character of local stock.

More recently, Arab blood has again been used to the extent that a certain amount of bastardization must occur and the ponies will be neither typical Connemara nor typical Arab. Several mares by Arab sires have been registered as *Connemara* ponies, and a stallion advertised in America, *registered Connemara*, a grandson of Naseel out of a part-Arab mare!

Today we notice that two Thoroughbred stallions Little Heaven and Winter and an Irish Light Draught stallion Mayboy have been introduced and presumably their progeny will call themselves Connemara. To this it seems fair to observe that in continental Studs where the breed is not 100 per cent *fixed*, it is sometimes the practice to use stallions of other breeds which *are* fixed to help retain the type desired or required.

The Connemara or native pony of Ireland must at one time have been one of the purest fixed breeds in these islands, but during the past sixty years its history shows us that man has caused it to become a mongrel breed. One wonders if there are any 'pure' Connemara ponies left?

CHAPTER SEVENTEEN

Conclusion

——————⊸⧫⧫⧫⧫⧫⊶——————

Forget the spreading of the hideous town:
Think rather of the packhorse on the down
                                    William Morris.

WE CANNOT forget. The world of the Atom Age is too much with us. But we can still think for ourselves, and not accept blindly the mechanically repeated assurances, the unfounded legends, the uncritical platitudes and generalizations founded on hearsay at fourth or fifth or sixth hand.

That is why there can be no conclusion. Or, rather, why the reader must draw his own. 'Disinterested intellectual curiosity', says George Macaulay Trevelyan, 'is the life-blood of real civilization.' And we would add that one of its hallmarks is not to be afraid of the word intellectual; it only means 'arising out of mental effort'. Without the horse—some kind of horse—there would have been no material western civilization as we know it. Without the pack-horse on the down there would have been no town, hideous or otherwise. To adopt, reluctantly, a mechanical metaphor, the horse in western civilization was like a starter motor that functioned for—let us say—three thousand years, until the vital spirit of mechanical propulsion was vaporized and compressed, the spark ignited it, and we were off. Leaving behind the horses; the Thoroughbred, that giant near-Arab, as a gambler's toy; the descendants of the Great Horse as raw material for Belgian *charcuterie*, and as a loss-leader for publicity-minded brewers; and the pony as the teenager's joy and an article of export ranking somewhere between poodles and whisky in value.

Of these three, the last is the one with the longest continuous history shared with the human population of Britain. We have tried as much as possible to place the evidence of that history before you, ladies and gentlemen of the jury, as it stands, both in pictures and in writing. For centuries the horse was not so much the right hand of British agriculture as of commerce. (In some places, such as the Fair Isle, there was no intermediate stage between ploughing with oxen and ploughing with tractors. In some places the steam plough almost bridged what gap there was.) Even taking into account the entire history of imports and crossings, it remains broadly true that the British pony breeds represent the descendants of the medieval horse stock of Britain, aside from the Great Horse of chivalry and an intermittent and very small trickling influx of hot-blood horses ultimately of Middle Eastern origin. But these medieval horses themselves were in the main only a legacy of the Roman occupation, and of the Celtic Iron Age stock before that. These are the only two general principles we have tried to establish from the evidence before you. Of course there have been crossings and admixtures, of course in some cases there has been wholesale bastardization. Pure is a relative term. But in spite of the skeletons in every cupboard from Mendip to Morpeth, in spite of the accidents in even the best regulated equine families, we believe that the Little Horses of Britain today are still in essence the same as the Little Horses of the Britons of old, blood of their blood and bone of their bone.

Coin of Aulerci Cennomani
(Department of Mayenne)

APPENDIX I: THE ROMAN POSTING SERVICE
(CURSUS PUBLICUS)

THE numbers of *paraveredi* or relay horses kept on the principal routes can be estimated by means of a formula worked out when passenger transport had once more reached the pitch of efficiency attained by the Romans in Britain. This did not happen until the first quarter of the nineteenth century, but it happened over exactly the same routes. Stagecoach proprietors in George IV's time reckoned that to keep a four-horse coach on the road required one horse per mile of route. The Roman post-chariot was pair-horsed, so only one *paraveredus* for each two miles was required. Over the main roads this would mean:

	Miles	Horses
Londinium–Eboracum–Corstopitum	277	138
Eboracum–Luguvallium	94	47
Londinium–Deva	180	90
Londinium–Viroconium	150	75
Londinium–Aquae Sulis–Isca Silurum	140	70
Londinium–Venta Belgarum–Isca Dumnoniorum	170	85
Clausentum–Londinium	76	38
Portus Lemanis–Londinium	60	30
Regnum (Noviomagus)—Londinium	62	31
Dubris–Londinium	70	35
Rutupiae–Londinium	74	37
		676

This is a minimum. Probably the establishments for the roads to Deva, Eboracum and Isca Silurum should be doubled. Probably there were in all 5,000 miles of Roman road in Britain, and something should be allowed for the fact that though Roman post-vehicles were lighter than the Georgian post-chaise, Roman harness, without a proper rigid collar, was less efficient. Together, these factors make for a total of something like 2,500 post-horses, all entire males. On 31st July 1960 there were only 931 stallions licensed by the Ministry of Agriculture.

We have another measure of the impression these horses made on the invading Saxons. They had, of course, no word for a post-horse in their own language, but there is evidence that they adopted the word *paraveredus* to mean a superior pacing horse or palfrey. As it happens, no document *written in Old English* has come down to us containing this word. But in the ninth century, when it had become fairly common, though not universal practice, to draw up legal documents in Latin, we find two examples where it is spelt *parafrithus*, one being in a charter of King Ecgbert of Wessex. Now plainly a spelling like this cannot have been arrived at by copying 'genuine' Roman documents. For one thing, the combination *th* hardly exists in 'genuine' Latin; for another, the Saxons used the letter *f* to represent the sound of *v*,

289

normally. Evidently this is a word which the clerk was accustomed to hear in the mouths of laymen every day, but pronounced in a form something like 'parav'reth', and he shuffled it back into Latin by adding '-us'.

On the Saxons of the Continent the Roman post-horses made an even stronger impression. In the language, which is called Old Saxon, of those who did not emigrate to Britain, the word for a horse in general became 'Perid', a contraction of *paraveredus* which displaced the native German word 'Ross' entirely. The latter survives now only as a dialect word in South Germany, and the universal word used by the Germans for a horse is *Pferd*.

APPENDIX II: MONASTIC HORSES

UNFORTUNATELY it is not until the eve of the Dissolution that we can get a really detailed picture of how the working and breeding stock of the abbeys was kept, but the Bursar's Expense Book of Durham may be taken as typical for north country economy of the years 1530–4. By this time of course monks and lay brothers had ceased to do any manual work of any kind, though they were up to their necks in very hard-boiled secular business. What they paid the abbey servants or 'famuli' for various duties can be seen from the wage accounts, per year, as under:

Head stableman 33s. 4d.   Carter 13s. 4d.   Stockman ·20s.   Wheel-
wright 33s. 4d.   Smith 10s., sometimes 16s.   Forage man 4s.   Groom
13s. 4d.

Prices paid for horses bought in these years will be the same as for the Jervaulx tenants' horses brought away from Flodden about twenty years earlier. Bought from William Duckett 14s.; from Robert Byddyk 17s. 6d.; from Thomas Blunt 17s.; from Widow Kechyng 20s.; from Robert Laxe 23s. 4d.; from Ripon Fair £2 16s. 3d.; from William Taylor 12s.

We can reconstruct a fairly complete catalogue of harness, saddlery, stable requisites and forage from the Bursar's Book, as follows:

Leather horse harness	10d.	Smithy halters (extra strong)	
Stirrup leathers, pr.	4d.	each	6d.
Flock for stuffing pack		Packsaddle	1s. 4d.
saddles per lb.	1d.	Bits, pr.	1s.
Stirrup irons, pr.	6d.	Wametows (bellybands)	2d.
Varnishing do.	2d.	Barley, per qtr.	4s. 9d.
Curry comb	2d.	Hay, per wainload	2s. 10d.
Web girths, pr.	5d.	Bait for 18 horses, one day	
Wainropes, each	4d.	(inn)	2s. 6d.
Large cartropes	1s. 4d.	Horse collar	3d.
Pin traces, pr.	8d.	Replacing skeps and	
Halter shanks, doz.	1s.	scoops, one year	1s. 6d.
Halters, doz.	2s.	Lock & key for oatbin	4d.

Oats is a smaller item than one would expect because horses in work were partly fed on bread of a special kind. One of their three verderers alone spent £3 11s. on horsebread in one year.[1] The four-wheeled wain (*plaustra*) probably held only about a ton of loose hay, approximately the yield of one acre. But mowing one acre cost 6d. at current piece rates, and all the other operations, collectively known as 'winning', might cost four times as much again, making 2s. 6d. As the price ex farm was unvarying at 2s. 10d. per wainload there was not much profit in selling hay off the farm.

Grass keep cost anything up to 6s. 8d. per head per season. While the brood mares appear to have 'lived rough' all the time, the importance of hand-feeding young stock was well understood in the north, as the custom of colthaver shows. 'Haver' is our north-country name for oats. Customary rents on some monastic property were paid in kind, known as colthaver—i.e. oats for young stock. The monks still ploughed with oxen, and their horses only went under the saddle and in carts and wains. They paid 16s. for a working bullock but only about 12s. for a beef steer. Some of the working bullocks went on the road, presumably in wains, since they were shod.

Where there are horses, near the Border, there are tinkers. These worked occasionally for the abbey, mending 'brekfastpotts' and the like, at about 8d. a day, about one-third as much again as a labourer got for mowing grass. Two individuals named Thomas and Alexander Tynkler so employed probably came out of Scotland.

The bursar's department had four horses to itself; one filly, one dun nag, one grey 'Audrey' and one grey 'Rippon' (the one that cost £2 16s. 3d.?). The last three were all mares.

The monks had seventeen horses 'on one side'. Since the property is occasionally divided for accounting purposes into East, West, North and South, the total kept was probably about sixty-eight. The vet's bill for one year details 'lybbyng 3 staggs' (gelding three colts) 6d.; other treatment, advice and medicine, 9s. 6d.

APPENDIX III: LIMITATIONS OF BITS AS EVIDENCE

OFTEN the only evidence of the use of horses the antiquary has is the finding of some imperishable item of harness—usually a bit, in Britain. The majority of these have been found, not on the sites of harness-makers' workshops, or on scrap-heaps, but in burials. From this something, but by no means everything, about the size of the deceased's horse can be assumed. Unfortunately the height of horses does not vary directly with their breadth across the bars

[1] The price of horsebread was controlled at ½d. per loaf (standard quart of dry meal), making 1,704 loaves, or rather less than five loaves a day; probably the ration for two horses. Innkeepers charged 2d. for a feed of bread, as we see from a sermon of Hugh Latimer's, at this time, but no one expected them to feed four loaves; more likely two, and the rest overheads and service charge.

of the mouth. The latter measurement may be identical in one animal with a broad muzzle and another, taller animal with a relatively narrow jaw.

In general, however, the following rough scale is applicable:

A three-inch bit fits a very small pony (Shetland or the like) ten hands or less.

A three-and-a-half inch bit fits an eleven-hand pony.

A four-inch bit fits a twelve-hand (say Exmoor) pony.

A four-and-a-half-inch bit fits a thirteen-hand pony.

A five-inch bit fits a fourteen-hand pony.

A five-and-a-half-inch bit fits a horse fifteen hands and upwards.

In the ordinary snaffle such as is found in Bronze Age and Iron Age burials, the relevant measurement is the length of the mouthpiece between the necks at each end where the mouthpiece bulges out to take the hole through which the rings are passed. The question now arises, for what sort of animal were the bits designed, such as that from Rise in East Yorkshire, where this measurement was less than two and a half inches? It is a fact that these miniature bits have never been found in conjunction with the skulls of the animals which wore them. One cannot escape the conclusion that there was a trade in special small bits similar to that in dress clothes without any back such as are supplied exclusively to the undertaking profession in America—in other words that there was a special sort of funerary harness, used by families who were too poor or too mean to inter the genuine article with their deceased kindred. It must be borne in mind that in the Bronze Age at least the metal *as such* had a high intrinsic value, and any saving in its bulk would be appreciated by the executors.

APPENDIX IV: MEMORY OF THE ROMAN POST-HORSE

THE reader may ask, as we have asked ourselves, how it is that the Latin *paraveredus* did not give rise in Old English, as it did in Dutch and German to some word like *paard* and *Pferd* respectively, meaning horse in general, but only to a roundabout and specialized derivative through French. The answer appears to be that such a word *was* taken into English but existed for some 1,400 years at a sub-literate level, that is it was used in the speech of grooms and nagsmen but not in the writing of their masters. Then, quite early in the eighteenth century, it surfaces in print as 'prad' meaning horse in general; not at all specialized, and in speech attributed to coachmen, horse-copers, etc. As the vogue for 'low-life' fiction, or low-life episodes in fiction, grew, its printed occurrence becomes more frequent. But not *too* low – it never formed a part of criminal slang. In terms of Dickens, it belongs to the vocabulary of Tony Weller but not of Bill Sykes (though Dickens himself did not use it). That it was not a part of what is now called 'stir talk' is proved by its absence from those works published around 1600, such as Thomas Dekker's *Bellman of London* and *Gull's Hornbook* or Robert Greene's *Cony-catching*, from which a very complete glossary of the cant terms used by the widespread and highly profitable horse-stealing industry could be compiled. Transpose the 'a' and the 'r' and you have something very like the German, and much more like the Dutch, equivalent. But such metatheses are not uncommon among Germanic languages, as Primitive Germanic *hros* = Anglo-Saxon *hors*.

Select Bibliography of Sources

Dates, not of first editions, but of those consulted.

THE ANGLO-SAXON CHRONICLE (tr. G. N. Garmonsway) London 1954

ANON RESPUBLICA, AN INTERLUDE London EETS 1905

MARGARET ASHDOWN ENGLISH AND NORSE DOCUMENTS London 1930

W. P. BAILDON NOTES ON THE RELIGIOUS AND SECULAR HOUSES OF YORKSHIRE York 1895 etc.

J. BARBOUR THE BRUS Edinburgh 1909

BEDE ECCLESIASTICAL HISTORY OF THE ENGLISH NATION London 1958

R. BEILBY and T. BEWICKE A GENERAL HISTORY OF QUADRUPEDS Newcastle upon Tyne 1800

BEOWULF (ed. Fr Klaeber) New York 1922
—— (tr. D. H. Crawford) London 1926

J. BILLINGSLEY GENERAL VIEW OF THE AGRICULTURE OF THE COUNTY OF SOMERSET 1797.

EDWARD BIRT (or BURT) LETTERS FROM A GENTLEMAN IN THE NORTH OF SCOTLAND London 1754

MARC BLOCH FEUDAL SOCIETY London 1960

JAMES BOSWELL THE LIFE OF DR JOHNSON 1790
JOURNAL OF A TOUR TO THE HEBRIDES 1786

G. JULIUS CAESAR WAR COMMENTARIES London 1935

SYLVIA CALMADY-HAMLYN Correspondence with Authors

EDMUND CAMPION HISTORIE OF IRELAND London 1633

G. CHESSMAN THE AUXILIA OF THE ROMAN IMPERIAL ARMY Oxford 1914

V. G. CHILDE PREHISTORIC MIGRATIONS IN EUROPE Oslo 1950

E. M. CLIFFORD BAGENDON, A BELGIC OPPIDUM Cambridge 1961

WILLIAM COBBETT RURAL RIDES (1830) London 1956

A. O. CURLE A ROMAN FRONTIER POST London 1911

GEORGE DAVIDSON Correspondence with Authors

DANIEL DEFOE A TOUR THROUGH THE WHOLE ISLAND OF GREAT BRITAIN London 1962

A. A. DENT and A. C. CAWLEY CHAUCER AND THE HORSE Leeds 1959

SIR HUMPHREY DE TRAFFORD (with SIR WALTER GILBEY) HORSES OF THE BRITISH EMPIRE London 1912

B. DICKINS RUNIC AND HEROIC POETRY Cambridge 1915

C. M. and A. I. DOUGLAS THE SHETLAND PONY Edinburgh 1913. Illustrated. Substantial appendix by J. C. Ewart on *The Making of the Shetland Pony*.

GAWIN DOUGLAS 'Works' (in MEDIEVAL SCOTTISH POETRY, ed. G. E. Todd) Edinburgh 1891

P. B. DU CHAILLU THE VIKING AGE London 1889

EXETER, BOOK OF (ed. B. Thorpe) London 1842

WILLIAM FITZSTEPHEN *see* JOHN STOW

SIR WALTER GILBEY THOROUGHBRED AND OTHER PONIES London 1900

GIRALDUS DE BARRY (CAMBRENSIS) TOPOGRAPHY OF IRELAND Dundalk 1957
—— ITINERARY THROUGH WALES London 1960

HENRY GOUGH SCOTLAND IN 1298 Edinburgh 1888

A. R. B. HALDANE THE DROVE ROADS OF SCOTLAND Edinburgh 1952

S. C. and A. M. HALL IRELAND London 1841–3
A WEEK AT KILLARNEY 1843

C. F. C. HAWKES and M. R. HULL CAMULODUNUM London 1947

M. O. HOWEY THE HORSE IN MYTH AND MAGIC London 1923

JERVAULX CHAPTER HOUSE BOOKS. Unpublished MS. in Public Record Office

SAMUEL JOHNSON A JOURNEY TO THE WESTERN ISLANDS OF SCOTLAND London 1775

J. KNOX A TOUR THROUGH THE HIGHLANDS Edinburgh 1786

L. LENGYEL L'ART GAULOIS DANS LES MÉDAILLES Mentrouge/Seine 1954

R. MAGNEN EPONA Bordeaux 1953

WILLIAM MARSHALL RURAL ECONOMY OF THE WEST OF ENGLAND London 1796

FYNES MORYSON ITINERARY London 1617

BARTHOLOMEN O'SULLIVAN THE CONNEMARA PONY Dublin 1939

SIR BERKELEY PIGGOTT and Others THE NEW FOREST London 1960

T. G. E. POWELL THE CELTS London 1958

T. TALBOT RICE THE SCYTHIANS London 1958

I. A. RICHMOND ROMAN BRITAIN London 1947
—— A HANDBOOK TO THE ROMAN WALL 1957

JAMES RITCHIE THE INFLUENCE OF MAN ON ANIMAL LIFE IN SCOTLAND Cambridge 1920

WILFRID ROBERTSON 'Adwalton Horse Fair' (in THE BRADFORD ANTIQUARY) Bradford 1927

W. SCROPE DAYS OF DEER STALKING London 1883

JOHN SPREULL AN ACCOMPT CURRENT BETWEEN ENGLAND AND SCOTLAND Edinburgh 1706

JOHN STOW THE ANNALS OF ENGLAND London 1600 (includes Fitzstephen's Description of London)

STRABO GEOGRAPHY (tr. H. E. Jones) London, Loeb Classical Library, 1917–32

JOHN STUART SCULPTURED STONES OF SCOTLAND Edinburgh 1856

SNORRI STURLUSON HEIMSKRINGLA (the History of the Kings of Norway) (tr. Samuel Laing) London 1844

P. CORNELIUS TACITUS GERMANIA London 1948
                          AGRICOLA London 1948
                          ANNALS New York 1942

B. J. TOZER THE HORSE IN HISTORY London 1908

JOHN OF TREVISA Translation of Bartholomew's *De Proprietatibus Rerum.* MS. in British Museum.

ROBERT TROW-SMITH HISTORY OF BRITISH LIVESTOCK HUSBANDRY London 1957–9

VIKING SOCIETY DIPLOMATARIUM ORCADENSE ET HJALTLANDENSE London 1907

GEORGE WALKER THE COSTUME OF YORKSHIRE London 1814

V. V. ZALENSKII. PRZEVALSKII'S HORSE London 1907. The Russian original was written in 1902, and first translated into German, from which language the English translation was made by Capt. M. H. Hayes and others. For this reason the author's name on the title-page is spelt 'W. Salensky' in the German manner. There is a valuable introduction by Professor J. C. Ewart, in which the Tarpan of Western Russia is also dealt with.

Index

Index

ABBEYS, 103, 290, 291
Acland, Sir T. Dyke, 249
Acland, Sir Thomas, 249
Adwalton Fair, 162–4
Aelfwold, Bishop of Crediton, 53
Aesc, 60
Agriculture, 28, 103, 145, 168, 172, 182, 278; P55
Altai Mountains, 17
Altamira, 21
Alesia (Alise-Ste-Reine), 11, 12
Alfred, King, 1, 7, 81, 99
Ambiorix, 10
Ambition, 185, 237
Ambler, 156, 158, 159
Ambrosius Aurelianus (Emrys Wledig), 44, 47
America, 18, 19, 131, 228, 240, 241
Anderida, Andredesweald, 8
Anderson, Capt. Magnus, 29
Anderson, Dr, 218
Aneirin the Bard, 45
Anglo-Saxons, 56–72
Angus, J. S., 199
Anne, Queen, 174
Antonine Wall, 38, 62, 211
Apocalypse, 185; P73
Apperly, C. J., 272
Armada, 147, 148, 192
Armies:
  Byzantine, 86
  Celtic, 30
  Edward I, 105–9
  Harold's, 2, 6
  Parliament, 167
  Robert the Bruce's, 108–12
  Roman, 10, 12, 30, 35, 37–45, 67
  William the Conqueror's, 1, 86, 92
Arran, 104, 175, 205, 208
Arrian, 37
Artemis, 10
Arthur, King, 46–8
Aryan, 9
Asa of Vestfold, Queen, 79, 80
Asia, 17
Asser, Bishop, 7
Atholl Stud, 213
Auxiliaries, 10, 37

Bagendon, 30n.
Baldishol, Norway, 8, 89; P27
Ball, John, 39, 90, 119; P35
Barbour, J., 109–10, 152
Barra, 176, 205, 207, 210, 212

Barra Head, 24
Bass, John (John Spreull), 169
Baudet de Poitou, 5
Bayeux Tapestry, 2–6, 92, 257
Bede, 55, 60
Beilby, R., 225, 226
Belesme, Robert de, 99, 100, 185
Bellfounder, 241
Benbecula, 206
Beowulf, 55, 56, 57, 69, 84
Berenger, Richard, 215, 276
Bewick, Thomas, Figs. 37, 38
Biddell, Hermann, 243, 244
Bill Bailey's Bank, 24
Birt, 152, 179–82
Birth, 10
Bits. *See* Harness
Black Demeter, 10
Blaze, 239, 240
Bloch, Marc, 200
Blundeville, Thomas, v, 143, 155–8, 239
Book of Fermoy, 104
Border, the, 150, 151
Borera (now Berneray), 174
Bos primigenius, 28, 102
Boswell, 177, 179
Boudicca, 39
Boule, M., 22
Brand, Rev. J., 201, 202
Brands, 165, 260
Breeding, 17, 22, 23, 62, 64, 65, 78, 95, 143, 199–286
Breeds:
  Andalusian 99, 159
  Appaloosa, 106
  Arab, 2, 31–4, 109, 158, 206, 208, 232, 258, 262, 263, 286
  Asturcones, *Asturión*, 37, 121, 122, 157, 205–14, 276
  Barb, 2, 32, 158, 249, 263, 276, 277
  Belgic Ardennais, 11
  Connemara, 93, 278, 280–6; P76, P77. *See also* Irish horses, etc.
  Dales, 27, 79, 101, 132, 135, 164, 165, 193, 194, 220–9
  Dartmoor, 246–61; P70
  Exmoor, 246–61; P71
  Faeroe, Faroe, 78, 206
  Fell, 56, 79, 101, 132, 133, 193, 220–9; P63, P65, P78
  Frisian 56, 221; P64
  Galloway, 137, 153, 155, 169, 170, 193, 194, 215–28, 259; Fig. 32; P61

299

Breeds—*continued*
  Gudbrandsal (*Dølehest*), 79–80, P24*b*
  Hackney, 112, 115, 117, 118, 120,
    129, 155, 227, 228, 236, 238, 241,
    270, 286; P66
  Hanoverian Cream, 60
  Highland, 209–14; Figs. 35, 36;
    P53, P54, P57, P58, P59
  Icelandic, 78
  Lipizzaner, 99, 159
  Mongolian: *Equus przevalskii*
    (Poliakov), 17, 22, 94, 95, 201
  Neapolitan, 99, 155
  New Forest, 4, 10, 143, 159, 189–92,
    246–61; P47, P72
  'Nordic pony,' 15
  Norfolk Cob. *See* Norfolk Roadster
  Norfolk Roadster, 197, 226, 227,
    230–45, 274; P68, P69
  Noriker, 47
  'North Atlantic pony,' 15, 16, 18,
    21–3, 38–9, 211
  Norwegian or Vestfjord, 79, 206,
    207; P24*b*
  Parthian, 157
  Persian, 47
  Shetland, 77, 94, 151, 174, 200–9;
    P56
  Spanish, 99, 209, 211; Fig. 21;
    P73
  Tarpan, 18, 23, 95
  Turke, 158
  Welsh, 100, 106, 159, 173, 218,
    262–74; Figs. 47, 48; P74
Britain, 1, 24, 74, 96, 176, 195–8, 216,
  217
British Museum, 23, 26, 96
Britons, 64
Brough Hill ponies, 223
Buchan, Alexander, 174–6
Burns, Robert, 188, 189; Fig. 31
Byng, John, Viscount Torrington, 194

Cabot, 20
Caedmon, 58
Caesar, Julius, 1, 10, 17
Calgary stud, 208
Calmady-Hamlyn, Miss S., 256
Cambridge, 183
Camerarius, 157
Campbell, Duncan, 208
Campion, Edmund, 278
Canterbury Psalter, 83, 84, 113; tail-
  piece, p. 84
Canterbury Tales, 115–20, 231
Canute, laws of, 56, 101, 257
Capul, 67, 119; Fig. 20; P35
Caradog, 16
Carew, Richard, 246, 254–7
Car-meidre, Fig. 29
Car-slaoid, Fig. 29
Carthage, 32, 33
Cartier, 20
Carts, 179–81, 193

Caspian Sea, 9, 16
Cassivellanus, 1
Carvings. *See* Monuments
Castor and Pollux, 48n.
Catterick, 45
Cavalry:
  Celtic, 10
  Gallic, 10, 13, 37
  Monmouth's, Duke of, 168
  Roman, 10, 14, 35, 37, 40 (Indiana,
    Sabiniana, Petriana, Classiana,
    Proculaiana, Agrippiana, II
    Sebosiana, First and Second
    Asturians, First Pannonians,
    Sarmatians, 37; Ala Prima
    Flavia Augusta Britannica, Ala
    Quinta Brittonum, 40)
  Ala Vocontiorum, 38
  Batavian, 12, 36
  First Thracian Cavalry, 38, 230
  First Vettones, 38
  Frisian, 36, 37, 38
    Cuneus Frisionum Aballaven-
      sis, 38, 221
    Prince Hnaufrid's Own, 37
  Tungrians, 36
Cave drawings, 23, 26, 200
Caxton, headpiece, p. 128
Cecil, Lord Arthur, 207, 228, 258,
  259, 285
Celtic coin, tailpiece, p. 288
Celts, 9–16, 29–46, 195–8
Cerdic, 58
Channel Isles, 24
Chapman horse, 155, 233
Chapmen, 164, 221
Chariots, 14, 29, 30, 49, 59, 60, 101,
  209, 230, 275, 276
Charles I, 159
Charles II, 168
Charlotte, Princess, Fig. 33
Chaucer, 74, 92, 113–20, 152, 198;
  Fig. 20
Church Litany, 13
Church Stretton. *See* Long Mynd
Churchill, Sir Winston, 160
Civilis, 12
Civil War, 166–8
Classicus, 12
Claudius, 16
Cleveland Bay, 155, 165
Clontarf, battle of, 80
Clydesdale, 152, 205, 207, 208, 213,
  218
Coaches, 235, 236
Coach-horses, 171–3, 232
Cob, 91, 92, 98, 105–8, 116, 117, 144,
  145, 234, 236, 265–71; Fig. 20;
  P50, P51
Cobbett, William, 192–4
Col, Laird of, 177
Coll, 177, 179, 207
Colours, 106–8, 114, 129–33, 151, 165,
  206, 214, 219, 221, 222, 237
Coltman Rogers, Mr Charles, 271–3

Combarelles Caves, 23
Commentaries, 10
Constantine, 10
Cordiner, Charles, 182, 202
Cornish ponies, Fig. 44
Cornwall, I.W., 31
Cornwall, 61
Cottager, 254
Country cart, 183, 279, 280; Fig. 30
Courser, 86, 91–100, 105–12, 138, 161, 216; P29
Cremation, 15
Crossland, Miss P., 223, 225
Cunedda, 43
Curle, J., 37
Cynewulf, 55, 71

Dargue, Mr J. S., 223
Dark Ages, 61
Darley Arabian, 235, 241
Dartmoor, 103, 227, 246–57
Darwin, 17
Defoe, Daniel, 168, 170–4
Descriptio Civitatis Londiniae, 97, 98
Diluvial. See *Forest*
Dogger Bank, 24
Domesday Survey, Book, 93, 94
Domestic horses, Fig. 16
Doncaster Cup, 115
Donkey, mule, ass, 13, 45; Figs. 7, 8
Dordogne, 23
Draught horse, 93
Dudley, Robert, Earl of Essex, 160
Dufton, 222, 223
Dun, 59, 104
Dykes, Mr T., 208, 213

Eastern counties, 167, 230–45
Edward I, 105–9
Edward III, 114, 115, 160
Edward the Confessor, 7
Elizabeth I, Queen, 125, 140, 143, 144, 148, 160, 162, 231, 234
Ellesmere MS., Fig. 20
Enclosures, 66, 102
England, 150
English, the, 1, 2, 6, 51, 53, 65, 71, 92, 98, 196
English art, 83, 84
Eocene, 19
Eohippus, 18, 19
Epona, 9–13, 35, 40, 61; P4, P7, P8, P9
Eponina, 12
Equestrian god, Fig. 14
Equi silvatici, 93
Equites, 36
Erik the Red, 19
Eriskay, 175
Ermine Street, 52
Essex, second Earl of, 166
Europe, 24
    map of, 25, 76, 123

Evans, G. E., 167
Ewart, Professor J. Cossar, 17, 21–3, 206, 211, 226, 285
Ewart Evans, Mr George, 243
Exmoor, 93, 103, 145, 171, 246–57; Frontispiece, P71
Eyre, George Edward Briscoe, 259

Faeroe, 24
Faestingmen, 72
Falkirk Roll, 105–8, 111, 163
fé, 19
Fens, 198, 226, 231
Fetlar ponies, 204
Fitzstephen, William (Stephanides), 96, 234
Flanders mares, 158
Flight into Egypt, 13
Flodden, 110, 133–5, 163, 221
Flying Childers, 228, 229, 232, 235, 238, 240
Forest, 2, 17, 18, 21, 22, 23, 26
Forteviot, Lord, 205
Frankland, Miss, 136
Frisian language, 56
Frisians, 56, 57
Froissart, Sir John, 112, 215
Fynes Moryson, 153, 154

Galatoi. *See* Keltoi
Galcantray, Colin of, 209
Galloway province, 153, 171, 187
Galway, 154
Galway curragh, P1
Gautier, 200
Garron, 154, 212, 218
Gaywood church, 160
Geddes, Jenny, 188
Gelding, 112, 131, 146, 215
George I, 155, 160, 171
George IV, 205
George V, 208
Gilbey, Sir Walter, 204, 212, 218, 222, 234, 235, 243, 252
Giraldus Cambrensis, 99–101, 154, 264, 276
Glenbruar, 208
Glenorchy, 209
Gobi Desert, 21, 22
Gocan, 208, 218
Gododdin, Manau, 45
Godolphin Arabian, 232, 240
Gokstad ship, 29, 80n.
Goonhilly pony, 198, 256
Gotland, 59, 66
Great Blizzard, 72
Great Horse. *See* Courser
Great mares, 5, 245
Greenland, 20
Grimm, 10
Gwito'r Glyn, 130
Gwynnedd (Venedotia), 44

302

Hadrian Line, 13, 43, 47, 57, 71, 96
Hadrian's Wall, 38, 157
Hakenay (*jaca*), 157
Hannibal, 33
Harald Hairfair, King, 77
Harald Hardraada, King, 81–2
Harness, 26, 27, 28, 40, 49, 56, 59, 74,
    100, 101, 129, 130, 154, 155, 179,
    180, 184, 209, 291 292; headpiece,
    p. 53; P6
Harold, King, 1–2
Hastings, 2–6, 8, 84; Fig. 10
Harris, 205, 206
Hatfield House, 160, 207, 258
Hay, Mr William, 203
Head, Richard, 152
Heathery Burn, 27
Heavy horses, 47, 49, 79, 81, 98, 114,
    117, 127, 152, 167, 226
Hebrides, 104, 146, 147
Hedeby, 81
Heimdall, 73
Henderson, Captain, 202
Hengest and Horsa, 41, 57, 60, 62
Henry I, 252
Henry II, 257
Henry VII, 128, 130; headpiece, p. 128
Henry VIII, 132, 138, 146, 155, 211;
    Fig. 22
Hephaestos, 13
Hercarius, 3
Highland chieftain, 104
Hinny, 157
Hipparion, 18, 19
Hobby, 111, 117, 119, 148, 152, 154,
    155, 156, 218, 234, 276
Hobilar, 111, 152
Holinshed, 155
Holy Roman Empire, 85
Homo sapiens, 16
Horse burials/remains, 19, 21, 26, 30,
    31, 38, 49, 59, 79, 80, 82, 230,
    231, 275
    coins, 33, 86
    cults, 9, 10, 56, 60, 69, 78, 82, 210
    cultures, 16
    fighting, 69, 70
    in art, 33, 86. *See also* Cave draw-
        ings, Rock carvings
    marks, 71
    plough, 98, 99, 127
Horseflesh, eating of, 31, 71
Howel the Good, 267
Humber, 8, 9
Hunter, 91, 124
Hunting, 7, 20, 28, 72, 73, 91, 92, 101,
    102, 122–6, 161, 209; Fig. 4;
    P42–6
Hutton, Mr Ernest, 185
Hutton, Mr John, 259
Huxley, 18

Ice Age, 17, 210, 211
Iceland, 19, 24, 69

Indo-European, 15
Ine, King of Wessex, 58
Ingvi-Frey, 60
Inner Hebrides, 24
Ireland, 24, 66, 67, 80, 100, 108, 148,
    154, 155, 275–88
Irish chieftain, Fig. 23
    draught horse, 286
    horses/ponies, 121, 155, 276, 277,
        278; Figs. 49, 50, 51; P75. *See
        also* Connemara
Islay, 205, 208

Jackson, Professor K., 195
Jalap, 232, 233; Fig. 39
James I, 149–51, 158, 159, 161, 211;
    Fig. 25
James II, 168
James V, 146, 211
James VI, 147, 211
Jennet, 156, 157, 158
Jervaulx, Chapter House Book of,
    130, 131
'Jerusalem pony,' 157
Jock, 160, 208
John, King, 103, 252
John of France, King, 114, 115
John of Trevisa, 68
Johnson, Samuel, v, 177, 178, 179,
    200, 207, 218
Jonson, Ben, 152, 153
Jónsson, Finnur, 74
Julius Sabinus, 12
Jura, 205
Jutes, 61, 62

Kaball, 46
Katerfelto, 250, 251
Kelso, Charter of, 211
Keltoi, 16
Kemble, 62
King's College, 168
Knight, Mr, 249–54
Knight, Sir Frederick, 249
Knights, 1, 86, 91, 103, 105–12, 118,
    126
Knights of the Round Table, 46
Knut, 72

Lady of Lynwood, Fig. 11
Lambarde, William, 259
Lancaster, Duchy of, 159
Langland, vii
Laplander, 25
Lascaux, 21
Lascelles, Hon. Gerald, 260
Leif the Lucky, 19
Lewis, 175, 205
Lincolnshire Trotter, 235
Ling Cropper, 222, 224
Lingay, 175
Londonderry, Marquis of, 204

Long Mynd, 69, 265, 273
Longslade Bottom, 190
Lousy Bank, 24
Lowe, G. S., 250
Lowlands, 187
Lugh, 13, 14
Lugudunum, 13
Luguvallium, 13
Lundholm, Bengt, 94
Lüneburg Heath, 153
Luttrell, Sir Geoffrey (Psalter), 113, 165
Lynwood, 8–10
Lyonesse, Land of, 25

MacEachern, 62
Macha. *See* Epona
Macleod, The, 174–6, 202
McMorough, Arthur, 126
Macneil, 207
Magna Carta, 101
Magnen, M., 11
Mail armour, 47
Mainland. *See* Highland ponies
Mambrino, 228, 240, 241
Mark (*March ab Meirchion*), 61
Markham, Gervase, 215, 234, 235, 239
Marks, 136
Marshall, Dugdale J., 239, 240
Marshall, William, 248
Marske, 257, 258
Marshland Shales, 229, 239; Fig. 40
Martin, Martin, 174–6, 202
Mary, Queen, 154
Master George, 285
May, Phil, 5
Meg, 188
Meleady, Thomas, 281–3
Merlin, 257, 268
Merlyn, 268, 269
Mesohippus, 19
Mesolithic, 26
Messenger, 240
Michaelmas cavalcade, 175, 176
Middle Ages, 85, 102–27
Middle March, 150
Miocene, 19
Mildenhall (Salver), 96, 231; P5
Mineral train, Fig. 34
'Minster' Stud, 5
Mohr, Dr Erna, 17, 94
Monarchy, 86, 160, 161
Mongolian Wild Horse. *See* Breeds
Monmouth, 168
Monro, Donald, High Dean of the Isles, 147, 206
Monuments, 173, 201, 209, 210, 275; Figs. 17, 18; P12, P13, P14, P15, P16, (carvings) P18, P19, P23, P37
Mosaic Law, 71
Mull, 205, 208
Munnings, Sir Alfred, 160
Murray Usher, Mrs, 219

Neolithic, 26, 27, 99, 210, 211
New Forest, 8–9, 187–92, 257–61
New Stone Age, 26
Newmarket Heath, 172
Nicholson, Sir A., 204
Nisean horses, 277
Nobis, Dr G., 80, 81
Norman Conquest, 92, 93, 99, 101
Normans, 2–6; Fig. 2
North Star, Fig. 42
North Uist, 175
Norway, 24
Nydam boat, 59

O'Donovan, Dr, 275
Offa, King of Mercia, 71
Olaf Tryggvason (King of Norway), 78, 82
Old English Cart Horse (Old Black), 266
Old Grey Shales, 229; P67
Old Mortality, P60
Old Stone Age, 25, 28
Old World, 16, 21
Oppian, 157, 277
Original Shales, 239, 240
Orkney, 187, 201, 202
Orkneyinga Saga, 79
Orkneys, 24
Oseberg, 79, 80; P24
Otadini. *See* Tribes: Votadini
Ottar, the Norwegian, 99
Otterburn, Sir Adam (King's Advocate and Recorder of Edinburgh), 146
Outer Hebrides (Long Island), 24
Oykel, 79

Paces, 158, 215, 276
Pack-horse, 4, 91, 92, 93, 97, 98, 111, 164, 193, 248, 253, 254; Figs. 3, 5, 43, 44; P48, P56
Pad, 171
Palaeolithic, 21, 22, 25
Palfrey, 4, 6, 91, 92, 97, 98, 101, 103–9, 116, 120, 125, 152, 158, 160, 162, 165, 171, 226, 237, 238, 264; Fig. 24
Paraveredi, palefroi, 50, 52
Paston Letters, 129, 130, 230
Pattisson, Miss M. B., 283, 284
Pembroke, Earl of, 236
Pevensey, 2
Phenomena, 185, 236, 237; P69
Philip III, 158
Philip of Castile, 129–30
Phoenicians, 31–3
Pictish War, 96
Piette, M., 22, 26
Place names and surnames, 63–70
Plateau, 18, 21, 22, 23, 26, 211
Pliny, Elder, 36, 37
Pluto, 13
Polo pony, 274

Pony, 194, 195–8, 220
Porcupine Bank, 24
Posting service, 49, 91, 236, 289, 290
Pottery, 9; Fig. 11
'Pownie,' 193, 220
Powys, 99, 263, 264
Prior, Miss Eve, 185; P74
Prosody, Dr, 203
Protohippus, 19

Racing, 49, 56, 65
Rakker, 131, 132
Ramsay, Allan, 187, 188, 192
Reindeer. *See* Palaeolithic
Relph, Mr, 224, 225
Respublica, 144
Remagen, 22
Rhiannon. *See* Epona
Rhine, 24
Rhum, 175, 184, 205, 207, 219, 258
Richmond, Earls of, 103
Ridler, Mr J. K., 184, 185
Ritchie, Professor James, 200, 206, 210, 211
Roads, 66
Robert the Bruce, 108–12
Robertshaw, Mr W., 162
Rockall Bank, 24
Rollon, Rou, Walking Rolf (first Duke of Normandy), 77, 80
Roman Britain, 10, 35–52
    Empire, 12, 31
    Occupation, 13, 20, 37, 91, 230, 262, 263
Roncesval, 6
Rory o' the Hills, 205
Rouncy. *See* Cob
Routes for shipping, 32
Rowlandson, J., 162; Figs. 43, 45
Ruler, 232, 233
Runes, 52, 54
Russell, Rev. John, 249

Saddles. *See* Harness
Sahara, 21
St Kilda, 174, 176
St Michael's Mount, 32
St Patrick, 45, 275
Sale of Horses Act, 144
Sampson, 240
Saracens, 6
Saxon Shore, Count of, 42
Saxons, 7; Figs. 4, 5
Scalloway, Court Book of, 151
Scandinavians, 74, 78; Fig. 19
Scandinavian invasions, 76, 80, 81–3
Scilly Is., 24, 32
Scotland, 77, 78, 146, 147, 150, 153, 170, 179, 202–14
Scott, Sir Walter 187, 189
Scythians, 9, 29, 59, 74, 166; Fig. 12
Sedgemoor, 168
Shadingfield Horse, 244

Shakespeare, 153, 154
Shetland Is., 24, 76, 77, 147, 151, 201–9
'Shelties,' 200, 204
Shepherds Meets, 225
Ships, 29, 59, 76, 92, 147, 148; Fig. 17
Shire, 152, 265
Sir George, 227, 272
Siwalik Hills, 18, 19, 39
Shrines, 14
Skagerrak, 24
Skraelings, 19
Skye, 175, 178, 179, 205
Slide-car, Fig. 28. *See also* Travois
Smithfield, 97, 98, 152, 171
Solutré, 21, 22
Somerset, 171
Song of Roland, 6
Song of Rig, 73
Spain, 123, 148, 156, 157, 173
Spenser, Edmund, 154
Stallion, 93, 95, 131, 140, 141
Statues, statuettes, 11, 13, 14; P2, P3, P4, P31, P179, P180, P181
Statutes of Henry VIII, 138, 143
Steed, 92
Steppe, 17, 21, 23; Fig. 15
Stirrups. *See* Harness
Stud cards, Figs. 39, 41
Sucellos, 13
Suffolk Punch, 231, 243–5
Sumburgh, 77, 204
Surnames. *See* Place names
Sussex, 3
Sutton Hoo, 48

Tacitus, 15, 30, 31
Taillefer, 6
Taliesin, 44, 46, 47n.
Tarpan. *See* Breeds
Tattersall, Mr R., 243
Tertiary, 17–21
Thor, 13
Thoroughbred, 172, 173, 199, 227, 246, 258
Thracian, 14
Tilbury, 160
Tinker, 27
Tiree, 205, 208
Tit, 155, 219
Tombstones, P10, P11, P12a, P17
Totemism, 10, 62
Travois, 178
Tribes:
    Aulerci Cennomani, tailpiece, p. 288
    Brigantes, 30, 60, 121, 122
    Catuvellauni, 30
    Dobuni, 30
    Epidii, 62
    Gallic, 12
    Iceni, 30, 203, 231
    Ingaevones, 60
    Leuci, 35

Novantae, 60
Ordovici, 44
Parisii, 40, 121, 230
Silures, 30
Trinovantes, 30
Turones, coin of, headpiece, p. 7
Veneti, 33, 122
Votadini (Otadini), 40, 44, 45, 121
Turbeville, 161–62

Udall, Nicholas, 145
Uist, 205, 206
Ussher, Mr, 284

Value of horses, 81, 103, 105–8, 126, 150, 151, 163, 164, 169, 170, 174, 208, 269, 278
Van Dyke, 159
Vercingetorix, 10
Vespasian, 11
Victoria, Queen, 258
Vikings, 53, 57, 59, 69, 70, 76, 77
Vortigern, 58, 60

Wales, 44, 99, 173, 262–74
Warren, Mrs Kathleen, 207, 208

Wayland, 13
Welsh Cart Horse, 264, 265, 266
Wessex, 61
Westbury, Wiltshire, 173
Western Isles, 77, 78, 147, 174–9
Westmorland, 184
'Whirlicote,' 165
William I, 8. *See also* William the Conqueror
William III, 2, 174
William the Conqueror, 81, 83, 92
Wills, 15, 53, 69, 126, 150
Wilson, Mr Christopher, 227, 253
Windmill Hill, 27
Wineland, 19
Woden, 62
Wulfric of Mercia, 96

Xenophon, 284

Yorkshire, 171–4, 186, 230; P48, P52, P62, P78
Yorkshire Coach-horse, 232
Youatt, William, 137, 203, 218, 226, 248, 268, 277
Young, Arthur, 279
Young Active, 232, 233